100

MATHS

LESSONS

This book m
another bo
upon appli

Ple
b

YEAR 1

Published by Scholastic Ltd,
Villiers House,
Clarendon Avenue,
Leamington Spa,
Warwickshire CV32 5PR

© **1999 Scholastic Ltd**
Text © Ann Montague-Smith 1999
4 5 6 7 8 9   1 2 3 4 5 6 7 8

SERIES CONSULTANT
Ann Montague-Smith

AUTHOR
Ann Montague-Smith

EDITOR
Joel Lane

ASSISTANT EDITOR
Clare Miller

SERIES DESIGNER
Joy White

COVER PHOTOGRAPH
Kim Oliver

ILLUSTRATIONS
Kirsty Wilson

British Library Cataloguing-in-Publication Data
A catalogue record for this book is available from the British Library.

ISBN 0-439-01693-2

The right of Ann Montague-Smith to be identified as the Author of this work has been asserted by her in accordance with the Copyright, Designs and Patents Act 1988.

ACKNOWLEDGEMENTS

The publishers wish to thank:
The Controller of HMSO and the DfEE for the use of extracts from *The National Numeracy Strategy: Framework for Teaching Mathematics* © March 1999, Crown Copyright (1999, DfEE, Her Majesty's Stationery Office).
Galt Educational and NES Arnold Educational Supplies for kindly loaning the equipment used on the front cover.

CONTENTS

INTRODUCTION

100 Maths Lessons is a series of year-specific teachers' resource books, for Reception to Year 6, that provide a core of support material for the teaching of mathematics within the National Numeracy Strategy *Framework for Teaching Mathematics* (March 1999) and within the structure of the 'dedicated mathematics lesson'. Each book offers three terms of medium-term planning grids, teaching objectives and lesson plans. At least 100 maths lessons are given in detail, with outlines for all the others needed to provide support for teachers for a whole year of maths teaching. Photocopiable activity pages and resources are included to support the learning. Regular assessment is built into the structure of the book, with assessment activity pages which can be kept as evidence of attainment.

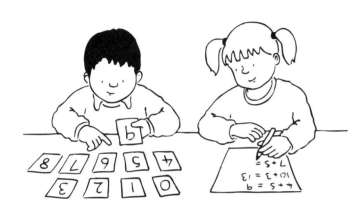

The activities in this book are designed to encourage pupils to develop mental strategies, to use paper and pencil methods appropriately, and to use and apply their mathematics in realistic tasks. There is a strong emphasis upon encouraging pupils to explain to each other the mathematics that they have used, the strategies that they employed and to compare these with each other to determine efficiency of method.

Each **100 Maths Lessons** book provides support across all the mathematics topics and learning objectives specified for a particular year group. However, the pages of the books have been hole-punched and perforated, so that they can be removed and placed in teachers' own resource files, where they can be interleaved with complementary materials from the school's existing schemes. This makes the integration of favourite material into this series very easy.

These books are intended as a support for the dedicated mathematics lesson for school mathematics coordinators, teachers and trainee teachers. The series of books can be used as the basis of planning, teaching and assessment for the whole school, from Reception to Year 6. These resources can be adapted for use by the whole school for single-aged classes, mixed-age classes, single- and mixed-ability groups, and for team planning across a year or a key stage. There is sufficient detail in the differentiated group activities within the 100 lesson plans to offer guidance to classroom assistants working with a group.

The content of these activities is appropriate for and adaptable to the requirements of Primary 1–2 in Scottish schools. In schools which decide not to adopt the National Numeracy Strategy, choose activities to match your planning.

USING THIS BOOK

THE MATERIALS

This book provides at least 100 maths lesson plans for Year 1, and further activity ideas to support all other dedicated maths lessons required during the year. Each maths lesson plan contains ideas for developing pupils' oral and mental maths, a detailed explanation of the main part of the lesson, ideas for differentiated activities, and suggestions for the plenary session. The book follows the Year 1 planning grid given in the National Numeracy Strategy *Framework for Teaching Mathematics* and so for each teaching section, whether one, two or three units of work, there are some detailed lesson plans and objectives, as well as outlined content for the other lessons. These materials should be regarded as a core for developing your own personalised folder for the year. More detail on planning and managing all aspects of the National Numeracy Strategy can be found in the *Framework for Teaching Mathematics*.

ADAPTING AND PERSONALISING THE MATERIALS

The materials are based upon the 'Teaching programme and planning grid' for Year 1 from the National Numeracy Strategy *Framework for Teaching Mathematics*. What follows is a suggested method of using this book to its full potential, but bear in mind that you may need to make adjustments to these materials in order to meet the learning needs of the pupils in your class.

● Separate the pages of the book and place them in an A4 ring binder.

● Check that the activities are of a suitable level for your pupils and agree with colleagues who teach higher and lower years that the entry level is a good match. If not, you can use materials from the **100 Maths Lessons** books for the previous or subsequent year, as appropriate.

● Add your own favourite materials in the relevant places.

● If your school uses a published scheme, insert suitable teacher and pupil resources into your file to supplement these materials.

PREPARING A SCHEME OF WORK

All schools are required to write detailed schemes of work, and this series has been designed to facilitate this process. The termly 'Planning grids' given in these books (see page 20 for example) are provided at the beginning of the work for each term and list all the learning objectives.

ORGANISATION

The **Organisation chart** outlines the key activities for each part of each maths lesson and can be used as a weekly plan.

LEARNING OUTCOMES	ORAL AND MENTAL STARTER	MAIN TEACHING ACTIVITY	PLENARY
LESSON 1 ● Know the number names and recite them in order to at least 20, from and back to zero. ● Describe and extend number sequences: **count on and back in ones from any small number**.	FINGER ADD: Children use their fingers to show additions for numbers to at least 5.	COUNTING RHYMES: Whole class activities involving counting games.	FINGER ADD.
LESSON 2 ● **Count reliably at least 10 objects**.	FINGER SUBTRACT: Children use their fingers to show subtractions for numbers to at least 5.	COUNT, TOUCH AND MOVE: Introduction of zero.	COUNTING PICTURES.
LESSON 3 ● **Count reliably at least 10 objects**.	FINGER ADD AND SUBTRACT: Counting waves around the class.	TOUCH AND COUNT: Counting games.	COUNTING PICTURES.
ORAL AND MENTAL SKILLS Know by heart: addition facts for all pairs of numbers with a total up to at least 5, and the corresponding subtraction facts.			

LESSON PLANS

After the **Organisation chart** comes a short section detailing which lessons are shown as full lesson plans and which are extensions of what has already been taught in a previous lesson. Some of these will be shown in grid form.

DETAILED LESSON PLANS

Each detailed lesson plan is written to the following headings:

Resources
Provides a list of what you need for that lesson.

Preparation

Outlines any advance preparation needed before the lesson begins, such as making resources or photocopying worksheets.

Learning outcomes

These are based upon the objectives in the 'Teaching programme: Year 1' from the *Framework for Teaching Mathematics*. All the objectives are covered at least once in this book. Key objectives for Year 1 are highlighted in bold as they are in the *Framework for Teaching Mathematics*. If a lesson does not cover an objective in its entirety, then only the portion which is intended to be covered is listed in the 'Learning outcomes' (or any of the grids provided).

The specific objectives for the **Oral and mental starter** and **Main teaching activity** are listed separately.

Vocabulary

The National Numeracy Strategy *Mathematical Vocabulary* booklet has been used to provide the vocabulary lists. New or specific vocabulary to be used during the lesson is listed. Use this vocabulary with the whole class so that all the children have a chance to hear it and begin to understand it. Encourage pupils to use the vocabulary orally, when asking or answering questions, so that they develop understanding of its mathematical meaning. Where flashcards are suggested these can be made by printing out onto card the appropriate sections from the CD-ROM which should have accompanied your school's copy of the *Framework for Teaching Mathematics*.

Oral and mental starter

This is designed to occupy the first 5–10 minutes of the lesson, but the duration of the work is not critical. This section contains activity suggestions to develop oral and mental work to be used with the whole class and is based on what has already been taught. Some suggestions for differentiated questioning are included to show how all the children can benefit. The detail in the lesson plan will help you to: provide a variety of sequentially planned, short oral and mental activities throughout the week; use a good range of open and closed questions; encourage all children to take part; target differentiated questions to individuals, pairs or small groups.

Main teaching activity

This sets out what to do in the whole-class teaching session and should last for about 30 minutes. In some lessons much of the time will be spent in whole-class, interactive teaching. In others, the whole-class session will be shorter, with differentiated activities for groups, pairs or individuals. The detailed lesson plan will help you to organise this part of the lesson appropriately.

Differentiation

This section suggests activities for differentiated group, paired or individual work, for the more able and less able children within the class. These activities will take the form of reinforcement, enrichment or extension, and many will provide challenges to encourage pupils to use and apply their mathematics.

Plenary

This session is a chance to bring the children together again for a 10-minute whole-class session. This offers opportunities to assess pupils' progress, summarise key facts learnt, compare strategies used, make links to other topics and to plan for the next topic.

EXTENSION LESSON PLANS

These provide activities which extend those already covered. They are less detailed, as they are based on one of the previous lessons for that week.

OUTLINE LESSON PLANS

These contain brief descriptions, as grids, of further lessons. They extend the scope of the book to give sufficient material for a year's work. Since they develop work already introduced, there are no vocabulary suggestions as the same range of words will be needed as in the previous, related lesson(s). For example:

RESOURCES	Photocopiable page 24 (Number mat); paper; pencils; dice: 1–6, 5–10, 10–15; 'big book' counting picture.
LEARNING OUTCOMES	**ORAL AND MENTAL STARTER** ● Know by heart addition facts for all pairs of numbers with a total up to at least 5, and the corresponding subtraction facts. **MAIN TEACHING ACTIVITY** ● **Count reliably at least 10 objects.**
ORAL AND MENTAL STARTER	Repeat the 'Finger add' and 'Finger subtract' activities. Count around the class from zero to 10, then 20, and back again.
MAIN TEACHING ACTIVITY	TOUCH AND COUNT: Ask children to count items on the Number mat, such as the bones, the flowers, the birds. Ask questions: *Which is more/fewer: the birds or the bones?* When they are confident, ask them to work in pairs, one rolls a 5–10 dice and draws that number of bones on paper, the other counts to check.
DIFFERENTIATION	Less able: use the 1–6 dice. More able: use the 10–15 dice.
PLENARY	Repeat the big book counting activity, using a different picture from the previous lesson.

USING THE LESSON PLANS

The plans are designed so that you can work through them in order, if you wish. However, you may prefer to choose the lessons that are appropriate for your pupils, and combine these with your favourite activities from other sources. By placing the pages of this book into a ring binder you can easily incorporate your own supplementary materials.

WEEKLY PLANNING

If you wish to use the ready-prepared plans, follow the Organisation chart which appears at the beginning of each unit or block of units of work.

If you prefer to plan your week using some of the lesson plans in the book, and some activities you have chosen yourself, then make some photocopies of the blank **Weekly planning chart** on page 12 of this book. These can then be completed with details of all the activities which you intend to use, those chosen from this book and those which you have taken from other sources.

MIXED-AGE CLASSES

If you have a mixed-age class, you will probably need to use the materials from more than one book in this series. You will find the blank **Weekly planning chart** on page 12 a useful planning tool, as you can combine planning from two books onto this chart.

BLANK WEEKLY PLANNING CHART

Make photocopies of this chart, complete a copy on a weekly basis and keep this in your planning file. You may prefer to enlarge the chart to A3.

Week beginning: *7 September*

Learning objectives for oral and mental skills	• Know the number names and recite them in order to at least 20, from and back to zero. • Describe and extend number sequences: **count on and back in ones from any small number, and in tens from and back to zero.** • **Count reliably at least 10 objects.**			
Oral and mental starter	Main teaching activity	Differentiation	Plenary	Resources
Finger add: children use their fingers to show additions for numbers to at least 5.	**Counting rhymes:** whole-class activities involving counting games and rhymes.	Less able: counting from O/1 to 5 and back. More able: counting on to 20 and back.	**Finger add:** as in the **Oral and mental** session.	Number rhymes such as 'One, two, three, four, five, Once I caught a fish alive' or 'Ten green bottles'.

CLASSROOM ORGANISATION

WHOLE-CLASS TEACHING

During a whole-class session it is important that all the children can see you, the board or flip chart and their table top. In many classrooms space is at a premium, so it is worth spending time considering how the furniture can best be arranged. If you have a carpeted area for whole-class work, think about whether the lesson you are planning to teach would work well with the children seated on the carpet, or whether they would be better placed at their tables, especially if you want them to manipulate apparatus, such as interlocking cubes, or they need to spread out numeral cards in front of them.

GROUP WORK

Again, it is important that the pupils sit so that they can see you, and the board or flip chart if necessary. While they are working in groups you may wish to ask whole-class questions, or remind pupils of how much time is left to complete their task, so eye contact will help to ensure that everyone is listening.

WORKING WITH OTHER ADULTS

If you have classroom helpers, brief them before the lesson starts on which group you would like them to work with; the purpose of the task; the vocabulary they should be helping to develop; and give some examples of the type of questions they should be asking. Check that all the resources needed are available or, if not, that the helper knows where to find them. You may want to ask a classroom helper to work with just one or two pupils; perhaps they are finding the work difficult, or have been absent and this is an opportunity to catch up on missed work. Whatever the reason, always ensure that the helper is well briefed before the lesson starts, and allow a few minutes after the lesson has finished to discuss any specific observations which the helper would like to make.

CHILDREN WITH SPECIAL EDUCATIONAL NEEDS

Include children with special educational needs in the whole-class work. If you have a classroom helper or support assistant ask him or her to sit beside the pupils with special needs to provide support. This could include repeating the questions quietly or encouraging them to use individual resources (such as counting apparatus, a number line or number cards) to find the answer. During differentiated questioning, ensure that some questions are specifically focused for these pupils and encourage them to answer appropriately.

To assist all pupils in reading new vocabulary, and particularly to help those with reading difficulties, make flash cards for the specific mathematics vocabulary which will be used in a series of lessons and encourage the children to read these.

Pupils who are partially sighted or deaf will need to sit close to you, so take this into account when considering the layout of the classroom for maths lessons. Those with emotional or behaviour difficulties will benefit from the structure and routines of the daily maths lesson and, where possible, from the support of a helper who can encourage on-task working. For children who are learning English as an additional language, speak more slowly, repeat instructions, and provide visual clues on worksheets or puzzle cards. For pupils who have an Individual Education Plan (IEP) which includes mathematics as an area of learning difficulty, use other books from this series to find activities of an appropriate level which can be linked to the work of the rest of the class.

HOMEWORK

For Year 1 pupils it is recommended that homework is given regularly on a weekly basis. These activities should be designed to be shared with a parent or carer, or could include

simple puzzles. A homework diary, which is completed by home and school, is a useful tool for logging what the homework is and how the pupil responded. Use a range of different types of task for homework:
● Choose favourite shared homework activities and send these home regularly. Suitable material may be found in *IMPACT Maths Homework* (Key Stage One titles) and *Mental Maths Homework for 6 year olds* all written by The IMPACT Project (published by Scholastic).
● Suggest a game to be played at home which will help the children to learn some number facts.
● Suggest some rhymes or songs to be sung at home that encourage the development of counting skills.

RESOURCES

PHOTOCOPIABLE SHEETS

These support the work and can be resource pages or activity sheets. They are marked with the photocopiable symbol.

Some sheets have many applications and are used throughout the book: these appear at the end of this 'Introduction' on pages 12–18. Others can be found at the end of the relevant unit(s).

Resource sheets

These include numeral and symbol cards, individual number lines and number fans, and can be found on pages 14–18. It is a good idea to make enough of these at the start of the year for each pupil to have at least one (set). You may wish to ask for help from parents and friends of the school to make these resources. Photocopy the pages onto card, then cut out and laminate as required.

For the numeral cards, consider whether to use different coloured card so that the children can put them away more easily, using the colour of their set as an aid. These cards can be stored in small polythene bags or tins so that the pupils can keep their resources in their own desks or trays. Alternatively, store these with a rubber band around each set and give them out at the beginning of the lesson. Store class sets of number lines, fans and trio cards (a rubber band around each set) in marked boxes.

Activity sheets

These are located at the end of the relevant unit(s) and relate to specific activities. They may offer practical activities, more traditional worksheets or games. Photocopy the pages onto A4 paper for the pupils; some activities may ask for an extra A3 enlargement for whole-class use.

Photocopiable activity 'cards' are also located at the end of the relevant unit(s) and relate to specific activities. Enlarge the page to A3, then cut into two A4 sheets. Enlarge again and photocopy onto card, then cut out.

CLASSROOM EQUIPMENT

All the equipment used in this book will normally be found within any primary school. The following list shows what will be needed on a regular basis. Alternatives are suggested where they would be equally appropriate. It is important that you create a mathematically-stimulating environment for the children, where they regularly encounter numbers. It is therefore assumed that all classrooms will have a long class number line with big numerals and a large 100 square. Ideally the children should be able to read all the numbers easily from their seats. A chalk board and chalk, or flip chart and marker pens, are essential for interactive whole-class sessions. You will also need:
● A 'washing line' strung across the room, with numbers 0 to 20 and beyond pegged on.
● Counting apparatus, such as counters, sorting toys, wooden cubes, beads and laces.
● Counting stick: a metre length of wood, divided into ten alternately-coloured sections.
● Cuisenaire or rods made from interlocking cubes, one colour for each 'number'.
● Measuring apparatus including 'junk' materials.
● Shape apparatus: for example, shape tiles, 3-D shapes, feely bag.
● Base 10 apparatus: ones and tens.

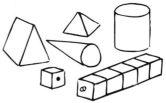

- Construction kits, Plasticine etc.
- Coins, preferably real.
- Dice: both 1–6 and blank.
- Roamer or PIP.
- Dominoes.
- Lots of interlocking cubes, such as Multilink.
- Straws.

USING INFORMATION AND COMMUNICATION TECHNOLOGY

Make use of your favourite mathematical games software as a paired or small group activity. Some of the activities in this book use a programmable toy such as Roamer or PIP. Pupils can use data-handling software to prepare simple graphs as part of the activity.

PUBLICATIONS

Do use your favourite mathematical stories, poems and rhymes as well as the published material available in school. The following Scholastic publications contain some useful ideas:

Oral and mental starter
Developing Mental Maths with 5–7 year olds
by Ros Leather

Main teaching activity
Maths Focus Number Kit 1
(several authors)
Practising Mental Maths:
Photocopiable activities for 6 year olds
by Ros Leather
Quick Mental Maths:
Mental recall practice for 6 year olds
by William Hartley

Homework
IMPACT Maths Homework (Years 1 & 2)
by the IMPACT Project
Mental Maths Homework for 6 year olds
by Helen Williams
Quick Mental Maths:
Mental recall practice for 6 year olds
by William Hartley

Assessment
Maths Focus Number Kit 1
(several authors)
Scholastic Portfolio Assessment:
Maths (Key Stage 1/Scottish Levels A–B)
by Jean Edwards and Ian Gardner

ASSESSMENT

During the week at the end of each half term, an assessment period of two lessons is built into the planning. This gives you the opportunity to make medium-term assessments of the key objectives for Year 1, listed in the National Numeracy Strategy. The aim of these assessments is to:

● Find out what progress each pupil has made, what he or she knows, understands and can do, whether he or she can apply and use their mathematics in context, and whether he or she has any weaknesses.

● Give you information on which to base feedback to pupils and their parents or carers. It will also help you to plan work for the next few weeks.

ASSESSMENT ADVICE

This is placed just before the assessment activity photocopiable sheets. Here you will find information on the aspects of mathematics which are to be assessed; some assessment activities for oral and mental starters which can be used with the whole class, others which can be used with groups, pairs and individuals; and advice on using the photocopiable assessment tasks provided.

ASSESSMENT ACTIVITIES

These activities have been designed so that you can observe pupils at work, and ask questions. Explain the purpose of the activity to them before they begin, as this will help them to demonstrate to you the things that you want to observe, such as clear recording, discussion of which strategy they used, why they used it, and so on. Target small groups for a specific activity and period of time, and work with them, observing how individuals respond to the activity. You may find it useful to have a notebook handy to make informal notes on observations and discussions.

If you have a classroom helper, he or she can also be involved in the assessment process. Explain the purpose of the assessment, what to do, and what to look for. After the lesson has finished make time to discuss observations and keep notes on individual pupils' achievements and weaknesses.

ASSESSMENT PHOTOCOPIABLE SHEETS

There are two photocopiable sheets for each half term assessment period. Each sheet has specific assessment criteria written at the bottom. Photocopy the pages for individual pupils to complete while you observe others undertaking the assessment activities.

Mark the completed sheets, then give pupils feedback on their strengths, and set targets for improvement in their areas of weaknesses. The sheets can be kept in a portfolio as part of the evidence of the children's achievement.

CLASS ASSESSMENT RECORDING SHEET

This will be found on page 13. It lists the key objectives for Year 1 from the National Numeracy Strategy *Framework for Teaching Mathematics*. Photocopy the sheet, enlarge it to A3, and record individuals' progress on it. By the end of the year, after six assessment sessions, you will have a wealth of assessment evidence to pass on to the children's next teacher.

Each half term assessment offers opportunities to assess all the relevant key objectives that have been taught. Some key objectives re-occur in later assessments. It is not necessary to assess every child each time. Use your assessment records to decide whether to re-assess a child or whether it is appropriate to leave a specific assessment objective which has already been learnt.

Weekly planning chart

(Photo-enlarge to A3.)

Week beginning:				
Learning objectives for oral and mental skills				

	Oral and mental starter	Main teaching activity	Differentiation	Plenary	Resources
Monday					
Tuesday					
Wednesday					
Thursday					
Friday					

Year 1: class assessment record sheet

Name	Count reliably at least 20 objects.	Count on and back in ones from any small number, and in tens from and back to zero.	Read, write and order numbers from 0 to at least 20; understand and use the vocabulary of comparing and ordering these numbers.	Within the range 0 to 30, say the number that is 1 or 10 more or less than any given number.	Understand the operation of addition and of subtraction (as 'take away' or 'difference'), and use the related vocabulary.	Know by heart all pairs of numbers with a total of 10.	Use mental strategies to solve simple problems using counting, addition, subtraction, doubling and halving, explaining methods and reasoning orally.	Compare two lengths, masses or capacities by direct comparison.	Suggest suitable standard or uniform non-standard units and measuring equipment to estimate, then measure, a length, mass or capacity.	Use everyday language to describe features of familiar 3-D and 2-D shapes.	Other:
Key Objectives: Year 1											

Numeral cards: 0 to 10

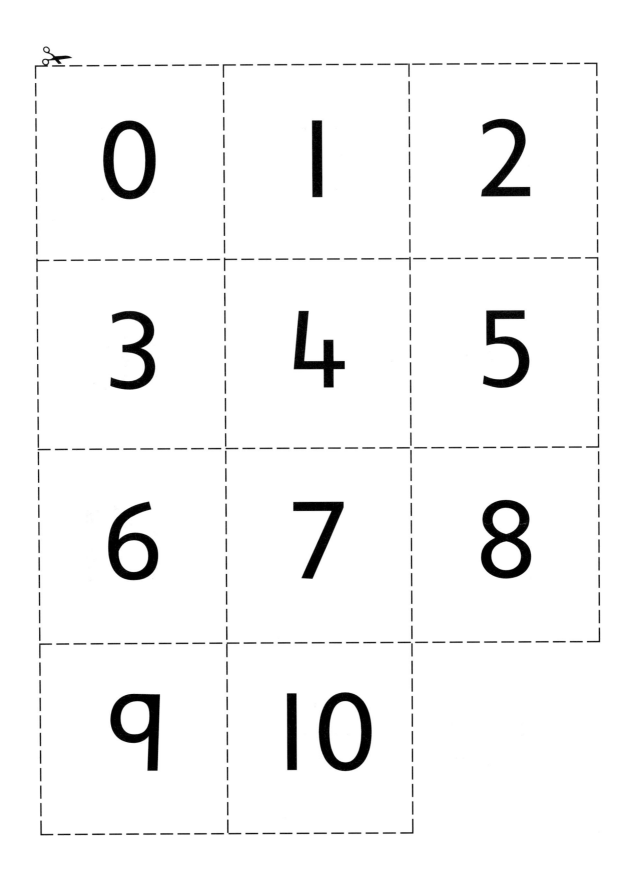

Numeral and symbol cards: 11 to 20, +, −

11	12	13
14	15	16
17	18	19
20	+	−

Numeral and symbol cards: 21 to 30, =

21	22	23
24	25	26
27	28	29
30	=	

Number fan

Photocopy this onto card. Cut out the number panels.
Drill holes as shown, and join the panels together, in number order,
with a paper fastener or bolt.

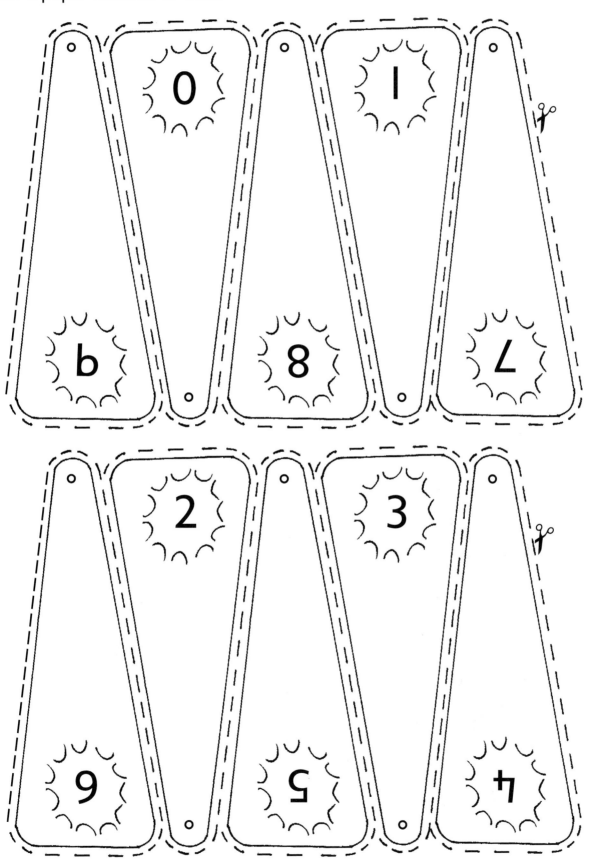

Number lines

Photocopy these onto card and cut them out.

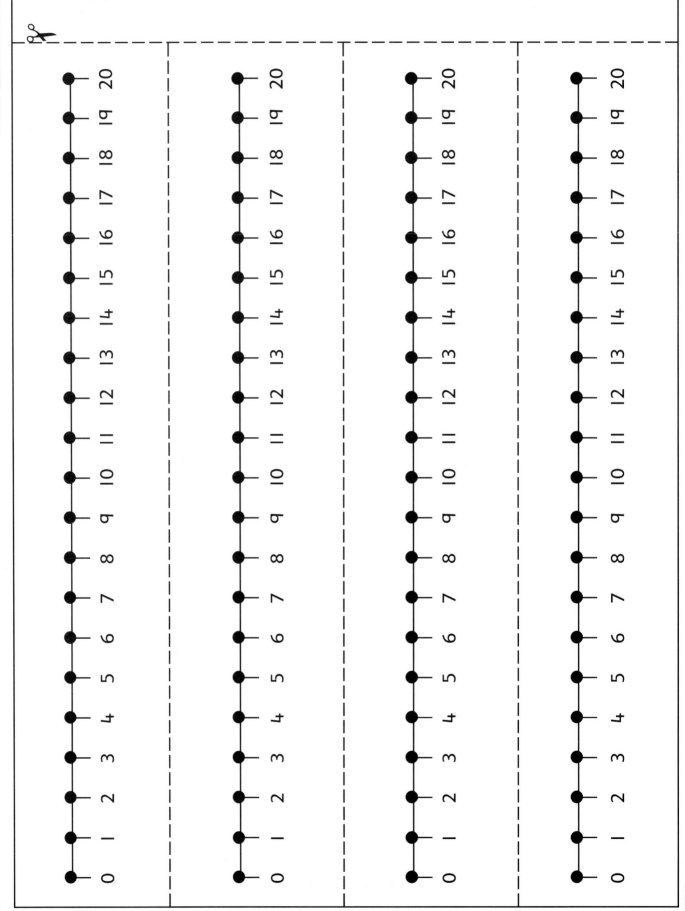

The emphasis in this term is on developing children's knowledge, skills and understanding with numbers to at least 10, then 20. Some mental strategies for addition are introduced. The children should begin to recall addition facts for all numbers to 5, and then addition facts with totals of 10. Subtraction as 'take away' and 'how many more to make?' are introduced. The children should learn to recognise all the coins, and equivalencies for 2p, 5p and 10p; solving 'real life' money problems. In 'Shape and space' the focus is on 3-D and 2-D shapes and their properties. In 'Measures', the children learn about direct comparisons, using non-standard units and metre sticks, and use this knowledge to solve problems. They begin to learn to tell the time and to know about time passing. In 'Organising and using data' the emphasis is on sorting data they have collected.

ENLARGE THIS SHEET TO A3 AND USE IT AS YOUR MEDIUM-TERM PLANNING GRID.

Oral and mental skills: Know by heart: addition facts for all pairs of numbers with a total up to at least 5, and the corresponding subtraction facts; addition doubles of all numbers to at least 5 (eg 4 + 4). Know the number names and recite them in order to at least 10, then 20, from and back to zero. **Count reliably at least 10 objects**. Describe and extend number sequences: **count on and back in ones from any small number**. Put the larger number first and count on in ones.

UNIT	TOPIC	OBJECTIVES: CHILDREN WILL BE TAUGHT TO
1	Counting and properties of numbers	● Know the number names and recite them in order to at least 20, from and back to zero. Describe and extend number sequences: **count on and back in ones from any small number. Count reliably at least 10 objects**.
2–4	Place value and ordering Understanding + and – Mental calculation strategies (+ and –) Money and 'real life' problems Making decisions	■ **Read and write numerals from 0 to at least 20. Order numbers to at least 20**, and position them on a number track. Begin to know what each digit in a two-digit number represents. Partition a 'teens' number and begin to partition larger two-digit numbers into a multiple of 10 and ones (TU). ■ **Understand the operation of addition, and use the related vocabulary**. Begin to recognise that addition can be done in any order. Begin to use the + and = signs to record mental calculations in a number sentence, and to recognise the use of ☐ to stand for an unknown number. ● Use knowledge that addition can be done in any order to do mental calculations more efficiently. For example: put the larger number first and count on in ones, including beyond 10 (eg 7 + 5); begin to partition into '5 and a bit' when adding 6, 7, 8 or 9, then recombine (eg 6 + 8 = 5 + 1 + 5 + 3 = 10 + 4 = 14). ● Recognise coins of different values. **Use mental strategies to solve simple problems** set in 'real life', money or measurement contexts, **using counting, addition, subtraction, doubling and halving, explaining methods and reasoning orally.** ● Choose and use appropriate number operations and mental strategies to solve problems.
5–6	Measures, including problems Shape and space Reasoning about shapes	● Understand and use the vocabulary related to length. **Compare two lengths, by direct comparison**; extend to more than two. Measure using uniform non-standard units or standard units. **Suggest suitable standard or uniform non-standard units and measuring equipment to estimate, then measure, a length**, recording estimates and measurements as 'about…'. **Use mental strategies to solve simple practical problems** set in measurement contexts, **using counting, addition, subtraction, doubling and halving, explaining methods and reasoning orally**. ■ **Use everyday language to describe features of familiar 3-D shapes**, including the cube, cuboid, sphere, cylinder, cone,… referring to properties such as the shapes of flat faces, or the number of faces or corners…. Make and describe models using construction kits, everyday materials, Plasticine,… . Begin to relate solid shapes to pictures of them. ● Solve simple mathematical problems or puzzles; recognise and predict from simple patterns and relationships. Suggest extensions by asking 'What if…?' or 'What could I try next?' Investigate a general statement about familiar shapes by finding examples that satisfy it. Explain methods and reasoning orally.
7	Assess and review	● **Read, write and order numerals from 0 to at least 20. Describe and extend number sequences: count on and back in ones from any small number. Count reliably at least 10 objects. Understand the operation of addition and use the related vocabulary. Use mental strategies to solve simple problems using counting, addition, subtraction, doubling and halving, explaining methods and reasoning orally. Use everyday language to describe features of familiar 3-D shapes. Compare two lengths by direct comparison. Suggest suitable standard or uniform non-standard units and measuring equipment to estimate, then measure, length. Use mental strategies and count reliably at least 10 objects.**

Oral and mental skills: Know by heart: all pairs of numbers with a total of 10 (eg 3 + 7); addition facts for all pairs of numbers with a total up to at least 5, and the corresponding subtraction facts; addition doubles of all numbers to at least 5 (eg 4 + 4). Begin to recognise the use of symbols ☐ or △ to stand for an unknown number. **Count reliably at least 10 objects. Describe and extend number sequences: count on or back in ones from any small number, and in tens from and back to zero.** Put the larger number first and count on in ones, including beyond 10 (eg 7 + 5); begin to partition into '5 and a bit' when adding 6, 7, 8 or 9, then recombine. Identify near doubles using doubles already known (eg 6 + 5). **Read and write numbers from 0 to at least 20**. Give a sensible estimate of a number of objects that can be checked by counting (eg up to about 15).

UNIT	TOPIC	OBJECTIVES: CHILDREN WILL BE TAUGHT TO
8	Counting and properties of numbers Reasoning about numbers	● Know the number names and recite them in order to at least 20, from and back to zero. Describe and extend number sequences: **count on and back in ones from any small number, and in tens from and back to zero. Count reliably at least 10 objects**. ● Solve simple mathematical problems or puzzles, recognise and predict from simple patterns and relationships. Suggest extensions by asking 'What if…?' or 'What could I try next?' Investigate a general statement about familiar numbers by finding examples that satisfy it. Explain methods and reasoning orally.
9–11	Place value, ordering, estimating Understanding + and – Mental calculation strategies (+ and –) Money and 'real life' problems Making decisions	● Begin to know what each digit in a two-digit number represents. Partition a 'teens' number and begin to partition larger two-digit numbers into a multiple of 10 and ones. Use the = sign to represent equality. Understand and use the vocabulary of estimation. Give a sensible estimate of a number of objects that can be checked by counting (eg up to about 15). ■ **Understand the operation of addition, and of subtraction (as 'take away' and 'how many more to make'), and use the related vocabulary**. Begin to recognise that addition can be done in any order. Begin to recognise that more than two numbers can be added together. ● Use knowledge that addition can be done in any order to do mental calculations more efficiently. For example: put the larger number first and count on in ones, including beyond 10; begin to partition into '5 and a bit' when adding 6, 7, 8, or 9, then recombine. Identify near doubles, using doubles already known (eg 6 + 5). Use patterns of similar calculations (eg 10 – 0 = 10, 10 – 1 = 9, 10 – 2 = 8). ● **Use mental strategies to solve simple problems** set in 'real life' or money contexts, **using counting, addition, subtraction, doubling and halving, explaining methods and reasoning orally**. Recognise coins of different values. Find totals and change from up to 10p. ● Choose and use appropriate number operations and mental strategies to solve problems.
12–13	Measures, and time, including problems Organising and using data	● Understand and use vocabulary related to time. Order familiar events in time. Know the days of the week and the seasons of the year. Read the time to the hour or half-hour on analogue clocks. Understand and use the vocabulary related to length. **Compare two lengths by direct comparison**; extend to more than two. **Suggest suitable standard or uniform non-standard units and measuring equipment to estimate, then measure, a length**, recording estimates as 'about…'. **Use mental strategies to solve simple problems** set in measurement contexts, **using counting, addition, subtraction, doubling and halving, explaining methods and reasoning orally**. ● Solve a given problem by sorting, classifying and organising information in simple ways, such as using objects or pictures. Discuss and explain results.
14	Assess and review	● **Know by heart all pairs of numbers with a total of 10. Count reliably at least 10 objects. Count on or back in ones from any small number and in tens from and back to zero. Read and write numerals to at least 20. Understand the operation of addition, and of lsubtraction (as 'take away'), and use the related vocabulary. Use mental strategies to solve simple problems using counting, addition, subtraction, doubling and halving, explaining methods and reasoning orally. Compare two lengths by direct comparison. Suggest suitable standard or uniform non-standard units and measuring equipment to estimate, then measure, length. Count on and back and use mental strategies.**

UNIT 1

ORGANISATION (3 LESSONS)

	LEARNING OUTCOMES	ORAL AND MENTAL STARTER	MAIN TEACHING ACTIVITY	PLENARY
LESSON 1	● Know the number names and recite them in order to at least 20, from and back to zero. ● Describe and extend number sequences: **count on and back in ones from any small number**.	FINGER ADD: Children use their fingers to show additions for numbers to at least 5.	COUNTING RHYMES: Whole class activities involving counting games.	FINGER ADD.
LESSON 2	● **Count reliably at least 10 objects**.	FINGER SUBTRACT: Children use their fingers to show subtractions for numbers to at least 5.	COUNT, TOUCH AND MOVE: Introduction of zero.	COUNTING PICTURES.
LESSON 3	● **Count reliably at least 10 objects**.	FINGER ADD AND SUBTRACT: Counting waves around the class.	TOUCH AND COUNT: Counting games.	COUNTING PICTURES.

ORAL AND MENTAL SKILLS   Know by heart: addition facts for all pairs of numbers with a total up to at least 5, and the corresponding subtraction facts.

Lessons 1 and 2 are shown in detail for Unit 1. Lesson 3 is an extension of what has already been taught and activity suggestions for it are shown after Lesson 2.

RESOURCES
A selection of favourite counting rhymes.

PREPARATION
Choose some counting rhymes which encourage counting on or back in ones, such as 'One, two, three, four, five, Once I caught a fish alive'; or '10 green bottles'.

LEARNING OUTCOMES

ORAL AND MENTAL STARTER
● **Know by heart**: addition facts for all pairs of numbers with a total up to at least 5.

MAIN TEACHING ACTIVITY
● Know the number names and recite them in order to at least 20, from and back to zero.
● Describe and extend number sequences: **count on and back in ones from any small number**.

VOCABULARY
Number; one, two, three, ...to 20 and beyond; how many...?; count; count (up) to; count on (from/to); count back (from/to); count in ones.

ORAL AND MENTAL STARTER
● FINGER ADD: Explain that when you say a number you want the children to hold up that number of fingers on one hand. You will then say a second number for them to hold up that number of fingers on the other hand. Ask: *How many fingers altogether?* Start with small numbers, such as 2 and 1, and extend to totals within 2 to 6.

MAIN TEACHING ACTIVITY
● COUNTING RHYMES: Explain that today's lesson is about counting. Recite together some counting rhymes such as 'One, two, three, four, five, Once I caught a fish alive'; c

'10 green bottles'. Now repeat counting up to 5, with rules such as: *1, 2, 3, 4, CLAP, 1, 2, …*, then change the number which should be clapped. Count individually around the class, first 1 to 5, then extend to 10. Count together on and back from zero to 10, then 20, and back again. Count on or back in ones from 2, or 3, or 4… to 20. Ask questions: *What is one before/after…?* Finish by counting around the circle in ones from 1 to 10, or 20, then back again.

DIFFERENTIATION

Target the questioning carefully, keeping the number range appropriate to individuals.
Less able: ask them to count on from 0 to 5, and back, then from 1.
More able: encourage them to count to and from 20, and beyond, and to count on from any small number.

PLENARY

Play 'Finger add' again. Ask the children to say number sentences, such as 'Three and two is five.'

LESSON 2

RESOURCES

Interlocking cubes or other counting apparatus in pots; copies of photocopiable page 24 (Number mat); a large counting picture such as those found in mathematics scheme 'big books'.

PREPARATION

On the tables place pots of counting apparatus and one copy of the photocopiable sheet for each child or pair of children.

LEARNING OUTCOMES

ORAL AND MENTAL STARTER
● **Know by heart**: addition facts for all pairs of numbers with a total up to at least 5, and the corresponding subtraction facts.

MAIN TEACHING ACTIVITY
● **Count reliably at least 10 objects**.

ORAL AND MENTAL STARTER

FINGER SUBTRACT: This is played in the same way as 'Finger add' on page 21. Limit the size of the first quantity to 5 or 6. Encourage the children to give a subtraction sentence such as, 'Five take away three is two'.

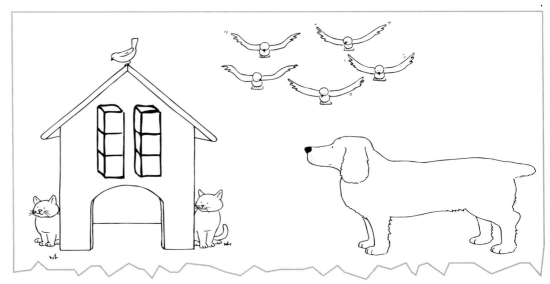

MAIN TEACHING ACTIVITY

COUNT, TOUCH AND MOVE: Ask the children to count out six cubes onto the dog's kennel on the sheet. Then re-count the cubes, simultaneously counting, touching and moving each one in turn onto the dog. Repeat this for different quantities. Introduce the concept of 'zero' as 'nothing' with examples. Ask: *Were there more/fewer cubes on the kennel or on the dog? Was the number still the same?* Then let the children decide how many to count out. Ask questions such as: *How many did you count? Who counted more/fewer than; had the same number as…?*

DIFFERENTIATION

The children will count out quantities within their confidence range. Check that they are counting suitable quantities for their skills. Encourage more able children to extend their counting out skills by counting larger quantities with increasing accuracy.

PLENARY

COUNTING PICTURES: Ask individuals to come out to touch and count objects on the 'big book' counting picture.

LESSON 3

RESOURCES	Photocopiable page 24 (Number mat); paper; pencils; dice: 1–6, 5–10, 10–15; 'big book' counting picture.
LEARNING OUTCOMES	**ORAL AND MENTAL STARTER** ● **Know by heart:** addition facts for all pairs of numbers with a total up to at least 5, and the corresponding subtraction facts. **MAIN TEACHING ACTIVITY** ● **Count reliably at least 10 objects.**
ORAL AND MENTAL STARTER	Repeat the 'Finger add' and 'Finger subtract' activities. Count around the class from zero to 10, then 20, and back again.
MAIN TEACHING ACTIVITY	TOUCH AND COUNT: Ask children to count items on the Number mat, such as the bones, the flowers, the birds. Ask questions: *Which is more/fewer: the birds or the bones?* When they are confident, ask them to work in pairs, one rolls a 5–10 dice and draws that number of bones on paper, the other counts to check.
DIFFERENTIATION	More able: use the 10–15 dice. Less able: use the 1–6 dice.
PLENARY	Repeat the big book counting activity, using a different picture from the previous lesson.

Number mat

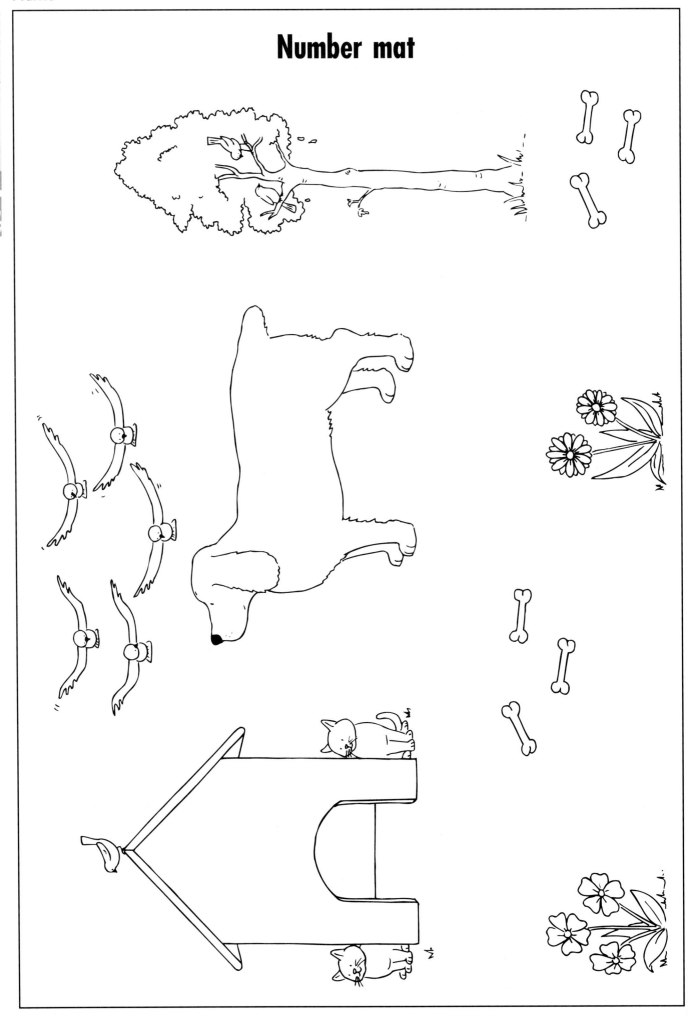

UNIT 1

UNITS 2-4

ORGANISATION (15 LESSONS)

	LEARNING OUTCOMES	ORAL AND MENTAL STARTER	MAIN TEACHING ACTIVITY	PLENARY
LESSON 1	• **Read and write numerals from 0 to at least 20.**	COUNTING STICK: Counting activities.	FIND THE NUMBER: Reading numbers.	Reading numbers.
LESSON 2	• **Read and write numerals from 0 to at least 20.** • **Order numbers to at least 20**, and position them on a number track.	FINGER ADD AND SUBTRACT.	FIND THE NUMBER ON A NUMBER LINE: Reading and writing numbers. Introduction of a number line.	Reading numbers.
LESSON 3 +4 +5	• **Understand the operation of addition, and use the related vocabulary.** • Begin to recognise that addition can be done in any order. • Begin to use the + and = signs to record mental calculations in a number sentence. • Use knowledge that addition can be done in any order to do mental calculations more efficiently. For example: put the larger number first and count on in ones, including beyond 10 (eg 7 + 5).	NUMBER LINE COUNT.	COMBINING SETS: Addition. Recording with numerals and symbols.	Checking results.
LESSON 6	• Recognise coins of different values.	SHOW ME ADD: Putting the larger number first.	COINS: Finding equivalent values of coins; games and recording.	FEELY BAG COINS.
LESSON 7	• Recognise coins of different values.	DOUBLES: Finding doubles up to 5 + 5.	EQUIVALENT VALUES: Finding equivalent values for coins.	Feedback from individuals.
LESSON 8	• Recognise coins of different values.	COUNTING STICK: Counting games.	SHOPPING: Choosing coins to pay for items.	Feedback from individuals.
LESSON 9 +10	• **Understand the operation of addition and use the related vocabulary.** • Begin to recognise that addition can be done in any order. • Begin to use the + and = signs to record mental calculations in a number sentence, and to recognise the use of p to stand for an unknown number. • Begin to partition into 5 and a bit when adding 6, 7, 8 or 9, then recombine (eg 6 + 8 = 5 + 1 + 5 + 3 = 10 + 4 = 14).	SHOW ME ADD: Putting the larger number first.	PARTITIONING: Developing mental strategies.	Feedback from pairs.

cont...

LESSON 11	● **Read and write numerals from 0 to at least 20.**	COUNTING CUBES: Touching and counting; pointing and counting.	READING AND WRITING NUMBERS: Playing games to develop number recognition.	NUMBER FAN ADD AND SUBTRACT: Adding and subtracting within 5.
LESSON 12 +13	● Begin to know what each digit in a two-digit number represents. Partition a 'teens' number and begin to partition larger two-digit numbers into a multiple of 10 and ones (TU).	NUMBER FAN ADD AND SUBTRACT: Adding and subtracting within 5.	TENS AND ONES: Bundling ones to make 10.	Discussion of recording of tens and units.
LESSON 14 +15	● **Use mental strategies to solve simple problems** set in 'real life', money or measurement contexts, **using counting, addition, subtraction, doubling and halving, explaining methods and reasoning orally.** ● Choose and use appropriate number operations and mental strategies to solve problems.	COUNTING: Counting to 20 and back.	PROBLEMS: Adding in 'real life' and with money.	Feedback from individuals.

ORAL AND MENTAL SKILLS **Know by heart:** addition facts for all pairs of numbers with a total up to at least 5; addition doubles of all numbers to at least 5 (eg 4 + 4). Know the number names and recite them in order to at least 10, then 20, from and back to zero. **Count reliably at least 10 objects.** Describe and extend number sequences: **count on and back in ones from any small number.** Put the larger number first and count on in ones.

Lessons 1, 2 and 3 are shown in detail for Unit 2. Lessons 4 and 5 are extensions of what has already been taught and activity suggestions are shown after Lesson 3. For Unit 3, Lessons 6, 8, 9 and 10 are shown in detail and Lesson 7 activity suggestions are shown after Lesson 6. For Unit 4 all lessons are shown in detail.

RESOURCES
A set of numeral cards for each child, 0–10 (page 14) or 0–20 (pages 14 and 15); teacher's set of large numeral cards 0 to 20; counting stick (see Introduction, page 4); flip chart and pen; pencils and tracing paper.

LEARNING OUTCOMES

ORAL AND MENTAL STARTER
● Describe and extend number sequences: **count on and back in ones from any small number.**

MAIN TEACHING ACTIVITY
● **Read and write numerals from 0 to at least 20.**

VOCABULARY
Counting numbers zero to 20.

ORAL AND MENTAL STARTER

COUNTING STICK: Explain that you would like the children to count together, from 0 to 10, and that you will point to the sections on the counting stick as you count. Explain that one end of the stick represents 0, and the other end 10. Ask the children to imagine where the counting numbers are placed on the stick. Count up to 10, then back again. Repeat this until the children are confident, then: count quietly; count loudly; count backwards from 10 to 0. Repeat, this time with one end of the stick representing 10 and the other end 20, counting forwards and backwards.

UNITS 2–4

MAIN TEACHING ACTIVITY

FIND THE NUMBER: Give each child a set of numeral cards. Hold up a large numeral card and ask the children to hold up the same numeral when you say *Show me*. Ask a child to read the number. Repeat this for other numerals. Then say: *Hold up the card with 9, or 4, or 10, or... on it*. On the flip chart, write the number 2, and ask the children to trace this number shape with their finger on the table top. Repeat this with other numbers. Ask individuals to come out and write specific numerals on the flip chart. Finally, ask the children to place their numeral cards in order, 0 to 9, then to trace the numerals in order onto tracing paper. Check that they start each numeral from the top.

DIFFERENTIATION

For the more able, extend the range of numbers up to 20.

PLENARY

Invite individuals to come out to write numerals on the flip chart, such as their age, house number, number of pets and so on.

RESOURCES

A number line for each child (page 18); teacher's set of large numeral cards 0 to 20; number word cards 'zero' to 'twenty'; washing line and pegs; class number line.

PREPARATION

Make number word cards and photocopy a number line for each child. Hang up the washing line and pin up a class number line so that everyone will be able to see it.

LEARNING OUTCOMES

ORAL AND MENTAL STARTER
● **Know by heart**: addition facts for all pairs of numbers with a total up to at least 5.
MAIN TEACHING ACTIVITY
● **Read and write numerals from 0 to at least 20**.
● **Order numbers to at least 20**, and position them on a number track.

VOCABULARY
Counting numbers zero to 10, then 20.

ORAL AND MENTAL STARTER

FINGER ADD AND SUBTRACT: Ask the children to hold up their fingers to show the answers to questions such as: *3 add 2; 6 take away 4; 2 plus 1...*

MAIN TEACHING ACTIVITY

FIND THE NUMBER ON A NUMBER LINE: Ask individuals to peg the large numeral cards on the washing line, in order. Read a number word card together and ask where it should go. Peg the word to the numeral. Continue to peg all the words to their numerals. Play 'Find the number', (see Lesson 1, page 26), but this time include number word and numeral cards. Using the class number line, say: *Start at 3; count on 2. What number have you reached?* Ask individuals to point to the 3, then count on 2 and say the answer. Check that they count on from the first number. Give examples for children to try on their own number lines.

DIFFERENTIATION

Less able: limit the range of numerals and words.
More able: extend the range to 20.

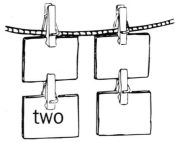

PLENARY

Shuffle the cards from the washing line, and ask individuals where they should be pegged to put them back up in order.

RESOURCES

A copy of photocopiable page 24 (Number mat) for each child; counting apparatus, including cubes; 0–5 dice; flip chart and pen; pencils; a class number line.

PREPARATION

Prepare the photocopiable sheets. The Main teaching activity may be easier if the children have A3 copies of the Number mat.

LEARNING OUTCOMES

ORAL AND MENTAL STARTER

● Know the number names and recite them in order to at least 10, from and back to zero. Describe and extend number sequences: **count on and back in ones from any small number**.

MAIN TEACHING ACTIVITY

● **Understand the operation of addition, and use the related vocabulary**.
● Begin to recognise that addition can be done in any order.
● Begin to use the + and = signs to record mental calculations in a number sentence.
● Use knowledge that addition can be done in any order to do mental calculations more efficiently. For example: put the larger number first and count on in ones, including beyond 10 (eg 7 + 5).

VOCABULARY
Add; more; plus; make; sum; total; altogether; one more; two more; equals; sign; plus.

ORAL AND MENTAL STARTER

NUMBER LINE COUNT: Count aloud from zero to 10 and back. Refer to the class number line and say *Start on 3; count on 4. What number have you landed on?* Repeat for other starting numbers.

MAIN TEACHING ACTIVITY

COMBINING SETS: Give each child a number mat. Ask the children to count out four cubes onto the dog, then one onto the kennel. Ask: *How many cubes are there altogether? Four, and one more. There are five.* Give other examples. Encourage them to count on in their heads from the larger number: *Three, four, five; there are five.* Write the sum 3 + 2 = 5 on the flip chart and explain what the + and = signs mean, using the terms 'and', 'add' and 'equals'. Repeat this for different quantities, asking children to come out and write the addition sums on the flip chart.

Then, in pairs, ask the children to throw two 0–5 dice; put out cubes for each number; write an addition sum on the dog on their sheet and count on from the larger number using the apparatus to find the total.

DIFFERENTIATION

Less able: use two 1, 1, 2, 2, 3, 3 dice.
More able: encourage them to count on in their heads (rather than touching and moving the cubes).

PLENARY

Invite individuals to read out one of their additions and ask the others to find the answer by counting on.

LESSON 4

RESOURCES	Photocopiable pages 24 (Number mat) and 18 (Number lines) per child; pack of 0–5 numeral cards per pair (page 14); pencils; counting apparatus (cubes).
LEARNING OUTCOMES	**ORAL AND MENTAL STARTER** ● Know the number names and recite them in order to at least 20, from and back to zero. ● Describe and extend number sequences: **count on and back in ones from any small number**. **MAIN TEACHING ACTIVITY** ● **Understand the operation of addition, and use the related vocabulary**. ● Begin to recognise that addition can be done in any order. ● Begin to use the + and = signs to record mental calculations in a number sentence. ● Use knowledge that addition can be done in any order to do mental calculations more efficiently. For example: put the larger number first and count on in ones, including beyond 10 (eg 7 + 5).
ORAL AND MENTAL STARTER	Repeat 'Number line count' from Lesson 3, page 28.
MAIN TEACHING ACTIVITY	Repeat 'Combining sets' from Lesson 3 page 28, changing the quantities in the examples used with the whole class. Pairs then take turns to turn over a card from a 0–5 pack, count on 2 on a number line and record the answer as an addition sum.
DIFFERENTIATION	Less able: use apparatus, putting out the card number in cubes, then counting out two more to count on 2. More able: include counting on 3 and 4.
PLENARY	Ask individuals to read out their sums and others to state the answer. Discuss what happens when zero is added to a number.

LESSON 5

RESOURCES	Two sets of 0–5 numeral cards (page 14) per pair; symbol cards for + and = (pages 14 and 15); photocopiable pages 24 (Number mat) and 18 (Number line) per child; flip chart and marker pens; paper and pencils.
LEARNING OUTCOMES	**ORAL AND MENTAL STARTER** ● Know the number names and recite them in order to at least 20, from and back to zero. ● Describe and extend number sequences: **count on and back in ones from any small number**. **MAIN TEACHING ACTIVITY** ● **Understand the operation of addition, and use the related vocabulary**. ● Begin to recognise that addition can be done in any order. ● Begin to use the + and = signs to record mental calculations in a number sentence. ● Use knowledge that addition can be done in any order to do mental calculations more efficiently. For example: put the larger number first and count on in ones, including beyond 10 (7 + 5).
ORAL AND MENTAL STARTER	Repeat 'Number line count' from Lesson 3, page 28.
MAIN TEACHING ACTIVITY	Repeat 'Combining sets' from Lesson 3, using numeral cards instead of counting apparatus. Children make the sums using numeral and symbol cards. Working in pairs using just the 0–5 cards in one stack, and 1, 2 and 3 cards in the other, they take turns to take two cards and make addition sentences, counting on a number line to find the total, and writing out the addition sums.
DIFFERENTIATION	Less able: one stack of 0–5 cards, the other all 1s. More able: two stacks of 0–5 cards.
PLENARY	Ask individuals to come out and write one of their sums on the flip chart for others to answer.

RESOURCES

Coins of all denominations; numeral cards (page 14) and a number line (page 18) for each child; large cards each with a picture of a different coin; large card labels of amounts (1p, 2p... up to 10p); washing line and pegs; flip chart and pen; feely bag.

PREPARATION

Make the required photocopies and coin cards. Put a selection of coins on each table.

LEARNING OUTCOMES

ORAL AND MENTAL STARTER

Put the larger number first and count on in ones.

MAIN TEACHING ACTIVITY

Recognise coins of different values.

VOCABULARY

Money; coin; pence; penny; pound; how much...?; total.

ORAL AND MENTAL STARTER

SHOW ME ADD: Ask the children to put the larger number first and count on in ones in their heads, then to hold up the relevant numeral card when you say *Show me*. Begin with adding 1: *3 add 1; 2 add 1*; then adding 2. Include some doubles, such as 2 + 2.

MAIN TEACHING ACTIVITY

COINS: Show a picture of a 1p coin. Ask a child to find the coin. Repeat for other coins to 10p. Ask individuals to peg the coin cards onto the washing line in order of value. When the children recognise the coins easily, ask them to find a specific coin, then show the picture for them to check. On the flip chart write 1p: *How much is this? Which coin do you need?* Repeat for 2p, 5p and 10p. Then ask the children to count out enough 1p coins to make 3p, 4p, and so on.

DIFFERENTIATION

Encourage everyone to join in. Observe who is confident with coin recognition, and who will need more support. This can be given during the next lesson.

PLENARY

FEELY BAG COINS: put a selection of coins into a bag and ask individuals to find a coin by touch.

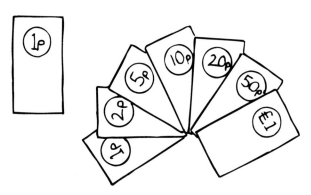

RESOURCES	Coins; number lines (page 18); large coin picture cards; large card labels of amounts 1p to 10p; washing line and pegs; flip chart and pen; photocopiable page 36 (Money boxes) with totals such as 4p, 6p, 7p written in, an A3 copy of this sheet; Blu-Tack; number fans (page 17).
LEARNING OUTCOMES	**ORAL AND MENTAL STARTER** ● **Know by heart**: addition doubles of all numbers to at least 5 (eg 4 + 4). **MAIN TEACHING ACTIVITY** ● Recognise coins of different values.
ORAL AND MENTAL STARTER	DOUBLES: Encourage counting on in ones to find simple doubles: 3 add 3; double 2;... up to 5 + 5. Children hold up a blade of their fans to show the answer.
MAIN TEACHING ACTIVITY	EQUIVALENT VALUES: Show the 2p coin card and explain that a 2p coin is worth two 1p coins. Record on the flip chart 2p = 1p + 1p. Show the 5p card and ask: *How many 1p coins are worth the same?* Ask children to find ways of making 5p using 1p and 2p coins. Record their results on the flip chart. Repeat for other values, such as 4p, 6p or 7p. Children then complete the worksheet by drawing in coins to make the totals. Encourage them to use the least number of coins possible for each box.
DIFFERENTIATION	Less able: work with this group, reinforcing understanding of coin values. More able: write in values such as 9p or 10p on another copy of the Money boxes sheet for the children to complete.
PLENARY	Work through the worksheet with the children, using the A3 copy attached to the flip chart with Blu-Tack.

RESOURCES

A selection of 1p, 2p, 5p and 10p coins available for each child; priced packages or labels with prices on them; flip chart and marker pen; paper and pencil.

PREPARATION

Prepare some priced packages for shopping or priced labels, using amounts from 1p to 10p. You may wish to set up a class shop to role play shopping and giving change.

LEARNING OUTCOMES

ORAL AND MENTAL STARTER

Know the number names and recite them in order to at least 20, from and back to zero. Describe and extend number sequences: **count on and back in ones from any small number**.

MAIN TEACHING ACTIVITY

Recognise coins of different values.

VOCABULARY
Money; coin; pence; penny; price; cost; buy; sell; pay; change; dear; costs more/ less; cheap; cheaper; how much...?.

ORAL AND MENTAL STARTER

COUNTING STICK: Repeat this activity from Lesson 1 page 26.

MAIN TEACHING ACTIVITY

SHOPPING: Hold up a priced package and ask: *How much is this...? Which coins shall I use to pay for it?* Children choose from their selection of coins, counting out enough to pay for the item. Ask, for 4p: *Which coins did you choose? How much does that make? What other way can we make 4p?* Write the range of responses on the flip chart:

    4p → 1p +1p + 1p + 1p
    4p → 1p + 1p + 2p
    4p → 2p + 2p

Discuss which way uses the least number of coins. Repeat with other examples. Encourage the children to choose the least number of coins. Ask them to work in pairs, taking turns to choose a price and count out coins, while their partners check that they have the least number of coins and record in the same way as on the flip chart.

DIFFERENTIATION

Less able: provide lower prices, to 5p.
More able: when they are confident with prices to 10p, extend the range to 20p.

PLENARY

Ask pairs to choose a price and write their choice of coins on the flip chart. Encourage the others to check that the result uses the least number of coins.

RESOURCES

Cuisenaire rods; interlocking cubes; two packs of numeral cards, shuffled together, for each pair; flip chart and pen; number line for each child; a copy of photocopiable page 37 (Number line add) for each child; an A3 enlargement of Number line add.

PREPARATION

For Lesson 10: Prepare a number line and a copy of photocopiable page 37 (Number line add) for each child. Enlarge one copy of the photocopiable sheet.

LEARNING OUTCOMES

ORAL AND MENTAL STARTER

Put the larger number first and count on in ones.

MAIN TEACHING ACTIVITY

● **Understand the operation of addition, and use the related vocabulary**.
Begin to recognise that addition can be done in any order.
Begin to use the + and = signs to record mental calculations in a number sentence, and to recognise the use of symbols $\square$ or $\triangle$ to stand for an unknown number.
● Begin to partition into '5 and a bit' when adding 6, 7, 8 or 9, then recombine (eg $6 + 8 = 5 + 1 + 5 + 3 = 10 + 4 = 14$).

VOCABULARY
Add; sum; total; altogether; one more; two more; equals; sign; plus.

ORAL AND MENTAL STARTER

Repeat 'Show me add' as in Lesson 6 (see page 30).

MAIN TEACHING ACTIVITY

PARTITIONING: Ask the children to put out a 6-rod with a 5-rod below. Ask: *Which rod do I need to add to the 5 rod to match the 6 rod?* (A 1 rod.) Repeat this, matching the 7 rod with the 5 rod and a 2 rod. Then use the 8 and 9 rods, making the numbers into '5 and a bit' each time. Write $5 + 6 =$ on the flip chart and ask children to use their rods as before, changing the 6 rod into a 5 rod and a 1 rod. Write $5 + 5 + 1 =$ on the chart. Ask: *What is 5 add 5? What is 10 add 1?* Encourage counting on to find the answer.

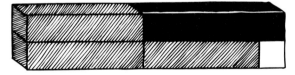 Working in pairs, the children take a numeral card from their stack and add the card number to 5. They must decide whether they need to partition the number into '5 and a bit' and then take turns to record the sum as you did on the flip chart.

DIFFERENTIATION

Less able: provide interlocking cubes or number lines if children have difficulty using the rods. This will allow them to count in ones.
More able: encourage the children to count on in their heads from 10.

PLENARY

Choose pairs to show their work. They can write some of their sums on the flip chart.

LESSON 10

Repeat Lesson 9, but in the **Main teaching activity** use a number line for counting on from 10, instead of the rods. The children can then complete photocopiable page 37 (Number line add). Make sure the children understand that the box after the = sign is for their answer – it represents a missing number to make the sum complete. In the Plenary session, complete an A3 enlargement of the worksheet with the children.

RESOURCES

About 10 cubes, buttons or other counting items for each child; large numeral cards 0 to 20, and word cards for 0 to 20; a number fan (photocopiable page 17) and a pack of numeral cards 0 to 20 for each child; a class number line; pegs.

LEARNING OUTCOMES

ORAL AND MENTAL STARTER
● **Count reliably at least 10 objects**.

MAIN TEACHING ACTIVITY
● **Read and write numerals from 0 to at least 20**.

VOCABULARY
Counting numbers 0 to 10, then 20.

ORAL AND MENTAL STARTER

COUNTING CUBES: Ask the children to count out a given number of cubes. Say: *Count out eight cubes. Put them in a straight line. How many have you? Put them in a circle. How many now?* Repeat this for other amounts.

MAIN TEACHING ACTIVITY

READING AND WRITING NUMBERS: Shuffle the large 0–10 numeral cards. Ask the children to take turns to find the next numeral to peg onto the number line. Extend this to 11–20. Remove all the cards, shuffle them, and ask individuals to peg the top card in the correct position on the line and explain why it has been pegged at that point. When the line is complete, ask for the number word cards to be pegged onto the numerals, 0–10, then to 20. Remove and shuffle them, and ask for them to be pegged once more to the correct numeral. Using their own numeral cards, ask the children to hold up the relevant card: *Find the card with '12' on* or, hold up a number word card: *Find the numeral card which matches this. Find the card which is one more/less than....*

DIFFERENTIATION

Less able: direct questions within their number range to them, encourage them to follow what the other children do.
More able: provide more challenging questions, such as: *Find me the number which is 3 more than this.*

PLENARY

Number fan add and subtract: Ask facts including doubles, using numbers to at least 5: *3 and 2; 5 subtract 1; 2 + 2; 4 + 4.* Encourage the children to count in their heads or use the class number line, and to hold up the relevant blade of their fans to answer.

RESOURCES

Number fan (photocopiable page 17) for each child; straws; elastic bands; flip chart and pen; pencils and paper. For lesson 13, Base 10 apparatus (Cuisenaire or Dienes blocks, instead of straws and elastic bands) and photocopiable page 38 (Base 10).

PREPARATION

Make the required photocopies.

LEARNING OUTCOMES

ORAL AND MENTAL STARTER

● **Know by heart**: addition facts for all pairs of numbers with a total up to at least 5.

MAIN TEACHING ACTIVITY

● **Read and write numerals from 0 to at least 20.**
● Begin to know what each digit in a two-digit number represents. Partition a 'teens' number and begin to partition larger two-digit numbers into a multiple of 10 and ones (TU).

VOCABULARY

Units; ones; tens; digit; figure; 'teens' number; exchange; the same number as; as many as; equal to.

ORAL AND MENTAL STARTER

Play 'Number fan add and subtract' from Lesson 11 on page 33.

MAIN TEACHING ACTIVITY

TENS AND ONES: Ask the children to count out 12 straws, then to bundle ten of them together with an elastic band. Ask: *How many in the elastic band? How many left? How many altogether? So 12 is the same as 1 ten and 2.* On the flip chart write: 12 ➔ 1 ten and 2 units. Repeat this for other quantities, to 20. Ask the children to work in pairs, taking turns to count a handful of straws, bundle 10, and record this on paper as you did on the flip chart.

DIFFERENTIATION

Less able: prepare a recording sheet for them, copying the lay out on the flip chart.
More able: encourage them to estimate how many there are before they count, and then to record their estimate as well.

PLENARY

Discuss children's recording and how a 'teens' number can be read as 'one 10 and …'

LESSON 13

As for Lesson 12, but in the **Main teaching activity** use Base 10 apparatus instead of the straws and elastic bands used in Lesson 12. Ask the children to put out a 10-rod, then to match it with 10 units. Ask: *How many units match the 10?* Next, ask children to count out 14 units, then to match these to a 10-rod. Ask: *How many match? And how many left? So fourteen is the same as one 10 and four units.* Record this on the flip chart like this:

		tens	units
14	➔	1	4

Repeat this for other quantities, so that children are confident with changing 10 units for a 10. For a whole-class demonstration, placing the Base 10 blocks on an OHP to make appropriate 'shadows' on a screen can be very effective. The children then complete photocopiable page 38 (Base 10), using Base 10 apparatus to help them.

LESSON 14 +15

RESOURCES

Number lines; interlocking cubes; Cuisenaire rods; coins; flip chart and pen.

PREPARATION

Put resources on the tables so the children can choose which to use for each problem.

LEARNING OUTCOMES

ORAL AND MENTAL STARTER

● Describe and extend number sequences: **count on and back in ones from any small number**.

MAIN TEACHING ACTIVITY
● **Use mental strategies to solve simple problems** set in 'real life', money or measurement contexts, **using counting, addition, subtraction, doubling and halving, explaining methods and reasoning orally**.
● Choose and use appropriate number operations and mental strategies to solve problems.

ORAL AND MENTAL STARTER

COUNTING: Ask the children to sit in a circle, and count with you forwards and back from zero to 10; then 20. Then count from, and back to, a small number such as 3, 5 or 2. Start from 0 and count around the class to 10, then back again, until everyone has had two turns. Repeat for zero to 20 and back.

MAIN TEACHING ACTIVITY

PROBLEMS: Explain to the children that during the next two lessons you will be asking some addition problems and would like them to answer these and explain how they worked out their answers. They can use any of the resources on the tables, or work mentally. Use the flip chart to record as children give their answers.
1. I am thinking of a number. Ask me questions. I can only answer 'yes' or 'no'.
2. There are two pencils in this jar and five in that. How many pencils are there altogether?
3. I have seven felt-tipped pens and my sister has five. How many do we have altogether?
4. My sister ate two cakes and I ate four. How many did we eat altogether? Who ate more/less?
5. I have some coins which total 6p. What might the coins be?
6. I want to buy a lolly for 9p. What coins might I use?
7. I want to buy a 2p sweet and a 3p lolly. Which coin shall I use?
In groups, ask the children to find some solutions to these problems:
8. I have some sweets in two bags. There are 10 sweets altogether. How many sweets could there be in each bag?
9. I have three coins in my pocket which total less than 10p. What might the coins be?
Ask them to record their results.

DIFFERENTIATION

Less able: ask a classroom assistant to work with them.
More able: encourage these children to work mentally where they can and to find as many different solutions as they can. Questions 8 and 9 are more challenging.

PLENARY

Choose a group to feed back their results for problem 8. Discuss the range of answers: are there more? Ask what strategies were used, which was best, and why?

LESSON 15

Repeat Lesson 14, but for the **Main teaching activity** challenge the children with different problems to those used in the previous lesson.

Money boxes

Total _____ p

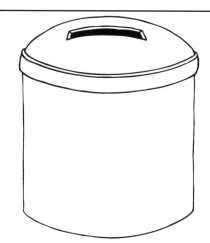

Total _____ p

Total _____ p

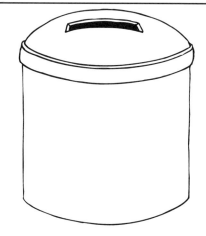

Total _____ p

Total _____ p

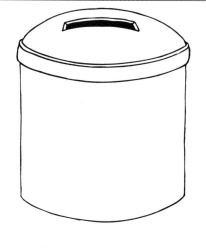

Total _____ p

Put coins in the money box. Write the total.

Number line add

Partition into 5 and a bit.
Use the number line to count on from 10.

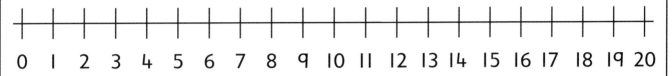

0 1 2 3 4 5 6 7 8 9 10 11 12 13 14 15 16 17 18 19 20

5 + 6 = ☐

5 + 8 = ☐

5 + 9 = ☐

5 + 7 = ☐

Now try these.

6 + 7 = ☐

7 + 9 = ☐

8 + 6 = ☐

9 + 6 = ☐

Base 10

Join matching pairs.

UNITS 5-6

ORGANISATION (8 LESSONS)

	LEARNING OUTCOMES	ORAL AND MENTAL STARTER	MAIN TEACHING ACTIVITY	PLENARY
LESSON 1	● Understand and use the vocabulary related to length. ● **Compare two lengths, by direct comparison**; extend to more than two.	COUNTING STICK: Counting activities.	COMPARING LENGTHS: Language of comparison of length; practical activities.	Feedback on activities.
LESSON 2	● Understand and use the vocabulary related to length. ● Measure using uniform non-standard units (eg straws, wooden cubes) or standard units (eg metre sticks). ● **Suggest suitable standard or uniform non-standard units and measuring equipment to estimate then measure a length**, recording estimates and measurements as 'about …'.	DOUBLES: Finding doubles up to 5 + 5.	MEASURING LENGTH: Using non-standard units; practical activities.	Feedback on solutions to problems.
LESSON 3 4	● Understand and use the vocabulary related to length. ● **Compare two lengths by direct comparison**; extend to more than two. ● Measure using uniform non-standard units (eg straws, wooden cubes,) or standard units (eg metre sticks.) ● **Suggest suitable standard or uniform non-standard units and measuring equipment to estimate, then measure, a length**, recording estimates and measurements as 'about…'. ● **Use mental strategies to solve simple problems** set in measuring contexts, **using counting, addition, subtraction, doubling and halving, explaining methods and reasoning orally**.	COUNTING STICK.	LENGTH PROBLEMS: Solving problems and explaining methods.	Feedback on solutions to problems.
LESSON 5	● **Use everyday language to describe features of familiar 3-D shapes**, including the cube, cuboid, sphere, cylinder, cone…, referring to properties such as the shapes of flat faces, or the number of faces or corners.	COUNTING ON: From a small number count on a small number.	SORTING 3-D SHAPES: Sorting by features of shape.	Discussion of features of shapes.
LESSON 6	● **Use everyday language to describe features of familiar 3-D shapes**, including the cube, cuboid, sphere, cylinder, cone…, referring to properties such as the shapes of flat faces or the number of faces or corners.	COUNTING CUBES: Counting out up to 10 objects.	BEHIND THE WALL: Describing 3-D shapes: properties of 3-D shapes; practical activities.	BEHIND THE WALL.
LESSON 7	● Make and describe models using construction kits, everyday materials, Plasticine…. ● Begin to relate solid shapes to pictures of them.	SHOW ME ADD.	MAKING MODELS: using apparatus to make models; drawing pictures of finished models.	Feedback on activities.

cont...

cont...

LESSON 8	● Solve simple mathematical problems; recognise and predict from simple patterns and relationships. Suggest extensions by asking 'What if...?' or 'What could I try next?' ● Investigate a general statement about familiar shapes by finding examples to satisfy it. Explain methods and reasoning orally.	SHOW ME ADD.	SHAPE PUZZLES: Solving problems and puzzles.	Feedback on activities.

ORAL AND MENTAL SKILLS   Know by heart: addition facts for all pairs of numbers with a total up to at least 5, and the corresponding subtraction facts; addition doubles of all numbers to at least 5 (eg 4 + 4). Know the number names and recite them in order to at least 20, from and back to zero. **Count reliably at least 10 objects**. Describe and extend number sequences: **count on and back in ones from any small number.**

For Unit 5 Lessons 1 and 2 are shown in detail. Lessons 3 and 4 are combined as a 'circus' of problem-solving activities. For Unit 6 Lesson 5 is also shown in detail, with Lessons 6 and 7 as extensions and Lesson 8 as a summative activity.

RESOURCES
Strips of coloured paper in different lengths; a range of items for comparing for each group, such as pencils, straws, ribbons, a metre stick, books...; large sheets (A3) of paper for recording, headed 'Shortest, Longer, Longest'; counting stick (see 'Introduction', page 9); numeral cards (pages 14 and 15) (as labels) and Blu-Tack.

PREPARATION
Prepare the recording charts.

LEARNING OUTCOMES

ORAL AND MENTAL STARTER
● Know the number names and recite them in order to at least 20, from and back to zero.
Describe and extend number sequences: **count on or back in ones from any small number**.

MAIN TEACHING ACTIVITY
● Understand and use the vocabulary related to length.
● **Compare two lengths by direct comparison**; extend to more than two.

ORAL AND MENTAL STARTER

COUNTING STICK: Explain that one end of the stick represents zero and the other end ten. Count, with the children, pointing to the stick's sections as you count. Count to ten; then back to zero. Point to any space and ask: *What number is this?* If the children are not sure, count and point from zero again. Repeat for other spaces on the stick. With a numeral card and the Blu-Tack, label one end of the stick '1', and the other end '11', and repeat. Then try with other number labels with a difference of ten, such as 3 and 13.

MAIN TEACHING ACTIVITY

COMPARING LENGTHS: Ask two children of different heights to stand back to back. Ask: *Who is taller? Who is shorter?* Repeat by comparing another child with each of the first two, ask: *Who is shortest? Who is tallest?* Repeat the activity with strips of coloured paper, emphasising that one end of the items to be compared must be placed level with one end of the other items. Show the range of items for comparing, and explain that the metre stick is used for measuring length.

VOCABULARY

Length; width; height; depth; long; short; tall; high; low; wide; narrow; deep; shallow; thick; thin; longer; shorter; taller; higher; longest; shortest; tallest; highest; metre; metre stick; measure; size; compare; guess; estimate; enough/not enough;too much; too little; too many; too few; nearly; roughly; close to; about the same as; just over/under.

Ask the children, working in groups, to compare two, then three items, order them by length, and record with pictures on the recording sheets. Repeat the activity by comparing width: narrowest, wider, widest.

DIFFERENTIATION

Less able: just compare two items: shorter/longer; wider/narrower.
More able: extend the vocabulary during the group activity to include depth.

PLENARY

Ask a group to explain their results, and to demonstrate how they made their comparisons. Take three different items and ask: *Which is the longest/shortest/widest/narrowest?*

RESOURCES

A large book; a flip chart stand or similar; access to the class library; a range of items with which to measure, such as pencils, metre sticks, straws, ribbons, Cuisenaire 'orange' (10) rods; interlocking cubes; recording charts for each group stating ' I used... My estimate is... My measure is about...'; pens and pencils; a number fan (see photocopiable page 17) for each child.

PREPARATION

Prepare the recording charts. These can easily be drawn up with the drawing or tabulation facility on the class computer. Three copies of the chart should fit on to one sheet of A4 paper; saving on photocopying. Alternatively, set up a table on the computer into which the children can key and then print out their results. Lay out the various measuring items on the tables.

I used	My estimate	My measure

LEARNING OUTCOMES

ORAL AND MENTAL STARTER
● **Know by heart**: addition doubles of all numbers to at least 5 (eg 4 + 4).

MAIN TEACHING ACTIVITY
● Understand and use the vocabulary related to length.
Measure using uniform non-standard units (eg straws, wooden cubes) or standard units (eg metre sticks).
● **Suggest suitable standard or uniform non-standard units and measuring equipment to estimate then measure a length**, recording estimates and measurements as 'about...'.

ORAL AND MENTAL STARTER

DOUBLES: Using their number fans to show the answers, ask the children to respond to doubles questions such as: *1 add 1* or *double 4*. Suggest the strategy of counting on in ones if they cannot recall any facts.

MAIN TEACHING ACTIVITY

MEASURING LENGTH: Stand a large book on the ledge of the flip chart stand and ask a child to make a tower of interlocking cubes that is about the same height as the book. Repeat this with the metre stick and Cuisenaire orange rods, asking first: *How many rods do you think will measure about the same as the metre stick?* Ask the children to work in small groups to estimate, measure, and record the length and width of two different-sized

VOCABULARY

Length; width; height; depth; long; short; tall; high; low; wide; narrow; deep; shallow; thick; thin; longer; shorter; taller; higher; longest; shortest; tallest; highest; metre; metre stick; measure; size; compare; guess; estimate; enough; not enough; too much; too little; too many; too few; nearly; roughly; close to; about the same as; just over; just under.

books, choosing their own non-standard units from the range of items supplied on their tables, and recording in a chart.

DIFFERENTIATION

Less able: work with this group, checking that they make a reasonable estimate before they measure.
More able: provide a wider range of non-standard units from which to choose, including some very small items (such as 1cm³ cubes) and some larger ones (such as 30cm lengths of ribbon).

PLENARY

Discuss the children's results, asking about the suitability of the units they chose and why they rejected particular units.

RESOURCES

A range of items for measuring, such as pencils, metre sticks, straws, ribbons, Cuisenaire rods, interlocking cubes; boxes; cylinders; counters; Roamer; string; card; adhesive; a hoop; chalk; paper; copies of photocopiable page 46 (Snake measure).

PREPARATION

Put the items (both to be measured and for measuring with) where they are easily accessible for the children. Decide whether the children will work with partners or in small groups. Make the required photocopies.

LEARNING OUTCOMES

ORAL AND MENTAL STARTER
● Describe and extend number sequences: **count on or back in ones from any small number**.

MAIN TEACHING ACTIVITY
● Understand and use the vocabulary related to length.
● **Compare two lengths by direct comparison**; extend to more than two.
Measure using uniform non-standard units (eg straws, wooden cubes,) or standard units (eg metre sticks).
● **Suggest suitable standard or uniform non-standard units and measuring equipment to estimate then measure length**, recording estimates and measurements as 'about …'.
● **Use mental strategies to solve simple practical problems** set in measuring contexts, **using counting, addition, subtraction, doubling and halving, explaining methods and reasoning orally**.

ORAL AND MENTAL STARTER

Repeat 'Counting stick' from Lesson 1, page 40.

MAIN TEACHING ACTIVITY

LENGTH PROBLEMS: Explain to the children that the next two lessons will be about solving problems to do with length, and that they will be asked to make comparisons, choose their (non-standard) units, make estimates, then measure and record their results. Remind them of the recording techniques they used in Lesson 2 (page 41) and encourage them to consider whether they chose suitable units for measuring. Select from these problems: 1–4 are easier, 5–8 should be suitable for most children and 9–12 are for the more able.
1. How many counters in a line make a row about the same length as your pencil?
2. Use Cuisenaire rods to estimate and measure a range of items. Choose the most appropriate rod to make the measurement as accurate as possible.

VOCABULARY

Length; width; height; depth; long; short; tall; high; low; wide; narrow; deep; shallow; thick; thin; longer; shorter; taller; higher; longest; shortest; tallest; highest; ruler; metre; metre stick; measure; size, compare; guess; estimate; enough; not enough; too much; too little; too many; too few; nearly; roughly; close to; about the same as; just over; just under.

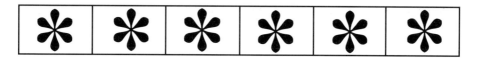

3. ROAMER MEASURE: Make Roamer move 1 unit forward. Estimate, then measure, how far that is with non-standard units.

4. Make and use a picture ruler (see figure) by stamping with a rubber stamp along the length of a piece of card. Use the ruler to estimate and measure. Make various rulers using different-sized pictures and decide which would be best for measuring each item.

5. SNAKE MEASURE: Complete photocopiable sheet 46, choosing appropriate units.

6. TIDDLYWINK FLIP: Flip a counter and estimate the distance it has gone, then measure using the most accurate non-standard unit that can be found.

7. BODY MEASURES: How long is the classroom? How wide is it? Estimate and measure in strides. Compare the results with a friend. Why are they different?

8. How long is a metre? Estimate and measure using body measures: hand spans; feet; strides; cubits (fingertip to elbow).

9. Stick some string on card to make a wavy pattern. How will you find out how long the string is?

10. Find the measurements of a box: height, and distance round (circumference). How will you find its circumference?

11. Find the depth and distance round a cylinder. How will you do this?

12. How far is one turn of a hoop? Devise a method for finding this (eg mark the point on the hoop where it rests on the floor; mark that point on the floor, with chalk; roll the hoop one turn; mark where the hoop finishes).

DIFFERENTIATION

Less able: start with activities 1 to 4. Work with the children, encouraging them to use the vocabulary of measures as they work.

More able: activities 8 to 11 are more challenging. Encourage the children to explain their thinking and to consider other possible solutions.

PLENARY

Ask questions about the results, such as: *Did everyone get the same number of units when they measured …? Why not?* Ask the children to explain how they solved the problem. Compare different methods and discuss which was most effective. Encourage the children to use the vocabulary of length carefully, and to refer to approximations saying whether it was 'nearly', 'just over' or 'about the same'.

RESOURCES

3-D shape models of cubes, cuboids, pyramids, cylinders and spheres (to have sufficient resources for a whole-class lesson you could use the wooden or plastic bricks found in early years classes); a teaching set of 3-D shapes; feely bag or box; flip chart and pen.

PREPARATION

Put sets of shapes on each table, so that all the children can reach them. Draw a chart on the flip chart to record how many flat faces, corners and edges each shape has.

Shape	No. of flat faces	No. of corners	No. of edges
Cube	6	8	12
Cuboid			
Pyramid			

LEARNING OUTCOMES

ORAL AND MENTAL STARTER

● Describe and extend number sequences: **count on or back in ones from any small number.**

MAIN TEACHING ACTIVITY

● **Use everyday language to describe features of familiar 3-D shapes**, including the cube, cuboid, sphere, cylinder, cone..., referring to properties such as the shapes of flat faces, or the number of faces or corners.

VOCABULARY

Solid/hollow shape; cube; cuboid; pyramid; sphere; cylinder; cone; face; flat/ curved face; round; edge; straight; corner; circle; triangle; square; rectangle; hollow; solid; point; pointed; end; sort.

ORAL AND MENTAL STARTER

COUNTING ON: Count from 0 to 10, then 20, and back in ones; then count on a given number from any small number, such as: *Start at 2; count on 3.* Repeat for other numbers.

MAIN TEACHING ACTIVITY

SORTING 3-D SHAPES: Ask the children to choose a shape and then point to: *a flat face; an edge; a corner.* Ask them to hold up their shape if it is: *a cube; cuboid; has a square/ rectangular/curved face; has a straight/curved edge.* Ask the children to choose a different shape and repeat the activity. Show the children the recording sheet on the flip chart, and ask: *How many flat faces/corners/edges has the cube?* Ask individual children to complete each part of the chart. Repeat the activity for each shape.

DIFFERENTIATION

Target questions to specific individuals, so that all the children can take part in this activity. Include one or two different shapes, such as triangular or hexagonal prisms, for the more able to describe and classify. Encourage the less able to compare their shapes with items in everyday life, such as 'box' for cube and cuboid, or 'ball' for sphere.

PLENARY

Show the children your teaching set of shapes as you put them into the feely bag. Ask a child to feel a shape in the bag and describe it for the others to guess which shape it is.

LESSON 6

RESOURCES	Cubes for counting; flip chart; large 3-D shapes; sets of 3-D shapes, feely bags and sorting circle diagrams (large sheet of paper with circles labelled cube, cuboid and so on, according to the shapes you have available) for each group.
LEARNING OUTCOMES	**ORAL AND MENTAL STARTER** ● **Count reliably at least 10 objects.** **MAIN TEACHING ACTIVITY** ● **Use everyday language to describe features of familiar 3-D shapes**, including the cube, cuboid, sphere, cylinder, cone, referring to properties such as the shapes of flat faces or the number of faces or corners.
ORAL AND MENTAL STARTER	COUNTING CUBES: Ask all the children to count out seven cubes. Say: *How many cubes do you have? Put two back, how many now? Take another three, now how many?* Repeat for other quantities.
MAIN ACTIVITY	BEHIND THE WALL: Hide a large 3-D shape behind the flip chart and gradually slide it up so that part of it can be seen. Ask: *What could this shape be?* Continue until someone guesses correctly. *How did you know?* Repeat this for other shapes. In groups, let the children play the feely bag game described in the Plenary session of Lesson 5 (above). Place each shape on to a sorting circle diagram as it is guessed.
DIFFERENTIATION	By outcome.
PLENARY	Play 'Behind the wall' again.

LESSON 7

RESOURCES	Number fans; copies of photocopiable page 47 (Models) and an A3 enlargement; construction kits such as LEGO, Clixi, Polydron; recycled materials; adhesive; Plasticine; construction kit project cards.
LEARNING OUTCOMES	**ORAL AND MENTAL STARTER** ● **Know by heart**: addition facts for all pairs of numbers with a total up to at least 5, and the corresponding subtraction facts. **MAIN TEACHING ACTIVITY** ● Make and describe models using construction kits, Plasticine, everyday materials... ● Begin to relate solid shapes to pictures of them.
ORAL AND MENTAL STARTER	SHOW ME ADD: Ask the children to hold up a blade of their fans to answer questions such as: *What is 3 add 2? 2 plus 4?* with answers up to 10. Each time ask the children how they worked out the answer, and encourage those who do not have rapid recall to use counting on.
MAIN TEACHING ACTIVITY	MAKING MODELS: Explain to the children that they can use a variety of different materials to copy the models in the outline pictures. Show examples of the pictures and the pieces of each construction kit, and ask individuals to come out and match the pieces to the picture. Set a time limit for completion of the models.
DIFFERENTIATION	Less able: provide simple outline pictures and ask them to find the construction pieces needed before they start. Ask them to compare their completed models with the pictures and to describe the differences. More able: ask them to sketch their models and compare their sketch with the original picture, explaining similarities and differences.
PLENARY	Look at the finished models. How are they similar to and different from the pictures? Discuss the shapes in the pictures, naming the 2-D faces and comparing them with the faces of the real 3-D shapes.

LESSON 8

RESOURCES	Interlocking cubes; Polydron or Clixi; recycled materials.
LEARNING OUTCOMES	**ORAL AND MENTAL STARTER** ● **Know by heart**: addition facts for all pairs of numbers with a total up to at least 5, and the corresponding subtraction facts. **MAIN TEACHING ACTIVITY** ● Solve simple mathematical problems, recognise and predict from simple patterns and relationships. Suggest extensions by asking 'What if...?' or 'What could I try next?'. ● Investigate a general statement about familiar shapes by finding examples to satisfy it. ● Explain methods and reasoning orally.
ORAL AND MENTAL STARTER	Repeat 'Show me add' as in Lesson 6 of Unit 3, page 30.
MAIN TEACHING ACTIVITY	SHAPE PUZZLES: Tell the children that this lesson will be about solving shape problems; they will be asked to find ways of solving the problems and to explain what they did and why. Encourage them by asking *What if...?* or *What else could you try?* Choose from these problems (most children should tackle 1–4 initially): 1. Use four interlocking cubes: how many different shapes can you make? 2. Go for a maths walk inside school: find examples of cubes, cuboids, pyramids, spheres, cylinders and cones. 3. Make a house to fit a small doll. 4. Work in pairs: one child builds a shape behind a screen or with his or her back turned, then describes the shape so his or her partner can build one to match. They then compare to see how similar the two shapes are. (This can be done with any construction materials.) 5. Make models that conform to given criteria: must have a hole in it; has more than six faces; is hollow; does not have more than one of each shape.
DIFFERENTIATION	Less able: begin with problems 1 and 2. More able: challenge the children to find a range of solutions to Problem 5.
PLENARY	Ask individuals to explain their challenge, what they did and how they solved their problem. Compare solutions from children who tackled the same problem.

Name

Snake measure

Choose different units.
Estimate the snake's length, then measure.
Fill in the chart.

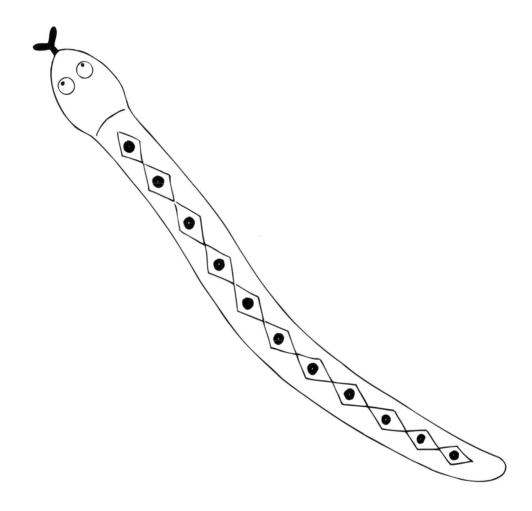

I chose	My estimate	My measure

Name

Models

Make these models.

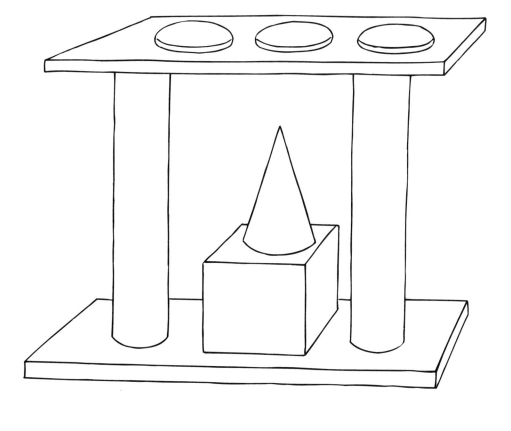

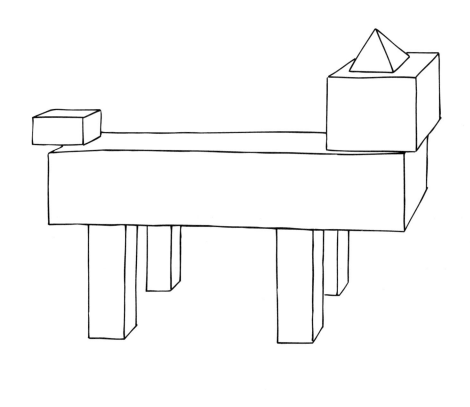

UNIT 7: Assess & Review

Choose from the following activities. During the group activities, some of the children can work with you on practical tasks, while others complete assessment worksheets 1A and 1B which assess their skills with reading and writing numbers, and addition. The specific assessment criteria for the assessment sheets can be found at the bottom of each sheet.

RESOURCES

Numeral cards for each child; sets of 3-D shapes and a label with each one's name; feely bag; strips of paper of differing lengths and widths such as 5cm wide and 20cm long, 5cm by 30cm, 2cm by 15cm, and so on; a selection of items for counting; a range of items to be used as non-standard units, and other items to measure; interlocking cubes; 1p, 2p, 5p and 10p coins; paper and pencils for recording.

ORAL AND MENTAL STARTER

ASSESSMENT

Can the children:
● Describe and extend number sequences: **count on and back in ones from any small number**?
● **Count reliably at least 10 objects**?
COUNTING: Ask the children to count with you, from zero to 10 and back, then from zero to 20 and back, then from any small number to 20 and back. Check who counts confidently and who needs more practice. This skill will be extended during subsequent work. Allow individual children opportunities to count the objects while you observe who can do this confidently.

GROUP ACTIVITIES

ASSESSMENT

Can the children:
● **Use everyday language to describe features of familiar 3-D shapes**?
● **Compare two lengths by direct comparison**?
● **Suggest suitable standard or uniform non-standard units and measuring equipment to estimate, then measure, length**?
● **Count reliably at least 10 objects**?
● **Use mental strategies to solve simple problems using counting, addition, subtraction, doubling and halving, explaining methods and reasoning orally**?
SHAPE SORT: Read the shape labels with the children. Ask them to take turns to choose a shape according to given criteria, such as: (3-D) a pyramid; flat faces; square faces; curved edges; six square faces; just one point. Place some of the shapes into a feely bag, and ask individuals to feel a shape and describe it to the others so that they can guess what it is. Check that they understand and use shape vocabulary appropriately.
COMPARING LENGTHS: Use 'Comparing lengths' (Unit 5 Lesson 1), using strips of paper to make comparisons. Check the children can understand and use the vocabulary of length.
COUNTING CUBES: Ask children to count a given quantity of cubes. Say: count out 5, 6, 7, 8, 9 and 10 cubes. Check they count accurately and can say how many cubes they have.
SOLVING PROBLEMS: Either choose some problems from Units 2–4, Lessons 14 and 15, or make up some similar ones. Provide counting materials such as cubes or coins. Encourage children to explain how they worked out their answer for each problem.
MEASURING LENGTHS: Use 'Measuring length' (Unit 5 Lesson 2), choosing different items to measure with and a range of non-standard units. Encourage the children to choose their own units, make estimates before they measure, talk about approximations, and justify their choice of non-standard units. Encourage them to discuss how many units something measured, and whether a different unit might have made the count easier, such as 'I tried to measure the table with cubes, but there were too many to count, so I used straws instead and I needed just a bit more than ten'.

Assessment 1A

Write the missing numbers.

● Read, write and order numbers from 0 to at least 20.

Name

Assessment 1B

Join matching pairs.

Write the answers to these sums.

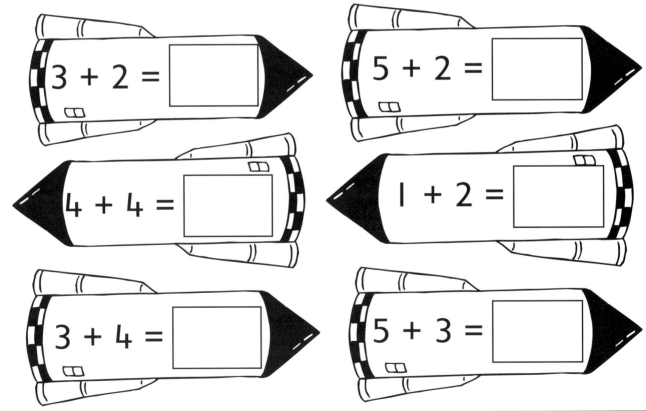

$3 + 2 =$

$5 + 2 =$

$4 + 4 =$

$1 + 2 =$

$3 + 4 =$

$5 + 3 =$

- Understand the operation of addition, and use the related vocabulary.
- Read, write and order numbers from 0 to at least 20.

UNIT 8

ORGANISATION (5 LESSONS)

	LEARNING OUTCOMES	ORAL AND MENTAL STARTER	MAIN TEACHING ACTIVITY	PLENARY
LESSON 1	● Know the number names and recite them in order to at least 20, from and back to zero. ● Describe and extend number sequences: **count on and back in ones from any small number, and in tens from and back to zero.**	SHOW ME ADD AND SUBTRACT: Recall of addition facts with numbers to 5.	COUNTING RHYMES: Favourite counting rhymes; counting patterns including counting in tens.	SHOW ME ADD AND TAKE.
LESSON 2 +3	● **Count reliably at least 10 objects.**	COUNTING: Counting on and back in ones.	COUNT BY TOUCHING OR POINTING: Synchronising touching or pointing and saying number names to count.	Counting.
LESSON 4	● Solve simple mathematical problems or puzzles, recognise and predict from simple patterns and relationships. Suggest extensions by asking: 'What if...?' or 'What could I try next?' ● Investigate a general statement about familiar numbers by finding examples that satisfy it. ● Explain methods and reasoning orally.	SHOW ME ADD AND TAKE: Recall of addition and subtraction facts with numbers to 5.	COUNTING PROBLEMS: Finding combinations to make 15. Encouraging counting on skills.	Comparing and discussing results.
LESSON 5	● Solve simple mathematical problems or puzzles, recognise and predict from simple patterns and relationships. Suggest extensions by asking: 'What if...?' or 'What could I try next?' ● Investigate a general statement about familiar numbers by finding examples that satisfy it. ● Explain methods and reasoning orally.	FINGER ADD: Finding complements to make 10.	COUNTING INVESTIGATION: Discovering that whatever order you count items, the number stays the same.	Comparing and discussing results.

ORAL AND MENTAL SKILLS   Know by heart: **all pairs of numbers with a total of 10** (eg 3+7); addition facts for all pairs of numbers with a total up to at least 5, and the corresponding subtraction facts. Describe and extend number sequences: **count on or back in ones from any small number, and in tens from and back to zero.**

Lesson 1 is an extension of what was taught earlier in the term and is outlined briefly at the beginning of this Unit. Lesson 2 is shown in detail. Lessons 3, 4 and 5 extend the work of Lesson 2 and are shown after it.

RESOURCES	Class number line; number fans (page 17); counting rhymes.
LEARNING OUTCOMES	**ORAL AND MENTAL STARTER** ● **Know by heart**: addition facts for all pairs of numbers with a total up to at least 5, and the corresponding subtraction facts. **MAIN TEACHING ACTIVITY** ● Know the number names and recite them in order to at least 20, from and back to zero. ● Describe and extend number sequences: **count on or back in ones from any small number, and in tens from and back to zero.**
ORAL AND MENTAL STARTER	SHOW ME ADD AND SUBTRACT: Ask children to use their number fans to show you the answers to questions such as: *3 add 1; 4 take away 1; 2 plus 3*. Encourage them to count on in ones in their heads if they do not have recall of a fact.
MAIN TEACHING ACTIVITY	COUNTING RHYMES: Recite favourite counting rhymes. Count in ones, from and back to zero, to 10, then 20 and beyond. Start on any small number, counting forwards and back to zero. Then show the children how to count in tens to a hundred, and back to zero, working along a number line. Try this as a class and repeat by counting individually around the class. Ask: *What comes before/next? Start on 3, count on 4, what number is that?*
DIFFERENTIATION	Encourage everyone to join in with reciting the counting patterns. Target the questioning by the size of the number and the count, and the individual's ability.
PLENARY	Repeat 'Show me add and subtract', from the oral and mental starter.

RESOURCES

Copies of photocopiable page 54 (Counting) for every child, plus one enlarged A3 copy; paper and pencils; flip chart and pen; Blu-Tack. Counters for Lesson 3.

PREPARATION

Enlarge one copy of Counting (page 54) to A3 for demonstration purposes. Attach this with Blu-Tack to the flip chart.

LEARNING OUTCOMES

ORAL AND MENTAL STARTER
● Describe and extend number sequences: **count on or back in ones from any small number, and in tens from and back to zero.**

MAIN TEACHING ACTIVITY
● **Count reliably at least 10 objects**.

VOCABULARY
Number; zero, one, two, three,... to 20 and beyond; nought; how many...?; count.

ORAL AND MENTAL STARTER

COUNTING: Count from zero to 20 and back in ones. Start on 2, 3, 4... and count to 20 and back. Ask: *Start on 5, count on 4, what number will we finish on? Count on from 3 to 8. How many did you count?*

MAIN TEACHING ACTIVITY

COUNT BY TOUCHING: Ask a child to touch and count items on the enlarged counting picture. Encourage the children to remember which items have/have not been counted. Now ask them to use their own copies. Say: *How many...? Are there more/fewer... than...?* Include the idea of zero by asking the children to count something not in the picture. Then ask them to work in pairs. They should each draw some spots on a piece of paper, swap papers, count and write how many, then check each other's work.

DIFFERENTIATION

Place children of similar ability together, so that they work within their counting range.

PLENARY

Repeat 'Counting' from the **Oral and mental starter**.

LESSON 3

Repeat Lesson 2, but in the **Main teaching activity** ask the children to estimate how many, then to point and count, without touching. Ask: *Have all the... been counted?* In pairs, children take turns to pick up some counters, spread them out, and challenge their partners to estimate, then count, how many without touching them.

RESOURCES	Sets of playing cards, dominoes, number fans; paper and pencils.
LEARNING OUTCOMES	**ORAL AND MENTAL STARTER** ● **Know by heart**: addition facts for all pairs of numbers with a total up to at least 5, and the corresponding subtraction facts. **MAIN TEACHING ACTIVITY** ● Solve simple mathematical problems or puzzles, recognise and predict from simple patterns and relationships. Suggest extensions by asking: *What if...?* or *What could I try next?* ● Investigate a general statement about familiar numbers by finding examples that satisfy it. ● Explain methods and reasoning orally.
ORAL AND MENTAL STARTER	SHOW ME ADD AND SUBTRACT: Repeat from Lesson 1, page 52.
MAIN TEACHING ACTIVITY	COUNTING PROBLEMS: Ask children to find combinations of two playing cards to make, for example, 15, counting the marks on the cards (hearts, clubs, and so on) and counting on from one card to the next. They should record their results as addition sums. Ask: *Do you think you have found all the pairs? What could you try next?*
DIFFERENTIATION	Less able: find combinations for smaller numbers using dominoes. More able: find combinations of three cards.
PLENARY	Ask pairs to show their results and explain their thinking.

RESOURCES	Counters, paper and pencils.
LEARNING OUTCOMES	**ORAL AND MENTAL STARTER** ● Describe and extend number sequences: **count on or back in ones from any small number, and in tens from and back to zero.** **MAIN TEACHING ACTIVITY** ●Solve simple mathematical problems or puzzles, recognise and predict from simple patterns and relationships. Suggest extensions by asking: *What if...?* or *What could I try next?* ● Investigate a general statement about familiar numbers by finding examples that satisfy it. ● Explain methods and reasoning orally.
ORAL AND MENTAL STARTER	FINGER ADD: Ask children to use their fingers to show you complements of 10. Say: *What do I add to 6 to make 10?*
MAIN TEACHING ACTIVITY	COUNTING INVESTIGATION: *Whichever order I count these in, the number always stays the same.* Ask the children to use counters to make different arrangements on paper such as a circle, a straight line, or a rectangular array, then re-count. They should draw their arrangements and write how many beside them.
DIFFERENTIATION	Less able: encourage them to use just a few counters. More able: encourage them to check for a range of quantities.
PLENARY	Invite individuals to show their results. Ask: *Does it matter in what order you count? Does the number stay the same? Does it matter how you arrange the counters?*

Counting

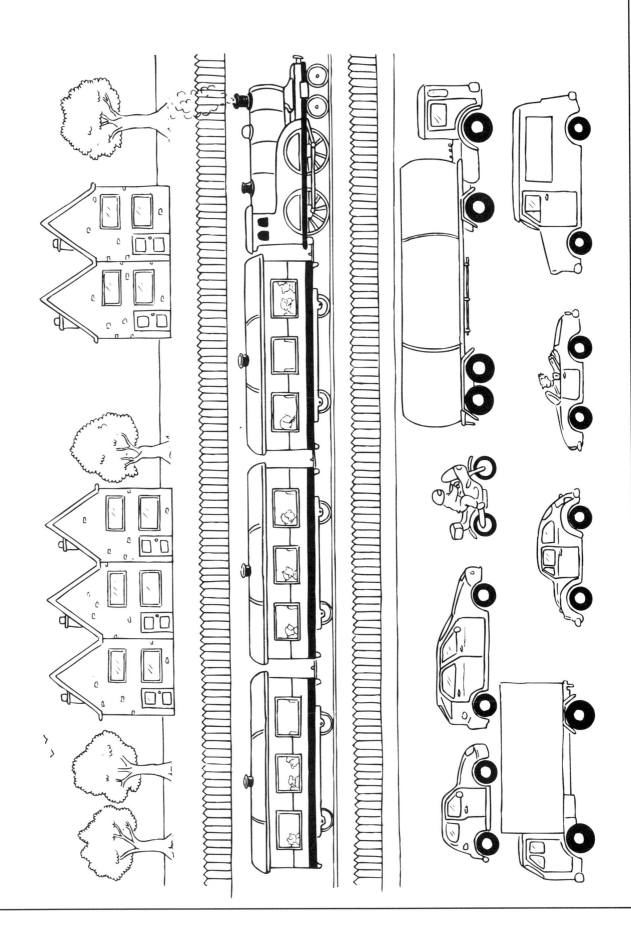

UNITS 9-11

ORGANISATION (15 LESSONS)

	LEARNING OUTCOMES	ORAL AND MENTAL STARTER	MAIN TEACHING ACTIVITY	PLENARY
LESSON 1	● Begin to know what each digit in a two-digit number represents. Partition a 'teens' number and begin to partition larger two-digit numbers into a multiple of 10 and ones (TU). ● Understand and use the vocabulary of estimation. ● Give a sensible estimate of a number of objects that can be checked by counting (eg up to about 15). ● Use the = sign to represent equality.	NUMBERS TO 20: Reading and writing numbers.	TENS AND UNITS: Using Base 10 apparatus to model numbers larger than 10.	Discussion of work.
LESSON 2	● Begin to know what each digit in a two-digit number represents. Partition a 'teens' number and begin to partition larger two-digit numbers into a multiple of 10 and ones (TU). ● Use the = sign to represent equality.	PUT THE LARGER NUMBER FIRST: Using this strategy in addition.	ARROW CARDS: Using arrow cards to represent tens and units.	Discussion of work.
LESSON 3	● Begin to know what each digit in a two-digit number represents. Partition a 'teens' number and begin to partition larger two-digit numbers into a multiple of 10 and ones (TU).	COUNTING STICK: Counting to 20 and back.	ABACUS NUMBERS: Using a paper abacus to represent tens and units.	Discussion of work.
LESSON 4	**Understand the operation of addition and use the related vocabulary**. ● Begin to recognise that addition can be done in any order. ● Use knowledge that addition can be done in any order to do mental calculations more efficiently. For example: put the larger number first and count on in ones, including beyond 10 (eg 7 + 5).	PUT THE LARGER NUMBER FIRST: Counting on in ones mentally.	PUT THE LARGER NUMBER FIRST: Counting on in ones mentally.	Discussion of counting on strategy.
LESSON 5	● **Understand the operation of addition and use the related vocabulary**. ● Begin to recognise that addition can be done in any order. ● Begin to recognise that more than two numbers can be added together. ● Use knowledge that addition can be done in any order to do mental calculations more efficiently. For example: begin to partition into '5 and a bit' when adding 6, 7, 8 or 9, then recombine (eg 6 + 8 = 5 + 1 + 5 + 3 = 10 + 4).	COUNTING TENS: Counting to 100 and back.	PARTITIONING AND RECOMBINING: Using number lines as an aid to addition.	Discussion of the addition sums generated and their answers.

cont...

UNITS 9–11

LESSON				
6	● **Understand the operation of addition and use the related vocabulary.** ● Begin to recognise that addition can be done in any order. ● Begin to recognise that more than two numbers can be added together. ● Use knowledge that addition can be done in any order to do mental calculations more efficiently. For example: begin to partition into '5 and a bit' when adding 6, 7, 8 or 9, then recombine (eg $6 + 8 = 5 + 1 + 5 + 3 = 10 + 4$). ● Recognise coins of different values.	COUNTING TENS: Counting to 100 and back in tens.	PARTITIONING AND RECOMBINING: Using coins.	MAKE 10P: Combining amounts to make 10p.
7	● **Understand the operation of addition and use the related vocabulary.** ● Begin to recognise that addition can be done in any order. ● Begin to recognise that more than two numbers can be added together. ● Identify near doubles, using doubles already known (eg $6 + 5$).	SHOW ME ADD: Finding the complements to make 10. Using o.	NEAR DOUBLES: Using known doubles to find near doubles.	Near doubles.
8	● **Understand the operation of addition and use the related vocabulary.** ● Begin to recognise that addition can be done in any order. ● Identify near doubles, using doubles already known (eg $6 + 5$).	COUNTING CUBES: Estimating how many and checking by counting.	DARTBOARD DOUBLE: Finding doubles and near doubles.	Discussion of doubling strategy.
9	● **Understand the operation of subtraction (as 'take away') and use the related vocabulary.** ● Use patterns of similar calculations (eg $10-0 = 10$; $10 – 1 = 9$; $10 – 2 = 8...$).	SHOW ME ADD AND SUBTRACT: Facts for numbers to 5.	TAKING AWAY: Using interlocking cubes to model taking away.	Discussion of results.
10	● **Understand the operation of subtraction (as 'take away') and use the related vocabulary.** ● Use patterns of similar calculations (eg $10 – 0 = 10$; $10 – 1 = 9$; $10 – 2 = 8...$).	SHOW ME ADD AND SUBTRACT: Facts for numbers to 5.	TAKING AWAY: Using a number line to count forwards and back.	Discussion of results.
11	● **Understand the operation of subtraction (as** 'how many more to make') **and use the related vocabulary.**	PARTITIONING: Beginning to partition into '5 and a bit' when adding.	COMPLEMENTARY ADDITION: Counting on in ones mentally.	Checking results.
12	● **Understand the operation of subtraction (as** 'how many more to make') **and use the related vocabulary.** ● Find totals and change from up to 10p.	PARTITIONING: Beginning to partition into '5 and a bit' when adding.	COMPLEMENTARY ADDITION WITH COINS:Using coins to count on.	Counting on.

cont...

LESSON 13	● **Understand the operation of subtraction (as** 'how many more to make') **and use the related vocabulary.** ● Find totals and change from up to 10p.	COUNTING STICK: Counting on and back from a small number.	GIVING CHANGE: Using the complementary addition strategy to work out change.	WHICH COINS?: Choosing coins to make small amounts.
LESSON 14 +15	● **Use mental strategies to solve simple problems** set in 'real life' or money contexts, **using counting, addition, subtraction, doubling and halving, explaining methods and reasoning orally.** ● Choose and use appropriate number operations and mental strategies to solve problems.	SHOW ME ADD AND SUBTRACT: Using rapid recall.	PROBLEMS: Number and money word problems.	Feedback on solving problems.

ORAL AND MENTAL SKILLS   Know by heart: all pairs of numbers with a total of 10 (eg 3+7); addition facts for all pairs of numbers with a total up to at least 5, and the corresponding subtraction facts. Put the larger number first and count on in ones, including beyond 10 (eg 7 + 5). **Count reliably at least 10 objects.** Describe and extend number sequences: **count on and back in ones from any small number, and in tens from and back to zero. Read and write numerals from 0 to at least 20.** Give a sensible estimate of a number of objects that can be checked by counting (eg up to about 15). Begin to partition into '5 and a bit' when adding 6, 7, 8 or 9, then recombine (eg 6 + 8 = 5 + 1+ 5 + 3 = 10 + 4 = 14). Begin to recognise the use of symbols to stand for an unknown number.

For Unit 9 Lessons 1, 2, 4 and 5 are shown in detail. Lesson 3 is a continuation of Lesson 2 and follows it. In Unit 10, Lesson 6 is an extension of what has been taught in Lesson 5. Lesson 7 is shown in detail, followed by Lesson 8, an extension of what has already been taught. Lesson 9 again is shown in detail and followed by its extension, Lesson 10. For Unit 11, Lessons 11, 14 and 15 are shown in detail, with Lessons 12 and 13 as continuations of Lesson 11.

RESOURCES

Flip chart and pen; Base 10 apparatus (tens and units) or Cuisenaire orange (tens) and white (ones) rods; numeral cards 0–9 (photocopiable page 14) for each child; a copy of photocopiable page 67 (Place value board): paper and pencils for each child.

PREPARATION

Make some A4-size place value boards for tens and units from photocopiable page 67 (Place value board). Put out sufficient Base 10 apparatus for each child to have access to it. Draw a large place value board on the flip chart.

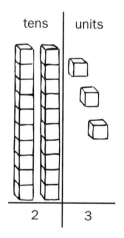

LEARNING OUTCOMES

ORAL AND MENTAL STARTER
● **Read and write numerals from 0 to at least 20**.

MAIN TEACHING ACTIVITY
● Begin to know what each digit in a two-digit number represents. Partition a 'teens' number and begin to partition larger two-digit numbers into a multiple of 10 and ones (TU).
● Understand and use the vocabulary of estimation.
● Give a sensible estimate of a number of objects that can be checked by counting (up to about 15).
● Use the = sign to represent equality.

ORAL AND MENTAL STARTER

NUMBERS TO 20: Ask questions such as: *Show me 15; the number 1 more than 3; the number 2 less than 10...* and invite individuals to write the answer on the flip chart.

MAIN TEACHING ACTIVITY

TENS AND UNITS: Begin by asking individual children to take a small handful of 'units'. Ask them to first guess how many they have, then check by counting. Encourage them to use the vocabulary of estimating such as 'I guessed 9, and counted 11. I was just under in my estimate.' Repeat this, checking that estimates become more accurate. Explain that the children will be using the Base 10 apparatus in order to model numbers larger than 10. Using the drawing on the flip chart explain how to use the place value board, by placing 10 rods in the tens column, units in the units column, and putting numeral cards into the spaces to represent the number. Ask all the children to show 14 on their board. Ask: *How many tens? How many units? So 14 is the same number as one 10 and four units.* Repeat for other numbers to 20, then extend to numbers between 20 and 30. Write some two-digit numbers on the flip chart. Ask the children to represent these on their place value boards, and to record in tens and units like this: 14 = 1 ten and 4 units. Write some tens and units, such as '2 tens and 3 units', on the flip chart and ask the children to use their place value boards to represent these numbers, recording like this: 2 tens and 3 units = 23.

DIFFERENTIATION

Less able: provide examples using teen numbers and extend to the twenties once the children are confident with these.
More able: challenge the children by asking for examples in the thirties and forties.

PLENARY

Ask individual children to give their answers, and discuss the fact that two-digit numbers are made up from tens and units.

RESOURCES

A set of arrow cards from photocopiable page 68 for each child; several different colours of card; scissors; flip chart and pen; numeral cards 11–20 for each pair (page 15); number fan for each child (page 17).

PREPARATION

Make up the arrow cards using various colours of card. If children sitting next to each other have a different coloured set of arrow cards, then they will find it easier to put away just their own cards, without muddling them with those of their neighbour.

LEARNING OUTCOMES

ORAL AND MENTAL STARTER
● Put the larger number first and count on in ones, including beyond 10 (eg 7 + 5).

MAIN TEACHING ACTIVITY
● Begin to know what each digit in a two-digit number represents. Partition a 'teens' number and begin to partition larger two-digit numbers into a multiple of 10 and ones (TU).
● Use the = sign to represent equality.

ORAL AND MENTAL STARTER

PUT THE LARGER NUMBER FIRST: Explain to the children that they are going to use the strategy of putting the larger number first, then counting on in ones in order to carry out some mental additions, such as 2 + 5 or 4 + 6. Write each example on the flip chart, then ask the children to use the strategy, and hold up a blade of their number fan to show the answer. Ask some children to explain how they worked it out. Repeat for other examples.

MAIN TEACHING ACTIVITY

ARROW CARDS: Write on the flip chart some examples of two-digit numbers, such as 15. Ask: *How many tens? How many units?* Then write: 15 = 1 ten and 5 units. Explain that the arrow cards can be used to show tens and units numbers. Show how to make 15 using the cards.

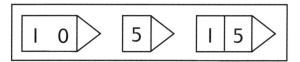

Say some two-digit numbers, and ask the children to use their arrow cards to make them. For each two-digit number, ask which two cards were used. Write these numbers on the flip chart: 15 = 10 and 5. Now ask the children to work in pairs. They should take turns to draw a card from their stacked numeral cards, make that number using their arrow cards, and record, for example: 17 = 10 and 7.

DIFFERENTIATION

Less able: provide Base 10 apparatus to support their use of the arrow cards.
More able: extend their number range, and ask them to record from 20 to 30.

PLENARY

Explain that you want to look at answers in number order. Ask: *What comes first?* then write on the flip chart: 11 = 10 and 1. Continue in order to 20 and discuss how 20 is two tens. Ask the more able children to extend the responses to 30.

RESOURCES	Flip chart and pen; counters; counting stick; numeral cards (pages 14, 15 and 16); Blu-Tack; blank A4 paper.
LEARNING OUTCOMES	**ORAL AND MENTAL STARTER** ● Describe and extend number sequences: **count on and back in ones from any small number.** **MAIN TEACHING ACTIVITY** ● Begin to know what each digit in a two-digit number represents. Partition a 'teens' number and begin to partition larger two-digit numbers into a multiple of 10 and ones (TU).
ORAL AND MENTAL STARTER	COUNTING STICK: Label one end of the stick zero, the other 10, then, pointing to the sections on the stick, count from zero to 10 and back again. Repeat for 10 to 20; 3 to 13; 6 to 16….
MAIN TEACHING ACTIVITY	ABACUS NUMBERS: Draw a two-spike abacus on the flip chart (see figure). Explain which spike represents tens and which units. Draw a counter on the 10 spike and ask what number that represents. Draw two on the units spike and ask what number this is. Ask the children to draw their own two-spike abacus on A4 paper and use counters to show numbers such as 13 and 21. Then ask them to work in pairs and, using up to three counters, find how many different numbers they can make on their abacus. They can record these by writing the numbers made, in order, from smallest to largest (1, 2, 3, 10, 11, 12, 20, 21, 30). If time allows, extend the activity by using four counters to find which numbers can be made (1, 2, 3, 4, 10, 11, 12, 13, 20, 21, 22, 30, 31).
DIFFERENTIATION	Less able: work with this group; provide Base 10 apparatus and ask them to model each number on the abacus with the apparatus. More able: extend the activity by providing five counters, and asking them to make all possible numbers between zero and thirty (as above, plus 5; 14; 23).
PLENARY	Write the results on the flip chart. Ask children to explain how they worked, and how they are sure that they have not missed any possible results.

RESOURCES

A number fan for each child (page 17); flip chart and pen; class number line; a set of numeral cards 0–5, and 0–10 (page 14) for each pair of children.

PREPARATION

Ask the children, working in pairs, to sort out the 0 to 5 cards from one set of numeral cards, so they have a 0–5 pile and a 0–10 pile.

LEARNING OUTCOMES

ORAL AND MENTAL STARTER

● Put the larger number first and count on in ones, including beyond 10 (eg 7 + 5).

MAIN TEACHING ACTIVITY

● **Understand the operation of addition and use the related vocabulary**.
● Begin to recognise that addition can be done in any order.
● Use knowledge that addition can be done in any order to do mental calculations more efficiently. For example: put the larger number first and count on in ones, including beyond 10 (eg 7 + 5).

VOCABULARY

Add; sum; total; altogether; one more; two more; equals; sign; plus; is the same as.

ORAL AND MENTAL STARTER

PUT THE LARGER NUMBER FIRST: As in Lesson 2 of this unit, page 58.

MAIN TEACHING ACTIVITY

PUT THE LARGER NUMBER FIRST: Write a sum on the board such as 3 + 5. Ask: *How can we work this out?* Accept children's suggestions, and then, if it has not been suggested, remind them that you can re-order the sum (as they would do in their heads if counting), and count on from the larger number: 5 + 3. Ask a child to count on 3 from the 5 on the class number line, then write the answer on the flip chart. Repeat for other sums.

The children (in pairs) take one card from the 0–5 pile and one from the 0–10 pile, use these to write an addition, decide which number to put first, and count on in their heads.

DIFFERENTIATION

Less able: make both piles of cards 0–5. Provide number lines (page 18) if needed.
More able: make both piles of cards 0–10.

PLENARY

Ask pairs to give some of their sums to others to try. Discuss the re-ordering strategy.

RESOURCES

A number line for each child (page 18); class number line; flip chart and pen; two 4–9 dice for each group; paper and pencils.

PREPARATION

Label blank dice or use self-adhesive stickers to renumber 1–6 dice with the numbers 4–9.

LEARNING OUTCOMES

ORAL AND MENTAL STARTER

● Describe and extend number sequences: **count in tens from and back to zero**.

MAIN TEACHING ACTIVITY

● **Understand the operation of addition and use the related vocabulary**.
● Begin to recognise that addition can be done in any order.

● Begin to recognise that more than two numbers can be added together.
● Use knowledge that addition can be done in any order to do mental calculations more efficiently. For example: begin to partition into '5 and a bit' when adding 6, 7, 8 or 9, then recombine (eg $6 + 8 = 5 + 1 + 5 + 3 = 10 + 4 = 14$).

ORAL AND MENTAL STARTER

COUNTING TENS: Count from 0 in tens to 100 and back again. Count around the class in tens. Ask: *What comes before/after 20; 50; Count on 3 tens from 20; 2 tens from 40....*

MAIN TEACHING ACTIVITY

PARTITIONING AND RECOMBINING: Explain that this lesson introduces another way to add, and suggest that children can use their number lines to help them if necessary. Write on the flip chart: $5 + 8$. Ask: *How shall we do this?* Encourage the partitioning and recombining strategy, and write: $5 + 5 + 3 = 10 + 3 = 13$. Highlight the double, $5 + 5$.

Try some more examples. Write $6 + 8$ and ask for a strategy. Encourage the children to partition both numbers and write: $5 + 1 + 5 + 3 = 5 + 5 + 1 + 3 =$. Explain how the numbers can be reordered, then complete the calculation by writing: $10 + 4 = 14$. Repeat this for other examples and, when the children have understood the process, omit the reordering step in the recording.

Next, working in small groups, ask the children to take turns to toss the two 4–9 dice and, independently, add the two numbers by partitioning and recombining, counting on in their heads or using their number lines where necessary. Each child should record the sum, and the answer, as was done on the flip chart, then compare their results.

DIFFERENTIATION

Less able: Provide one 5–9 dice, and ask them to add their score to 6.
More able: Encourage them to count on in their heads, rather than using a number line.

PLENARY

Ask for some of the sums that have been generated, and write them on the board. Encourage all the children to partition, recombine and to count on in their heads to calculate. Emphasise that this is a new strategy for addition.

VOCABULARY

Add; sum; total; altogether; one more; two more; equals; sign; plus; is the same as.

LESSON 6

RESOURCES	Price cards from 5p–9p; 1p and 5p coins; paper, pencils; flip chart, pen.
LEARNING OUTCOMES	**ORAL AND MENTAL STARTER** ● Describe and extend number sequences: **count in tens from and back to zero.** **MAIN TEACHING ACTIVITY** ● **Understand the operation of addition and use the related vocabulary.** ● Begin to recognise that addition can be done in any order. ● Begin to recognise that more than two numbers can be added together. ● Use knowledge that addition can be done in any order to do mental calculations more efficiently. For example: begin to partition into '5 and a bit' when adding 6, 7, 8 or 9, then recombine (eg $6 + 8 = 5 + 1 + 5 + 3 = 10 + 4 = 14$). ● Recognise coins of different values.
ORAL AND MENTAL STARTER	Repeat 'Counting tens' from Lesson 5 of this unit (above).
MAIN TEACHING ACTIVITY	PARTITIONING AND RECOMBINING: Repeat Lesson 5, but this time using money, explaining with coins how to partition 6p +7p into 5 pence coins and pennies, then recombine. Children work in groups, turning over two price cards at a time, using coins to help them, and recording their money additions as on the flip chart.
DIFFERENTIATION	Less able: choose one price card and add this to 5p. More able: ask them to recombine left over 'bits' to make another 5p where appropriate. Introduce 2p and 10p coins.
PLENARY	MAKE 10p: adding mentally, ask the children to combine amounts of money to make 10p, such as 3p and 7p.

RESOURCES
Interlocking cubes; a dice marked d ,d, d, d+1, d+1, d+1 (d for double, and d+1 for double add one) and a pack of numeral cards 0–10 (page 14) for each pair; paper and pencils; flip chart and pen.

PREPARATION
Make the dice by writing on blank ones or covering the numbers on regular dice with labelled self-adhesive stickers.

LEARNING OUTCOMES

ORAL AND MENTAL STARTER
● **Know by heart all pairs of numbers with a total of 10** (eg 3 + 7).
● Begin to recognise the use of symbols such as [] or [] to stand for an unknown number.

MAIN TEACHING ACTIVITY

● **Understand the operation of addition and use the related vocabulary**.
● Begin to recognise that addition can be done in any order and that more than two numbers can be added together.
● Identify near doubles, using doubles already known (eg 6 + 5).

VOCABULARY

Add; sum; total; altogether; one/two more; equals; sign; plus; double; near double; half; halve.

ORAL AND MENTAL STARTER

SHOW ME ADD: Write on the flip chart questions which involve finding the complement to make 10, such as 6 + ☐ = 10; 3 + ☐ = 10. Suggest that the children count on from the first number to 10 to find the missing number. Ask a child to write in the missing number for each addition sentence.

MAIN TEACHING ACTIVITY

NEAR DOUBLES: Hold up one stick of five interlocking cubes, then another, and ask: *How many is this... and this... and how many altogether?* Add one cube to one of the sticks and ask: *How many now? How did you work that out?* Encourage the children to use the double facts that they already know. Write on the board: 5 + 6 = 5 + 5 + 1 = 11. Repeat this for other amounts until the children are confident with the strategy. Show a stick of 10 and ask: *How much is half of this?* Ask a child to break the stick in half to check, and repeat for other even amounts.

Now ask the children to work in pairs, taking turns to take a card from a stack of numeral cards and throwing the d/d + 1 dice. If they throw a 'd' they double the number; if they throw a 'd+1' they double and add one. For double 4 they write: 4 + 4 = 8; for double 4 add one they write: 4 + 5 = 9.

DIFFERENTIATION

Less able: limit the cards in their pack to 1–5.
More able: introduce cards for numerals beyond 10, such as 11–15 (page 15).

PLENARY

NEAR DOUBLES: Ask some oral doubles and near doubles questions, and some halves, differentiating the questions according to the ability range, such as double 2; double 6; double 15; 3 + 2; 7 + 6; 12 + 13; half of 8; half of 20 and so on. Each time ask the children to explain their calculating strategy.

RESOURCES	A copy of photocopiable page 69 (Dartboard doubles) for each child, plus an A3 enlargement attached to the flip chart; flip chart and pen; paper and pencils; number lines (page 18); cubes for counting.
LEARNING OUTCOMES	**ORAL AND MENTAL STARTER** ● **Count reliably at least 10 objects.** ● Give a sensible estimate of a number of objects that can be checked by counting (eg up to about 15). **MAIN TEACHING ACTIVITY** ● Understand the operation of addition and use the related vocabulary. ● Begin to recognise that addition can be done in any order. ● Identify near doubles, using doubles already known (eg 6 + 5).
ORAL AND MENTAL STARTER	COUNTING CUBES: Take a handful of cubes and ask the children how many they think you have. Ask a child to count them. Repeat for other handfuls, including child handfuls.
MAIN TEACHING ACTIVITY	DARTBOARD DOUBLE: Explain that for each number on the outer ring of the board, they must write either the double or the double add one, as marked on the inner ring. Complete one of these together on the enlarged page, then ask them to complete the others themselves.
DIFFERENTIATION	Less able: provide number lines for counting on when necessary. More able: challenge the children to make up some more dartboard double sums for themselves.
PLENARY	Discuss strategies for solving the dartboard sums.

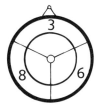

RESOURCES

A number fan for each child; interlocking cubes; flip chart and pen.

LEARNING OUTCOMES

ORAL AND MENTAL STARTER

● **Know by heart:** addition facts for all pairs of numbers with a total up to at least 5, and the corresponding subtraction facts.

MAIN TEACHING ACTIVITY

● **Understand the operation of subtraction (as 'take away') and use the related vocabulary.**

● Use patterns of similar calculations (eg 10 – 0 = 10; 10 – 1 = 9; 10 – 2 = 8...).

VOCABULARY
Take; take away; subtract; one less; two less; three less...; make; leave; is the same as; equals; sign; minus; how many are left?; how many are left over?; how many are gone?.

ORAL AND MENTAL STARTER

SHOW ME ADD AND SUBTRACT: Ask the children to use their number fan to show you the answer to addition and subtraction facts for numbers to 5.

MAIN TEACHING ACTIVITY

TAKING AWAY: Say that this lesson is about taking away. Show the children a stick of seven cubes. Snap off three cubes. Ask: *How many cubes are there altogether? How many did I take away? How many are left?* Write on the flip chart: 7 – 3 = 4. Explain that the minus sign means take away, minus or subtract. Repeat for other numbers. Ask the children to use cubes to make a stick for 6, and to find all the take away sums for 6 in order. Do one or two on the flip chart: 6 – 0 = 6; 6 – 1 = 5. Ask the children to write them down in order.

DIFFERENTIATION

Less able: work with the group, ensuring that they understand what 'take away' means.
More able: challenge them to find the subtraction pattern counting on or back mentally.

PLENARY

Discuss the children's results and discuss the pattern. Ask the children to find the pattern for 5–0; 5–1 and so on. Encourage them to use the pattern to predict the answers.

RESOURCES	Individual number lines (page 18); class number line; paper and pencils; number fans (page 17).
LEARNING OUTCOMES	**ORAL AND MENTAL STARTER** ● **Know by heart:** addition facts for all pairs of numbers with a total up to at least 5, and the corresponding subtraction facts. **MAIN TEACHING ACTIVITY** ● **Understand the operation of subtraction (as 'take away') and use the related vocabulary.** Use patterns of similar calculations (eg 10–0=10; 10–1=9; 10–2=8…).
ORAL AND MENTAL STARTER	Repeat 'Show me add and subtract' from Lesson 9 of this unit, page 63.
MAIN TEACHING ACTIVITY	**Taking away:** Discuss taking away, using a number line to count back or forward. Ask the children to write take away sums for the pattern 8–0; 8–1…; 9–0; 9–1….; and 10–0; 10–1…; using their number lines to help them where necessary.
DIFFERENTIATION	Less able: provide cubes if necessary. More able: suggest that they try to do these by counting on or back in their heads.
PLENARY	Discuss results, and the patterns that emerge.

RESOURCES

Interlocking cubes; flip chart and pen; one set per pair of 0–10 numeral cards (page 14).

LEARNING OUTCOMES

ORAL AND MENTAL STARTER

● Begin to partition into '5 and a bit' when adding 6, 7, 8 or 9, then recombine
(eg 6 + 8 = 5 + 1+ 5 + 3 = 10 + 4 = 14).

MAIN TEACHING ACTIVITY

● **Understand the operation of subtraction (as** 'how many more to make'), **and use the related vocabulary.**

VOCABULARY

How many more to make…?; make; leave; sign; minus; equals.

ORAL AND MENTAL STARTER

PARTITIONING: Ask the children to partition into '5 and a bit', then recombine as they add mentally. Write the addition sums on the flip chart, for example 5 + 7 =, and ask children to suggest how this would be tackled. Write: 5 + 5 + 2 = 10 + 2 = 12. Give other examples for adding 5 and a larger number.

MAIN TEACHING ACTIVITY

COMPLEMENTARY ADDITION: Make a tower of six cubes and ask: *How many more cubes do we need to have 10?* Ask for suggestions of how to do this. Encourage the children to count on in ones, mentally, to 10. Write on the flip chart: 6 + 4 = 10. Explain that one way of subtracting is to count on and write 10 – 6 = 4. Repeat this for other examples.

Now ask the children to work in pairs, taking turns to draw two cards, and finding how many more need to be added to the smaller number to make the larger. They should record these as subtractions, using the minus and equals signs.

DIFFERENTIATION

Less able: provide interlocking cubes for counting on. You could also limit the size of the numbers by using 0–6 cards only.
More able: extend the number range by including cards 11 and 12 (page 15).

PLENARY

Choose a pair to call out two numbers and challenge the others to find the answer ('how many more make…?') quickly by counting on in their heads from the smaller number.

LESSON 12

RESOURCES	Flip chart and pen; 1p coins; dice marked 1p, 2p, 3p, 4p, 5p, 6p.
LEARNING OUTCOMES	**ORAL AND MENTAL STARTER** ● Begin to partition into '5 and a bit' when adding 6, 7, 8 or 9, then recombine (eg 6 + 8 = 5 + 1 + 5 + 3 = 10 + 4 = 14). **MAIN TEACHING ACTIVITY** ● **Understand the operation of subtraction** (as 'how many more to make') **and use the related vocabulary.** ● Find totals and change from up to 10p.
ORAL AND MENTAL STARTER	Repeat 'Partitioning' from Lesson 11 of this unit, page 64.
MAIN TEACHING ACTIVITY	COMPLEMENTARY ADDITION WITH COINS: Repeat Lesson 11, page 64, using coins. Ask the children to use 1p coins to count on from 2p to 5p. Ask: *How much did you need?* Repeat this for other amounts until the children are confident. Extend to counting on to 10p. Working in pairs, ask children to take turns to roll a dice, then count on from the dice amount in pennies to 10p. They should record this as subtractions, using minus and equals signs: 10p – 5p = 5p.
DIFFERENTIATION	Less able: limit the amounts on the dice to 1p, 1p, 2p, 2p, 3p, 3p and find the complements to 5p. More able: when they are confident with this, encourage them to count on to 15p.
PLENARY	Write some amounts on the flip chart, such as 7p. Ask: *How much more to make 10p?* Repeat for other amounts.

LESSON 13

RESOURCES	Counting stick; numeral cards (pages 14, 15 and 16) and Blu-Tack for labels; photocopiable page 70 (Change); coins; price labels or packages.
LEARNING OUTCOMES	**ORAL AND MENTAL STARTER** ● Describe and extend number sequences: **count on and back in ones from any small number.** **MAIN TEACHING ACTIVITY** ● **Understand the operation of subtraction (as** 'how many more to make') **and use the related vocabulary.** ● Find totals and change from up to 10p.
ORAL AND MENTAL STARTER	COUNTING STICK: Label one end of the stick '5', the other end '15', and count forwards and backwards, pointing to the divisions on the stick. Change the end numbers to, for example, 2 and 12, and repeat.
MAIN TEACHING ACTIVITY	GIVING CHANGE: Show a price label or package for 3p and a 5p coin. Ask how much change the shopkeeper will give. Encourage the children to count on from 3p, in ones, in their heads. Ask: *Which coin(s) will be used?* Encourage the children to suggest the least number of coins that could be used for the change (one 2p coin). Repeat for other amounts and extend to a 10p coin, always encouraging the use of the least number of coins. Ask the children to complete photocopiable page 70 (Change). You may need to work through an example first.
DIFFERENTIATION	Less able: ask the children to give change from 5p. More able: when they are confident with change from 10p, extend to 20p.
PLENARY	WHICH COINS?: Explain that you have, for example, 7p. Ask which coins you might have. Repeat for other amounts.

LESSON 14 +15

RESOURCES
Flip chart and pen; individual number lines (page 18); some 1p, 2p, 5p and 10p coins for each child; number fans (page 17); pencils and paper. Photocopiable page 71 (Problems) for Lesson 15.

PREPARATION
Make the required photocopies for both lessons.

LEARNING OUTCOMES

ORAL AND MENTAL STARTER
● **Know by heart: all pairs of numbers with a total of 10** (eg 3+7); addition facts for all pairs of numbers with a total up to at least 5, and the corresponding subtraction facts.

MAIN TEACHING ACTIVITY
● **Use mental strategies to solve simple problems** set in 'real life' or money contexts, **using counting, addition, subtraction, doubling and halving, explaining methods and reasoning orally.**
● Choose and use appropriate number operations and mental strategies to solve problems.

VOCABULARY

Work out; answer; right; wrong; what could we try next?; how did you work it out...?; add; sum; total; altogether; one more; two more; equals; sign; plus; money; coin; pence; penny; price; cost; buy; sell; pay; change; dear; costs more; costs less; cheap; cheaper; how much...?; spend; spent.

ORAL AND MENTAL STARTER

SHOW ME ADD AND SUBTRACT: Using their number fans to show the answer, ask some addition and subtraction questions, such as *Five add three; 10 subtract four; How many more do you need to add to seven to make 10?* Each time, ask a child how he or she worked it out. Encourage counting on as a strategy.

MAIN TEACHING ACTIVITY

PROBLEMS: Explain that the purpose of the lesson is to find a solution to a problem. Begin by asking: *I am thinking of a number, then I add 3; the answer is 7. What is my number?*

Ask the children to explain the strategies that they used to solve the problem and compare strategies. Ask: *Did everyone use the same one? Which was best? Why?* Ask the children to put out two 5p coins, a 2p and two 1p coins. Ask: *How shall we find out how much there is in total?* Encourage the children to count the larger coins first, using doubling, then count on in ones. Repeat for other combinations of coins.

Then choose from the following problems, adapting them to make new problems as needed. For the money problems, encourage the children to use their coins, and to use doubling, counting on, adding and subtracting strategies.
1. Jenny has six sweets and Charles has three. How many do they have altogether? How many more sweets does Charles need to have the same as Jenny?
2. Noel rolled double 6 on his dice. What was his score?
3. There were 10 biscuits in the pack. There are seven left. How many have been eaten?
4. I doubled 10 and added 1. What number did I have then?
5. There are four pencils in each packet. How many in two packets?
6. The box says eight; now there are only five biscuits left. How many have been eaten?
7. If I buy a 4p lolly with a 10p coin, how much change will I be given?
8. I had 6p in my pocket. Now I have just 2p. How much have I spent?
9. I paid 7p for some toffees. Which coins could I use?
10. Find different ways to make 9p exactly.
11. Mohammed had 10p. He spent 8p. How much does he have left?
12. Marian spent 3p and 5p on sweets. What change will she get from 10p?
13. Oranges are 6p each. What do two cost? Which two coins can I use to pay for them? Encourage the children to use mental strategies. If necessary, they can use a number line or coins as an aid. Ask the children to work in pairs for about five minutes to make up some word problems for sums such as: 3 + 6 = 9; 5 + 2 = 7.

DIFFERENTIATION

Less able: simplify the numbers in the problems.
More able: encourage them to make up word problems, then to swap these with a partner and solve them.

PLENARY

Discuss the word problems which the children made up. Ask individuals to explain how they would solve them.

Place value board

tens

units

Arrow cards

Photocopy these onto card and cut them out.

1	1 0	1 0 0
2	2 0	2 0 0
3	3 0	3 0 0
4	4 0	4 0 0
5	5 0	5 0 0
6	6 0	6 0 0
7	7 0	7 0 0
8	8 0	8 0 0
9	9 0	9 0 0

Dartboard doubles

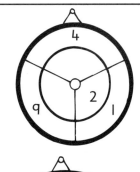

Double these numbers.
Write the answers on the dartboard, like this:

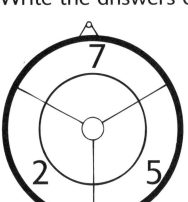

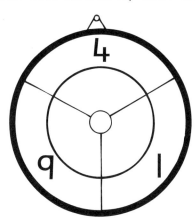

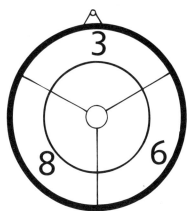

Double these and add 1.

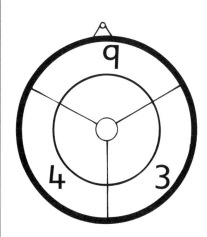

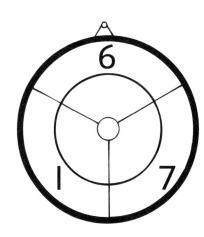

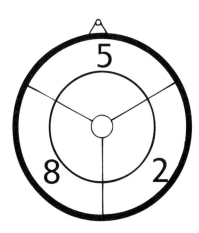

Make up your own sums.

Double   Double add 1

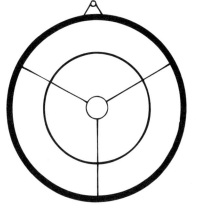

Change

Write how much change.

 p

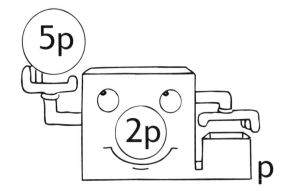 p

 p

 p

 p

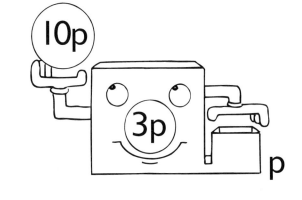 p

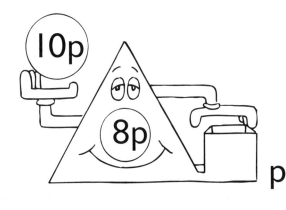 p

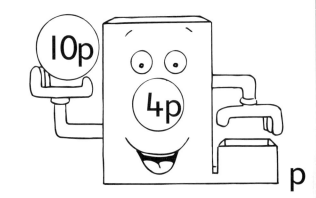 p

Problems

Write a sum for each picture.

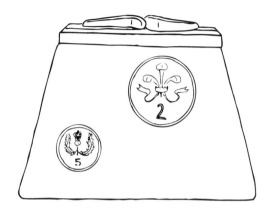

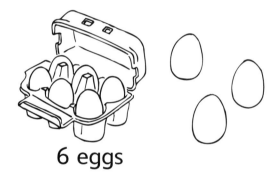

6 eggs

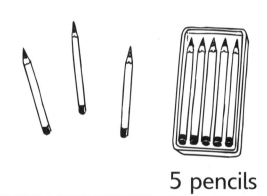

5 pencils

10 toffees

6 jam tarts

UNITS 12-13

ORGANISATION (10 LESSONS)

	LEARNING OUTCOMES	ORAL AND MENTAL STARTER	MAIN TEACHING ACTIVITY	PLENARY
LESSON 1	● Understand and use the vocabulary related to time. ● Order familiar events in time. ● Know the days of the week and the seasons of the year. ● Read the time to the hour on analogue clocks.	NEAR DOUBLES: Oral doubles and near doubles questions.	SEQUENCING EVENTS: Sequencing events in time order.	Discussion of clocks and time-telling.
LESSON 2	● Understand and use the vocabulary related to time. ● Order familiar events in time. ● Know the days of the week and the seasons of the year. ● Read the time to the hour on analogue clocks.	COUNTING: Counting out at least 10 objects.	TELLING THE TIME: Understanding o'clock times.	Reciting the names of days and seasons.
LESSON 3	● Understand and use the vocabulary related to time. ● Order familiar events in time. ● Know the days of the week and the seasons of the year. ● Read the time to the hour or half-hour on analogue clocks. ● Solve a given problem by sorting, classifying and organising information in simple ways, such as using objects or pictures. ● Discuss and explain results.	FINGER ADD: Complements to 10.	TELLING THE TIME: Understanding o'clock; recording bedtimes on a data-handling chart.	Discussion of the data collected.
LESSON 4 +5	● Understand and use the vocabulary related to time. ● Order familiar events in time. ● Know the days of the week and the seasons of the year. ● Read the time to the hour or half-hour on analogue clocks. ● **Use mental strategies to solve simple practical problems set in measurement contexts, using counting, addition, subtraction, doubling and halving, explaining methods and reasoning orally.**	COUNTING TENS: Counting in tens.	TIME PROBLEMS: What can you do in one minute? In two or five minutes?	TELLING THE TIME: Understanding o'clock and half past.
LESSON 6 +7	● Solve a given problem by sorting, classifying and organising information in simple ways, such as in a list or simple table. Discuss and explain results.	COUNTING TENS: Counting in tens.	SORTING: Sorting data onto diagrams.	Discussion of the data collected.

cont...

cont...

8 **+9** **+10**	● Solve a given problem by sorting, classifying and organising information in simple ways, such as in a list or simple table. Discuss and explain results. ● Understand and use the vocabulary related to length. ● **Compare two lengths by direct comparison;** extend to more than two. ● **Suggest suitable standard or uniform non-standard units and measuring equipment to estimate, then measure, a length,** recording estimates and measurements as 'about...'.	FINGER ADD: Complements to 10. Near doubles.	LENGTH PROBLEMS: Using knowledge of measuring and data recording.	Discussion of methods used to solve problems.

ORAL AND MENTAL SKILLS   Know by heart: all pairs of numbers with a total of 10 (eg 3+7); addition doubles of all numbers to at least 5 (eg 4 + 4). **Count reliably at least 10 objects.** Describe and extend number sequences: **count on and back in ones from any small number, and in tens from and back to zero.** Identify near doubles using doubles already known (eg 6 + 5).

In Unit 12, Lessons 1 and 4 are shown in detail. Lessons 2, 3 and 5 are continuations of what has already been taught and follow on sequentially. In Unit 13, Lesson 6 is shown in detail with Lesson 7 as its continuation. Lessons 8, 9 and 10 are shown as one lesson, containing a variety of activities to be chosen for each day.

LESSON 1

RESOURCES

Paper, pencils and crayons; adhesive; date chart; a copy of photocopiable page 79 (Sequencing) for each child, plus an A3 enlargement of the top sequence on this page (which can be coloured in and the pictures cut out); large pictures depicting the seasons such as those found in a mathematics scheme 'big book', or in sets of 'seasons' posters; teaching clock.

PREPARATION

Make a days of the week and date chart, which can be changed on a daily basis (the figure below shows an example). Make the required photocopies.

LEARNING OUTCOMES

ORAL AND MENTAL STARTER
● Know by heart addition doubles of all numbers to at least 5 (eg 4 + 4).
● Identify near doubles using doubles already known (eg 6 + 5).

MAIN TEACHING ACTIVITY
● Understand and use the vocabulary related to time.
● Order familiar events in time.
● Know the days of the week and the seasons of the year.
● Read the time to the hour on analogue clocks.

ORAL AND MENTAL STARTER

NEAR DOUBLES: Ask some oral doubles and near doubles questions, for all numbers to at least 5, such as double 2; 3 add 4; 5 plus 4.... Extend the number range for the more able. Each time ask the children for their calculating strategy.

VOCABULARY

Time; days of the week: Monday, Tuesday, …; seasons: spring, summer, autumn, winter; day; week; weekend; morning; afternoon; evening; night; today; yesterday; tomorrow; now; soon; early; late; before; after; o'clock; hour; clock; watch; hands; midnight; bedtime; dinnertime; playtime; next; last.

MAIN TEACHING ACTIVITY

SEQUENCING EVENTS: Ask: *What day is it today?* and ask a child to place the day's card on the date chart. Ask: *What will it be tomorrow? What was it yesterday? What comes before/after …?* Say the days of the week in order. Ask questions such as: *Which days do we come to school? Which days do you stay at home?* Ask about the season, which season it is and how you can tell, discussing the weather. Show the pictures of the seasons, and ask the children to explain which is which.

Ask individuals to describe what they have done so far today, and to put this information in event order, such as 'I got up; washed; had my breakfast; came to school'. Pin up the pictures from photocopiable page 79 (out of sequence) and ask the children to describe the pictures and put them in order. Then ask them to cut out the pictures from the top part of their own photocopies, and sequence those, sticking them onto paper in the correct order, then to do the same for the pictures from the bottom of the sheet.

DIFFERENTIATION

Less able: discuss where each picture should go in the sequence and why.
More able: encourage them to make their own sequencing puzzles, then swap with a partner to try out each other's puzzles.

PLENARY

Show the teaching clock; talk about the hands, name them, then count around the clock. Set it to o'clock times and encourage the children to say what time it is.

LESSON 2

RESOURCES	Cubes; copies of photocopiable page 80 (Clock) copied onto card; paper fasteners; teaching clock; scissors.
LEARNING OUTCOMES	**ORAL AND MENTAL STARTER** ● **Count reliably at least 10 objects.** **MAIN TEACHING ACTIVITY** ● Understand and use the vocabulary related to time. ● Order familiar events in time. ● Know the days of the week and the seasons of the year. ● Read the time to the hour on analogue clocks.
ORAL AND MENTAL STARTER	COUNTING: Ask children to count out 9 cubes. Say: *How many are there? Put one more; how many now? Take away three; how many do you have now?...* Repeat this for other amounts.
MAIN TEACHING ACTIVITY	TELLING THE TIME: Repeat the days of the week activity from Lesson 1. Draw a circle on the board and ask the children to help to write in the numbers on the clock face. Using the teaching clock, show o'clock times. Ask children to cut out the clock and hands on the photocopiable sheet, and to fix the hands on with a fastener. Ask them to respond to 'Show me' setting the hands on their clock to given o'clock times.
DIFFERENTIATION	Encourage everyone to join in. Differentiation is by outcome.
PLENARY	Say the names of the days, then the seasons, in order.

RESOURCES	Teaching clock; card clocks; large paper circles each labelled with a different bedtime (eg 7 o'clock, half past 7); paper and pencils.
LEARNING OUTCOMES	**ORAL AND MENTAL STARTER** ● **Know by heart all pairs of numbers with a total of 10** (eg 3+7). **MAIN TEACHING ACTIVITY** ● Understand and use the vocabulary related to time. ● Order familiar events in time. ● Know the days of the week and the seasons of the year. ● Read the time to the hour or half-hour on analogue clocks. ● Solve a given problem by sorting, classifying and organising information in simple ways, such as using objects or pictures. ● Discuss and explain results.
ORAL AND MENTAL STARTER	FINGER ADD: Children show on their fingers what to add to a number to make 10, such as *What do I add to 5 to make 10?*
MAIN TEACHING ACTIVITY	TELLING THE TIME: Repeat the days of the week activity from Lesson 1. Children use their cardboard clocks to show given o'clock times; extend to half past, using the teaching clock to demonstrate. Ask them to draw a small picture of their face on a piece of paper, then take turns to stick it onto the large paper circle labelled with their bedtime.
DIFFERENTIATION	Encourage everyone to join in. Differentiation is by outcome.
PLENARY	Discuss the collected data: *How many children go to bed at...? Which is the most/least popular bedtime? Which is the earliest/latest bedtime?*

RESOURCES

One-minute sandtimers; teaching clock; cardboard clocks; interlocking cubes; pencils and paper; flip chart and pen; a copy of photocopiable page 81 (Timing activities) for each child. For Lesson 5: empty plastic water or lemonade bottles (about 1 litre); access to a sink or water play area; stop clock or watch; 2 or 5 minute sandtimers.

PREPARATION

Make a hole in each bottle, so that water flows out of the holes at different rates. These can then be used as timing devices. Make the required photocopies.

LEARNING OUTCOMES

ORAL AND MENTAL STARTER
● Describe and extend number sequences: **count in tens from and back to zero.**

MAIN TEACHING ACTIVITY
● Understand and use the vocabulary related to time.
● Order familiar events in time.
● Know the days of the week and the seasons of the year.
● Read the time to the hour or half-hour on analogue clocks.
● **Use mental strategies to solve simple problems** set in measurement contexts, **using counting, addition, subtraction, doubling and halving, explaining methods and reasoning orally.**

ORAL AND MENTAL STARTER

COUNTING TENS: Together count in tens from zero to 100 and back. Start at 20, count five tens; start at 30 count six tens....

MAIN TEACHING ACTIVITY

TIME PROBLEMS: Begin by asking questions such as: *If it is now 5 o'clock: what time will it be in one hour's time? Two hours? One hour ago?* Ask individual children to use the teaching clock to count forward or back to show the answer. Show the one minute sand timer, and let the sand run through, explaining this will take about a minute. Ask: *How many*

VOCABULARY

Hour; o'clock; half past; clock; watch; hands; takes longer; takes less time; quick; quicker; quickest; quickly; fast; faster; fastest; slow; slower; slowest; slowly.

cubes could you fix together in one minute? How many times could you do up and undo your shoe/ write your name/ skip...? Set each group of children a different challenge, ask them to decide how they will keep a count, make an estimate, and record on photocopiable page 81. They may find it easier

I think I can ...	I counted
Fit **20** cubes together	**26** cubes
Do up my shoe **5** times	**3** times

to work in pairs, one doing the activity, the other counting. Turn the sand timer over, and say *Go!* They record their results, then swap activities. Discuss their results with them, and ask them whether their estimates improved over time.

DIFFERENTIATION

Less able: ensure that the size of the count is manageable.
More able: ask questions such as: *If you can do... in 1 minute, how many do you think you will do in 2 minutes? Try it. Was your estimate reasonably accurate?*

PLENARY

TELLING THE TIME: Children show different o'clock and half past times on their clocks.

LESSON 5

Repeat the activities for Lesson 4. Introduce other timing devices, such as home-made water clocks, the second hand on a stop clock or watch, and 2 and 5 minute sand timers. Repeat the timing activities. For the water clocks ask: *How long do you think it will take for the water to run out? A minute? More? Less?* Children can experiment, comparing the bottles with the sand timers. Then ask the children to shut their eyes, and keep them closed for a minute. Discuss how accurate they were in their estimate.

RESOURCES

Large hoops or rings made from skipping ropes; large paper labels; red, blue, green and yellow bricks; large sheets of paper; coloured pencils and paper; scissors; adhesive.

PREPARATION

Make paper labels with 'Blue bricks', 'Not blue bricks'; 'Red bricks';

MY BIRTHDAY

Jan Feb Mar Apr May Jun Jul Aug Sep Oct Nov Dec

'Yellow bricks'; 'Green bricks'. Prepare a large sheet for a pictogram entitled 'My birthday', with the months along the x-axis (see figure above).

LEARNING OUTCOMES

ORAL AND MENTAL STARTER
● Describe and extend number sequences: **count on and back in ones from any small number, and in tens from and back to zero.**

MAIN TEACHING ACTIVITY
● Solve a given problem by sorting, classifying and organising information in simple ways, such as: in a list or simple table. Discuss and explain results.

VOCABULARY

Count; sort; group; set; vote.

ORAL AND MENTAL STARTER

Repeat 'Counting tens' from Lesson 4 of this unit, page 76.

MAIN TEACHING ACTIVITY

SORTING: Place two large hoops on the floor. Without stating the criterion, sort some children into each hoop, perhaps by gender; colour of jumper/shoes/eyes, then ask how you have sorted. Repeat for different criteria. Put the 'Blue bricks' label in one hoop and the 'Not blue bricks' label in the other hoop. Ask the children to take turns to sort the bricks into the hoops. Ask: *How many are blue? How many are not blue? Are there more blue bricks or more that are not blue?* Place the labels 'Blue bricks', 'Red bricks', 'Green bricks', 'Yellow bricks', in a line on the floor, and ask the children to line the bricks up above their colour label to show the sorting. Ask: *Which line has most bricks? How many bricks in total?* Ask the children to draw a picture of themselves on a small piece of paper, then stick this onto a class pictogram entitled: 'My birthday'.

DIFFERENTIATION

Encourage all the children to join in.
Less able: check that they understand the idea of 'is' and 'is not' by asking questions, such as: *Which are blue? Which are not blue?*
More able: ask more complex questions, such as: *Are there more blue bricks or more that are not blue?*

PLENARY

Using the birthday pictogram, ask questions such as: *Which month has the most/least birthdays? Which months have more birthdays than...? When is your birthday?*

LESSON 7

Repeat the ideas for Lesson 6, sorting different items such as shapes, toy cars, the children themselves. Record the sorting by matching the count with pictures or blocks of colour on a block graph. Make a class pictogram for favourite snacks and ask questions such as: *Which is most/least popular? How many more like... than...?*

RESOURCES

Items for measuring such as bricks, cubes, straws, paper strips, books or pencils; pencils and paper;

hoops; labels with 'Longer than 6 cubes', 'Shorter than 6 cubes' 'About as long as 6 cubes'; gummed coloured paper squares; picture rulers (sse figure); recording tables.

PREPARATION

Make some picture rulers (the figure above shows an example). Make a recording table for each child, pair or small group. This could be done on the class computer.

LEARNING OUTCOMES

ORAL AND MENTAL STARTER

● **Know by heart: all pairs of numbers with a total of 10** (eg 3+7); addition doubles of all numbers to at least 5 (eg 4 + 4).
● Identify near doubles using doubles already known (eg 6 + 5).

MAIN TEACHING ACTIVITY

● Solve a given problem by sorting, classifying and organising information in simple ways, such as: using objects or pictures; in a list or simple table. Discuss and explain results.
● Understand and use the vocabulary related to length.
● **Compare two lengths by direct comparison;** extend to more than two.
● **Suggest suitable standard or uniform non-standard units and measuring equipment to estimate, then measure, a length,** recording estimates and measurements as 'about...'.

Length; width; height; depth; long; short; tall; high; low; wide; narrow; deep; shallow; thick; thin; longer; shorter; taller; higher; longest; shortest; tallest; highest; count; sort; group; set.

ORAL AND MENTAL STARTER

Repeat 'Near doubles' from Lesson 1 (page 74) and 'Finger add' from Lesson 3 (page 76).

MAIN TEACHING ACTIVITY

LENGTH PROBLEMS: Ask the children to write number sentences, using +, –, and = as appropriate, in order to find the answers to questions such as: *Three cubes are as long as one pencil. How long will two pencils be?* or *The toy car is as long as three cubes, and the toy bus is as long as four cubes. If I put them together, how long would they be?* Choose from the following challenges and read them to the children, asking them to record their estimates and measures for each activity in a simple recording table (for example, with columns headed 'I am measuring', 'My units are', 'My estimate is' and 'My measure is').

1. Sort toys into hoops labelled 'Longer than 6 cubes' 'Shorter than 6 cubes' and 'About as long as 6 cubes'.

2. Find items in the classroom and draw pictures of them in circles labelled 'Longer than a metre' and 'Not longer than a metre'.

3. How far away is the classroom door? Children choose a non-standard unit to measure (cane, metre stick, stride), and record their estimate and measure.

4. How much longer is the classroom than it is wide? Children decide how to solve this problem, choosing their own non-standard units to measure. They write a subtraction sentence to show their answer.

Longer than a metre | About the same as a metre | Shorter than a metre

5. Estimate, then measure, the length of a straw, using non-standard units. Repeat with other units. Which was the most appropriate unit to use?

6. How long is an elastic band? Children work in pairs, estimating, then stretching the elastic band gently to find out how long it might be, measuring with their chosen non-standard units.

7. Find the height, width, and length of a table. Children choose their units and estimate, then measure.

8. Which paper ruler would you use? Children decide which one to use to measure items such as a pencil, shoe, book. They write their measurements on a simple chart (for example, with columns headed 'I chose', 'I measured with' and 'I counted').

9. How long is a metre? Children use different non-standard units to estimate, then measure the metre stick.

10. Mark a line on the floor. Children jump across the line, then measure how far they have jumped, agreeing on a non-standard unit to use. They make a simple block graph, writing their names on the x-axis, and using one coloured gummed square to represent one unit.

11. Children stand behind a line and throw a bean bag. They measure their throw using agreed non-standard units, and record on a block graph (as for activity 10).

12. Who has the widest hand span? Working as a group, children measure each others' hand span using a paper ruler, then record their measure on a pictogram with their names along the x-axis.

DIFFERENTIATION

Less able: start with activities 1 and 2.
More able: activities 9 to 12 are more challenging.

PLENARY

Ask the children to explain how they solved the problem. Compare different methods and discuss which was most effective. Encourage them to make approximations saying whether it was 'nearly'; 'just over' or 'about the same'. Compare their sorting diagrams and ask questions about the data, such as: *Whose is most/longest/furthest? How many ....?*

LESSONS 9 AND 10

Repeat Lesson 8, choosing different problems to challenge the children in the **Main teaching activity.**

Sequencing

Cut out the pictures.
Put them in order.

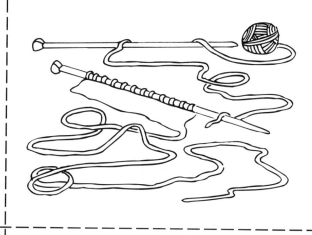

Clock

Photocopy this onto card and cut it out.
Fix the hands with a paper fastener or bolt.

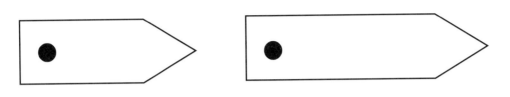

12

11

1

10

2

9

3

8

4

7

5

6

Timing activities

Write your estimate and measure.
In I minute...

I think I can ...	I counted
Fit [ ] cubes together	[ ] cubes
Do up my shoe [ ] times	[ ] times
Write my name [ ] times	[ ] times
Skip [ ] times	[ ] times
Write your own here.	

UNIT 14: Assess & Review

Choose from these activities. During the group activities, some children can be completing assessment worksheets 2A and 2B (which assess their skills with reading and writing numbers to 20, addition and subtraction) while others work with you on practical tasks. On sheet 2B you may need to point out to the children that the answer to each sum provides them with the first number in the next sum. The specific assessment criteria for the assessment sheets are to be found at the bottom of each sheet.

RESOURCES

Assessment photocopiables 2a and 2b; paper and pencils for recording; numeral cards for each child; counters; a collection of items which can be used for making direct comparisons of length, such as ribbons, strips of paper of various widths or toy cars; a collection of items which can be used as non-standard units, such as straws, cubes or pencils of the same length; metre sticks; packs of playing cards with 'spots' on.

ORAL AND MENTAL STARTER

ASSESSMENT

Do the children:
● **Know by heart:** all pairs of numbers with a total of 10?
COUNTING IN ONES AND TENS: Count forwards and backwards in ones from zero to twenty. Say, *Start at 5, count to 15. Start at 8, count on 4. What numbers do you reach? Count back from 18 to 12. How many did you count?* Suggest to the children that they use their fingers to help them keep count. Repeat counting in tens from zero to one hundred and back. Say: *Count on three tens from twenty: count back two tens from eighty.*
SHOW ME ADD: Ask children to hold up the number which will make 10 when added to the number you say; so, for '7', they hold up '3'. Note who is confident, and who will need more practice.

GROUP ACTIVITIES

ASSESSMENT

Can the children:
● Count reliably at least 10 objects.
● Compare two lengths by direct comparison.
● Suggest suitable standard or uniform non-standard units and measuring equipment to estimate, then measure, a length.
● Use mental strategies to solve simple problems using counting, addition, subtraction, doubling and halving, explaining methods and reasoning orally.
COUNTING: Ask children to take a handful of about 10 counters, estimate how many, then check by counting. Ask them to rearrange their counters, then say: *How many are there now?* Check that they have understood that the quantity does not change. Repeat for another handful.
COMPARING LENGTHS: Ask children to choose two items from the collection and, by making a direct comparison, say which is longer/shorter/wider/narrower. Check that they place one end of each object level with the other so that they make a direct comparison. Ask them to repeat this with two more items, then extend to more than two. Encourage children to use the vocabulary of length in explaining their response each time.
MEASURE A METRE: Ask children to estimate, then measure, a metre stick, choosing their own units. Ask them to explain why they have chosen their units.
SOLVING PROBLEMS: Repeat the activities in Unit 8, lesson 4, this time using counting to find combinations of playing card spots to make thirteen. Ask children to find combinations using two cards, then if they are confident at this, extend to three cards. Check that they count the spots accurately.

Assessment 2A

Read the words.
Write the numbers.

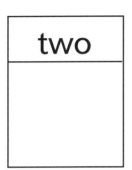 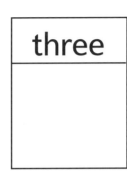 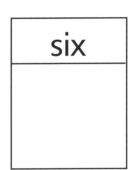 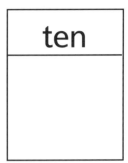

two	three	six	ten

Read the numbers.
Write the words.

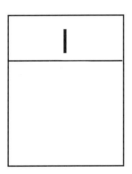 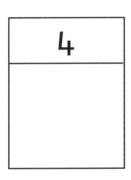 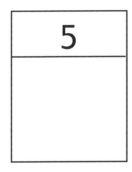 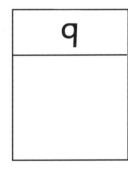

I	4	5	q

Write the missing numbers.

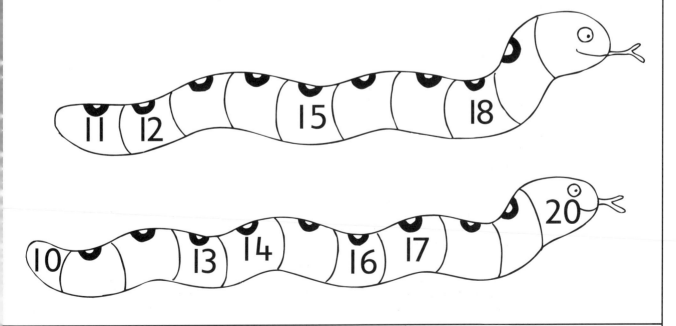

● Read and write numbers to at least 20.

Assessment 2B

Write the answer to each sum on the next leaf.
The first one has been done for you.

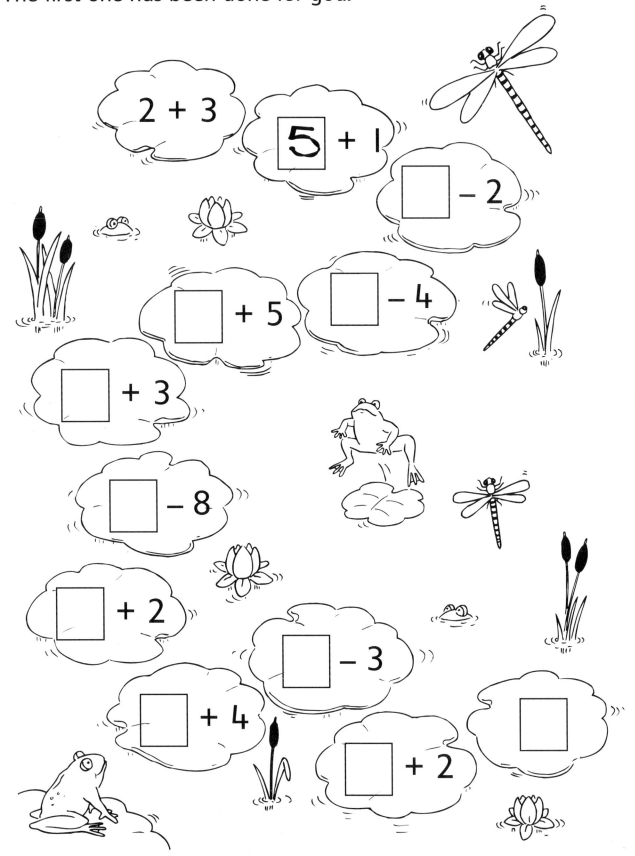

2 + 3

5 + 1

□ − 2

□ + 5

□ − 4

□ + 3

□ − 8

□ + 2

□ − 3

□ + 4

□ + 2

□

● Understand the operation of addition, and of subtraction (as 'take away'), and use the related vocabulary.

This term's work reinforces that of Term 1. It develops knowledge, skills and understanding with numbers to 20, and extends the use of mental strategies for addition. Subtraction, both as 'take away' and as 'difference' is taught, and children begin to recall subtraction facts for numbers to 10. They continue their work on money, and extend their use of coins to include totals to 20p, and giving change from 20p. In 'Shape and space' the focus on 3-D and 2-D shapes and their properties from Term 1 continues. In 'Measures' the children learn about direct comparisons, using non-standard units, and use this knowledge to solve problems involving mass. They continue to learn to tell the time. When 'Organising and using data' the emphasis is upon collecting data, using objects and pictures to represent the data, and discussing and explaining results.

TERM 2 PLANNING GRID

Oral and mental skills: **Know by heart: all pairs of numbers with a total of 10;** addition facts for all numbers to at least 5, and corresponding subtraction facts; addition doubles of all numbers to at least 5 (eg 4 + 4). **Count reliably at least 10, then 20 objects.** Describe and extend number sequences: **count on and back in ones from any small number, and in tens from and back to zero.** Begin to partition into '5 and a bit' when adding 6, 7, 8, or 9, then recombine (eg 6 + 8 = 5 + 1 + 5 + 3 = 10 + 4 = 14).

UNIT	TOPIC	OBJECTIVES: CHILDREN WILL BE TAUGHT TO
1	Counting and properties of numbers	● Know the number names and recite them in order to at least 20, from and back to zero. Describe and extend number sequences: **count on or back in ones, from any small number, and in tens from and back to zero;** count on in twos from zero, then one, and begin to recognise odd or even numbers to about 20 as 'every other number'.
2–4	Place value and ordering	● **Read and write numerals from 0 to at least 20.** Begin to know what each digit in a two-digit number represents. Partition a 'teens' number and begin to partition larger two-digit numbers into a multiple of 10 and ones (TU). **Within the range 0 to 30, say the number that is 1 or 10 more or less than any given number. Order numbers to at least 20,** and position them on a number track.
	Understanding + and –	● **Understand the operation of subtraction (as 'difference' and 'how many more to make') and use the related vocabulary.** Begin to use the – and = signs to record mental calculations in a number sentence. Begin to recognise that more than two numbers can be added together.
	Mental calculation strategies (+ and –)	● Put the larger number first and count on in ones, including beyond 10 (eg 7 + 5). Add 9 to single-digit numbers by adding 10 then subtracting 1. Use patterns of similar calculations (eg 10 – 0 = 10; 10 – 1 = 9; 10 – 2 = 8...).
	Money and 'real life' problems	● **Use own mental strategies to solve simple problems** set in 'real life' or money contexts, **using counting, addition, subtraction, doubling and halving, explaining methods and reasoning orally.** Recognise coins of different values. Find totals and change from up to 10p. Work out how to pay an exact sum using smaller coins.
	Making decisions	● Choose and use appropriate number operations and mental strategies to solve numerical problems.
5–6	Measures, including problems	● Understand and use the vocabulary related to mass. **Compare two masses by direct comparison,** extend to more than two. Measure using uniform non-standard units, or standard weights. **Suggest suitable standard or uniform non-standard units and measuring equipment to estimate, then measure, a mass,** recording estimates and measurements as 'about as heavy as 20 cubes'. **Use mental strategies to solve simple problems** set in measurement contexts, **using counting, addition, subtraction, doubling and halving, explaining methods and reasoning orally.**
	Shape and space	● **Use everyday language to describe features of familiar 2-D shapes,** including the circle, triangle, square, rectangle... referring to properties such as the shapes of flat faces, or the number of faces, or corners... or the number and types of sides. Fold shapes in half, then make them into symmetrical patterns.
	Reasoning about shapes	● Solve simple mathematical problems or puzzles; recognise and predict from simple patterns and relationships. Suggest extensions by asking 'What if...?' or 'What could I try next?' Investigate a general statement about familiar shapes by finding examples that satisfy it. Explain methods and reasoning orally.
7	Assess and review	● **Know by heart: all pairs of numbers with a total of 10. Count reliably at least 20 objects.** Describe and extend number sequences: **count on and back in ones from any small number, and in tens from and back to zero. Read, write and order numbers to at least 20. Within the range 0 to 30, say the number that is 1 or 10 more or less than any given number. Understand the operation of subtraction (as 'difference') and use the related vocabulary. Use mental strategies to solve simple problems,** using counting, addition, subtraction, doubling and halving, explaining methods and reasoning orally. Compare two masses by direct comparison. Suggest suitable standard or uniform non-standard units and measuring equipment to estimate, then measure, a mass. Use everyday language to describe features of familiar 2-D shapes.

Oral and mental skills: **Count reliably at least 20 objects. Know by heart: all pairs of numbers with a total of 10** (eg 3 +7); addition facts for all numbers to at least 5, and the corresponding subtraction facts; addition doubles of all numbers to at least 5 (eg 4 + 4). Begin to know: addition facts for all pairs of numbers with a total up to at least 10, and the corresponding subtraction facts. Describe and extend number sequences: **count on and back in ones from any small number, and in tens from and back to zero;** count on in twos from zero, then one, and begin to recognise odd and even numbers to about 20 as 'every other number'. Use known number facts and place value to add or subtract a pair of numbers mentally within the range 0 to at least 10, then 20. Begin to recognise that more than two numbers can be added together. **Within the range 0 to 30, say the number that is 1 or 10 more or less than any given number.** Read the time to the hour or the half hour on analogue clocks.

UNIT	TOPIC	OBJECTIVES: CHILDREN WILL BE TAUGHT TO
8	Counting and properties of numbers	● Know the number names and recite them in order to at least 20, from and back to zero. **Count reliably at least 20 objects.** Describe and extend number sequences: **count on and back in ones from any small number, and in tens from and back to zero;** count on in twos from zero, then one, and begin to recognise odd and even numbers to about 20 as 'every other number'.
	Reasoning about numbers	● Solve simple mathematical problems or puzzles; recognise and predict from simple patterns and relationships. Suggest extensions by asking 'What if...?' or 'What could I try next?' Investigate a general statement about familiar numbers by finding examples that satisfy it. Explain methods and reasoning orally.
9–10	Place value, ordering, estimating	● **Read and write numerals from 0 to at least 20. Understand and use the vocabulary of comparing and ordering numbers,** including ordinal numbers to at least 20. Use the = sign to represent equality. Compare two familiar numbers, say which is more or less, and give a number which lies between them. **Within the range 0 to 30, say the number that is 1 or 10 more or less than any given number.**
	Understanding + and –	● **Understand the operation of addition and of subtraction (as 'take away' or 'difference') and use the related vocabulary.** Begin to recognise that addition can be done in any order. Begin to use the + and = signs to record mental calculations in a number sentence, and to recognise the use of symbols such as □ or △ to stand for an unknown number. Begin to recognise that more than two numbers can be added together.
	Mental calculation strategies (+ and –)	● Put the larger number first and count on in ones, including beyond 10 (eg 7 + 5). Use known number facts and place value to add or subtract a pair of numbers mentally within the range 0 to at least 10, and later 20. Use patterns of similar calculations (eg 10 – 0 = 10; 10 – 1 = 9; 10 – 2 = 8...).
	Money and 'real life' problems	● **Use mental strategies to solve simple problems** set in 'real life' or money contexts, **using counting, addition, subtraction, doubling and halving, explaining methods and reasoning orally.** Recognise coins of different values. Find totals and change from up to 20p. Work out how to pay an exact sum using smaller coins.
	Making decisions	● Choose and use appropriate number operations and mental strategies to solve numerical problems.
11–12	Measures, and time, including problems	● Understand and use the vocabulary related to length and mass. **Compare two lengths or masses by direct comparison;** extend to more than two. Measure using uniform non-standard units, or standard units. **Suggest suitable standard or uniform non-standard units and measuring equipment to estimate, then measure, length or mass,** recording estimates and measurements as 'about as heavy as 20 cubes'. Understand and use the vocabulary related to time. Order familiar events in time. Know the days of the week and the seasons of the year. Read the time to the hour or half hour on analogue clocks. **Use mental strategies to solve simple problems** set in measurement contexts, **using counting, addition, subtraction, doubling and halving, explaining methods and reasoning orally.**
	Organising and using data	● Solve a given problem by sorting, classifying and organising information in simple ways, such as: using objects or pictures. Discuss and explain results.
13	Assess and review	● **Know by heart all pairs of numbers with a total of 10.** Describe and extend number sequences: **count on and back in ones from any small number, and in tens from and back to zero. Count reliably at least 20 objects. Read, write and order numbers from 0 to at least 20;** understand and use the vocabulary of comparing and ordering these numbers. **Within the range 0 to 30, say the number that is 1 or 10 more or less than any given number. Understand the operation of addition, and of subtraction (as 'take away' or 'difference'), and use the related vocabulary.**

UNIT 1

ORGANISATION (3 LESSONS)

	LEARNING OUTCOMES	ORAL AND MENTAL STARTER	MAIN TEACHING ACTIVITY	PLENARY
LESSON 1	● Know the number names and recite them in order to at least 20, from and ba ck to zero. ● Describe and extend number sequences: **count on or back in ones from any small number, and in tens from and back to zero;** count on in twos from zero, then one, and begin to recognise odd or even numbers to about 20 as 'every other number'.	DOUBLE IT: Doubling numbers by counting on.	COUNTING RHYMES: Counting in ones and twos; identifying odd and even numbers.	Counting in twos.
LESSON 2	● Describe and extend number sequences: count on in twos from zero, then one, and begin to recognise odd or even numbers to about 20 as 'every other number'.	DOUBLE IT: Doubling numbers by counting on.	ODDS AND EVENS: Playing a dice game.	Discussion of the sums: odds and evens.
LESSON 3	● Describe and extend number sequences: **count on and back in tens from and back to zero.**	DOUBLE IT: Doubling numbers by counting on.	COUNTING IN TENS: Using a hundred square.	Counting in tens.

ORAL AND MENTAL SKILLS   Know by heart: addition doubles of all numbers to at least 5 (eg 4 + 4).

Lesson 1 is shown in detail. Lessons 2 and 3 are extensions of Lesson 1.

RESOURCES

Numeral cards 0–10 (page 14); paper and pencils; flip chart and pen; interlocking cubes; a selection of favourite counting songs.

PREPARATION

Choose some favourite counting songs, including some that count in twos. Make and photocopy a two-column chart for 'odd' and 'even' numbers which the children can fill in.

VOCABULARY

Number; zero, one, two, three... to 20 and beyond; zero, 10, 20... to one hundred; none; count in ones... twos... tens...; odd; even; every other; how many times?; pattern; pair.

LEARNING OUTCOMES

ORAL AND MENTAL STARTER
● **Know by heart:** addition doubles of all numbers to at least 5 (eg 4 + 4).

MAIN TEACHING ACTIVITY
● Know the number names and recite them in order to at least 20, from and back to zero.
● Describe and extend number sequences: **count on or back in ones from any small number, and in tens from and back to zero;** count on in twos from zero, then one, and begin to recognise odd or even numbers to about 20 as 'every other number'.

ORAL AND MENTAL STARTER

DOUBLE IT: Explain to the children that you will be asking them to double numbers. They should hold up a numeral card to show the double fact. Suggest that if they do not know the answer they count on in their heads.

MAIN TEACHING ACTIVITY

COUNTING RHYMES: Sing or say some counting rhymes, including those which count in twos. Ask the children to count with you in ones from zero to 20 and back, then from any small number to 20 and back to zero. Count around the class, then back again, until everyone has had two turns. Repeat for counting in tens. Now count in twos to 20 starting from zero, then from 1. Say which numbers are odd and which are even. Make a stick of 10 cubes and ask a child to count them in twos. Ask: *Is 10 odd or even?* Repeat for other numbers. Count slowly in ones, writing each number on the flip chart under 'odd' or 'even'. Now ask the children to make sticks of up to 20 cubes, count them in twos, then write the quantity in an 'odd' or 'even' column on their paper.

DIFFERENTIATION

Less able: limit the number of cubes in the sticks to about 10.
More able: decide whether to extend the number of cubes to more than 20.

PLENARY

Count again in twos, first from zero to 20, then from 1. Remind the children which are odd and which are even numbers.

LESSON 2

RESOURCES	1–6 dice; paper (or photocopied recording chart, see Lesson 1, above) and pencils; interlocking cubes.
LEARNING OUTCOMES	**ORAL AND MENTAL STARTER** ● **Know by heart:** addition doubles of all numbers to at least 5. **MAIN TEACHING ACTIVITY** ● Describe and extend number sequences: count on in twos from zero, then one, and begin to recognise odd or even numbers to about 20 as 'every other number'.
ORAL AND MENTAL STARTER	Repeat 'Double it' from Lesson 1 in this unit, page 87.
MAIN TEACHING ACTIVITY	ODDS AND EVENS: Ask the children to make a stick of 8 cubes. *Can you make two sticks the same size from this one? Is 8 odd or even?* Try with other numbers. Ask the children (in pairs) to throw two dice, add the scores and write the sum under 'odd' or 'even' depending on the answer.
DIFFERENTIATION	Less able: provide number lines to help them to add if necessary. More able: challenge them to find all odd and all even numbers to 20.
PLENARY	Discuss the sums made. Which have odd and which even totals?

LESSON 3

RESOURCES	Class hundred square; photocopiable pages 89 (Hundred square) and 90 (Counting in tens); A3 enlargement of 'Counting in tens'.
LEARNING OUTCOMES	**ORAL AND MENTAL STARTER** ● **Know by heart:** addition doubles of all numbers to at least 5. **MAIN TEACHING ACTIVITY** ● Describe and extend number sequences: **count on and back in tens from and back to zero.**
ORAL AND MENTAL STARTER	Repeat 'Double it' from Lesson 1. Include some 'near doubles' (eg 3 + 4) once the children are confident.
MAIN TEACHING ACTIVITY	COUNTING IN TENS: Count in tens, from and back to zero. Point to the pattern of tens on the hundred square. The children use their fingers to keep count as you say: *Count on three tens from 20... from 50... from 60. Count back five tens from 100... from 60... from 80.* Count around the class in tens, from zero, to 100 and back again, then from 30, 50 and so on. Invite children, using their hundred squares to help them, to say the number that is 10 more/fewer than, for example, 20, writing on the flip chart 10 → 20 → 30. They should then complete page 90.
DIFFERENTIATION	Less able: encourage them to count in tens to answer the questions. More able: on the back of the sheet, challenge them to write the first decade number, the next one, and then the one that is 20 more.
PLENARY	Count in tens again, from and back to zero, then from 10, 40....

Hundred square

0	1	2	3	4	5	6	7	8	9
10	11	12	13	14	15	16	17	18	19
20	21	22	23	24	25	26	27	28	29
30	31	32	33	34	35	36	37	38	39
40	41	42	43	44	45	46	47	48	49
50	51	52	53	54	55	56	57	58	59
60	61	62	63	64	65	66	67	68	69
70	71	72	73	74	75	76	77	78	79
80	81	82	83	84	85	86	87	88	89
90	91	92	93	94	95	96	97	98	99

Counting in tens

Write in the missing tens.

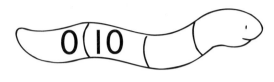 0 10

 20 40

 30

 50

 70 60

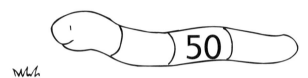 100 80

 10 30

 20 30

 30 40

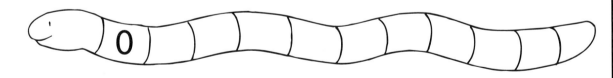 0

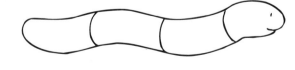

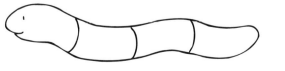

UNITS 2-4

ORGANISATION (15 LESSONS)

LEARNING OUTCOMES	ORAL AND MENTAL STARTER	MAIN TEACHING ACTIVITY	PLENARY
LESSON 1 +2 • Begin to know what each digit in a two-digit number represents. Partition a 'teens' number and begin to partition larger two-digit numbers into a multiple of 10 and ones (TU).	DOUBLE IT: Doubling small numbers.	ARROW NUMBERS: Playing a place value game.	Discussion of the mental strategies used.
LESSON 3 +4 • **Read and write numerals from 0 to at least 20.** • **Within the range 0 to 30, say the number that is 1 or 10 more or less than any given number.** • **Order numbers to at least 20,** and position them on a number track. • Add 9 to single-digit numbers by adding 10 then subtracting 1.	COUNTING: Counting out cubes, synchronising counting, touching and moving.	NUMBER TO 20: Ordering numbers on a number line.	Discussion of the mental strategies used.
LESSON 5 +6 • **Understand the operation of subtraction (as 'difference') and use the related vocabulary.** • Begin to use the − and = signs to record mental calculations in a number sentence.	COUNT IN TENS: Counting to 100 and back to zero in tens.	FINDING THE DIFFERENCE: Developing the concept of difference.	Discussion of the mental strategies used.
LESSON 7 • **Understand the operation of subtraction (as 'difference') and use the related vocabulary.** • Begin to use the − and = signs to record mental calculations in a number sentence. • Use patterns of similar calculations (eg 10-0=10; 10-1=9; 10-2=8…).	FAST 10: Finding the complement to make 10.	FINDING THE DIFFERENCE: Using patterns to find differences.	FAST 10.
LESSON 8 • Recognise coins of different values. Work out how to pay an exact sum using smaller coins. • Begin to recognise that more than two numbers can be added together. • Put the larger number first and count on in ones, including beyond 10 (eg 7 + 5).	FAST 10.	20P IN COINS: Making 20p using different combinations of coins.	Discussion of results.
LESSON 9 • Recognise coins of different values. • Work out how to pay an exact sum using smaller coins.	FAST 10.	EXACT AMOUNTS: Using coins to make exact amounts of money.	WHICH COINS HAVE I?: Totalling three coins.
LESSON 10 • **Understand the operation of subtraction** (as 'how many more to make') **and use the related vocabulary.** • Recognise coins of different values. Find totals and change from up to 10p. Work out how to pay an exact sum using smaller coins.	PARTITIONING: Partitioning into '5 and a bit' to add.	GIVING CHANGE: Giving change for amounts to 10p.	Discussion of results.

cont…

UNITS 2–4

LESSON 11	● **Understand the operation of subtraction (as** 'how many more to make'**) and use the related vocabulary.** ● Recognise coins of different values. Find totals and change from up to 10p. Work out how to pay an exact sum using smaller coins.	COUNTING: Counting in ones then tens, forwards and back to zero.	GIVING CHANGE: Using the least number of coins to give change.	Discussion of the work.
LESSON 12	● **Understand the operation of subtraction (as** 'how many more to make'**) and use the related vocabulary.** ● Begin to recognise that more than two numbers can be added together. ● Recognise coins of different values. Find totals and change from up to 10p. Work out how to pay an exact sum using smaller coins.	FAST 10.	SHOPPING: Choosing two items to total, then giving change from 10p.	FAST 10.
LESSON 13 +14 +15	● **Use mental strategies to solve simple problems** set in 'real life' or money contexts, **using counting, addition, subtraction, doubling and halving, explaining methods and reasoning orally.** ● Choose and use appropriate number operations and mental strategies to solve numerical problems.	FAST 10.	PROBLEMS: Solving problems.	Discussion of solutions.

ORAL AND MENTAL SKILLS Know by heart: **all pairs of numbers with a total of 10** (eg 3 + 7); addition doubles of all numbers to at least 5 (eg 4 + 4). **Count reliably at least 10 objects.** Describe and extend number sequences: **count on and back in ones from any small number, and in tens from and back to zero.** Begin to partition into '5 and a bit' when adding 6, 7, 8 or 9, then recombine (eg 6 + 8 = 5 + 1 + 5 + 3 = 10 + 4 = 14).

In Unit 2, Lessons 1, 3 and 5 are shown in detail, with Lessons 2 and 4 as extended versions of Lessons 1 and 3. In Unit 3, Lessons 8 and 10 are shown in full. Lessons 6, 7 and 9 are a continuation of what has already been taught and are shown in less detail. In Unit 4, Lessons 11 and 12 are continuations of what has already been taught. Lesson 13 is shown in detail with Lessons 14 and 15 as extensions of this work.

RESOURCES

A set of arrow cards from photocopiable page 68 (Arrow cards) and a number fan (page 17) for each child; a supply of number lines (page 18); flip chart and pen; a 1–6 and a 4–9 dice for each pair of children; paper and pencils; counters.

PREPARATION

Make the required photocopies. Make the 4–9 dice.

LEARNING OUTCOMES

ORAL AND MENTAL STARTER

● **Know by heart:** addition doubles of all numbers to at least 5 (eg 4 + 4).

MAIN TEACHING ACTIVITY

● Begin to know what each digit in a two-digit number represents. Partition a 'teens' number and begin to partition larger two-digit numbers into a multiple of 10 and ones (TU).

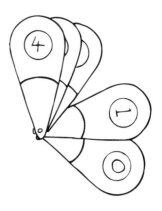

ORAL AND MENTAL STARTER

DOUBLE IT: Show the children how to hold up two blades of their fans to make two-digit 'teens' numbers. Using their number fans, ask the children to show you their answers to double and near double facts, such as: 5+5; 4+5; 3+3; double 4…

MAIN TEACHING ACTIVITY

ARROW NUMBERS: Write some 'teens' numbers on the flip chart and ask the children to say the numbers. Then ask them to spread out their arrow cards and show them how to combine the 10 card with a single-digit card to make a 'teens' number.

Explain to the children that you will say a number and that you would like them to make it with their arrow cards. Say: *Show me …18; …the number that is a 10 and four units; the number that is two tens* and so on until they are confident with doing this.

Now ask them to work in pairs, taking turns to throw the two dice. One child adds the dice score and shows it with arrow cards, the other says the 'teens' number. They record by writing an addition sum.

DIFFERENTIATION

Less able: provide number lines (page 18) for counting on.
More able: use two 4–9 dice.

PLENARY

Discuss the strategies that the children used to combine their dice scores.

LESSON 2

Repeat as for Lesson 1, but in the **Main teaching activity**, ask the children to make a paper abacus as in Unit 9, Lesson 3 of Term 1 (see page 59). Ask them to model numbers on the abacus, using their counters, then to use their arrow cards to show what the number underneath is. Say: *Show me 16. How many tens? How many units? Show me 18. What does the 'one' mean? What does the 'eight' mean? Show me 23; 25; 30; 45….*

Working in threes, tell the children to take turns to say a 'teens' number, make it with a tens and a units arrow card, and model it on the paper abacus with counters. Each time, they should check that they have all made the same number.

LESSON
3
+4

RESOURCES

Washing line and pegs; flip chart and pen; a copy of photocopiable page 89 (Hundred square) for each child; sets of numeral cards 0 to 20 (pages 14 and 15), number word cards and large numeral cards, counting cubes, paper and pencils.

PREPARATION

Hang up the washing line. Make the required photocopies.

LEARNING OUTCOMES

ORAL AND MENTAL STARTER
● **Count reliably at least 10 objects.**

MAIN TEACHING ACTIVITY

● **Read and write numerals from 0 to at least 20.**
● **Within the range 0 to 30, say the number that is 1 or 10 more or less than any given number.**
● **Order numbers to at least 20,** and position them on a number track.
● Add 9 to single-digit numbers by adding 10 then subtracting 1.

VOCABULARY

More; greater; larger; less; smaller; fewer; fewest; least; smallest; before; after; most; biggest; largest; greatest; one more; one less; 10 more; 10 less.

ORAL AND MENTAL STARTER

COUNTING: Ask each child to count out 10 cubes. Say: *Put out one more, how many have you now? Take away 2; now how many do you have? Add 3…. Take away 5….?* Repeat this for different amounts, and check that the children all count, synchronising touching and moving the cubes, and saying the number names in order.

MAIN TEACHING ACTIVITY

NUMBERS TO 20: Ask individuals to take turns to peg the numerals 0–20 onto the washing line. Then ask other individuals to remove numbers: *Take the number one before/after…; three before/after …; the number next to….* Take the cards off the line and ask: *What is 1 more/less than 6; …7? What number is 1 before/after 5? Which is more, 5 or 10? Which is least, 19, 2 or 18?* Using their hundred squares to help them ask the children: *What number is 10 more/less than 4? …40?* Think about '9 more' together. Explain that a way of adding 9 is to add 10 and subtract 1. Again using their hundred squares ask the children to find the answers to questions, such as: *5 add 9*, by counting 10 squares and subtracting/moving back one. Encourage them to explain the pattern on the hundred square.

Working in pairs, ask the children to play a game where they take turns to draw a card from a face-down, shuffled, 0–20 pack, and place it on the table. The aim of the game is to order the cards, remembering to leave gaps for missing cards.

DIFFERENTIATION

Less able: limit the ordering of cards to 10.
More able: encourage the children to respond to 10 more/less without using their hundred square.

PLENARY

Ask the children to peg the numerals and number word cards on the washing line so that each position on the line has both cards.

LESSON 4

Repeat Lesson 3, but in the hundred square activities from the **Main teaching activity** encourage the children to quickly find 10 more/less, then move on to adding 9 by adding 10 and subtracting 1. When the children are confident with this, ask them to try some questions without using their hundred square.

Next, ask them to work in pairs, taking turns to draw a card from a 0 to 9 pack. They must add 9 to each card drawn, and write an addition sum. Ask them to count on 10 in their heads and to subtract one. If any children lack confidence, provide them with hundred squares for counting on 10.

RESOURCES

Interlocking cubes or Cuisenaire rods; 1–6 and 4–9 dice; paper and pencils; flip chart and pen; numeral cards 0–10 (page 14) and a number line (page 18) for each child.

PREPARATION

Make the 4–9 dice; put two packs of numeral cards together for each pair of children.

LEARNING OUTCOMES

ORAL AND MENTAL STARTER

● Describe and extend number sequences: **count in tens from and back to zero.**

MAIN TEACHING ACTIVITY

● **Understand the operation of subtraction (as 'difference') and use the related vocabulary.**
● Begin to use the – and = signs to record mental calculations in a number sentence.

VOCABULARY

Difference between; one less; two less; makes; leaves; is the same as; equals; sign; minus; how many fewer is … than …?; how much less is … than …?; how many/much more is … than …?

ORAL AND MENTAL STARTER

COUNT IN TENS: Together, count from zero to one hundred and back in tens. Count around the class, zero, 10,… to one hundred, then back to zero. Ask: *What is 10 more/less than 20? Count in tens from 20 to sixty; keep a count with your fingers; how many tens?*

MAIN TEACHING ACTIVITY

FINDING THE DIFFERENCE: Hold up a tower of eight cubes and ask how many. Repeat this for a tower of six. Hold the two towers alongside each other, and ask: *How many more cubes in this* (pointing to the eight) *than this* (pointing to the six)*? What is the number difference between eight and six?* Repeat this for other cube towers, asking: *How many more? How many fewer? How much less? What is the difference…?* until the children are confident with the concept of difference. Repeat, counting on number lines. Ask the children to try some examples mentally, counting on in ones from the smaller number. Explain that the number sentence for difference is written as a subtraction, then ask *What is the difference between 7 and 3?* and write the number sentence on the flip chart with the answer: 7 – 3 = 4. Ask: *What is the difference between 3 and 8?* Then choose a child to write the subtraction sentence on the flip chart, and to explain the mental strategy used.

Give each pair of children two dice (1–6 and 4–9). Ask them to take turns to throw the dice, write a 'difference number sentence', and the answer, using the strategy of counting on in ones from the smaller number.

DIFFERENTIATION

Less able: provide a 1, 1, 1, 2, 2, 2 and a 1-6 dice. Work with this group and help them to count on in ones from the smaller number.
More able: provide two 4–9 dice.

PLENARY

Invite pairs of children to write some of their number sentences on the flip chart and explain their mental strategy for finding the answer.

LESSON 6

Repeat Lesson 5, but in the **Main teaching activity** remind the children of the concept of difference by asking some difference questions which they can work out using their number lines: *What is the difference between 4 and 6? How many more is 8 than 4? How many less is 3 than 9?* Ask some more questions, this time encouraging the children to count along or back on their 'mental number line' (the one they can 'see' in their heads) to find the answer.

In pairs, using two packs of numeral cards, ask children to take two cards each time, find the difference between the two numbers, and write a subtraction sentence.

DIFFERENTIATION

Less able: limit the number range of cards to 5.
More able: challenge them to write number stories for some of their difference sentences, such as 'Mark has four sweets and I have 10. I have six more than Mark. He has six fewer than me.'

RESOURCES	Copies of photocopiable page 101 (Finding the difference) and an A3 enlargement; flip chart and pen; numeral cards 0-10 (page 14) for each child; number lines (page 18).
LEARNING OUTCOMES	**ORAL AND MENTAL STARTER** ● **Know by heart: all pairs of numbers with a total of 10** (eg 3 + 7). **MAIN TEACHING ACTIVITY** ● **Understand the operation of subtraction (as 'difference') and use the related vocabulary.** ● Begin to use the – and = signs to record mental calculations in a number sentence. ● Use patterns of similar calculations (eg 10–0=10, 10–1=9, 10–2=8...)
ORAL AND MENTAL STARTER	FAST 10: Explain that you will say a number less than 10. Ask the children to hold up, as quickly as they can, the numeral card for the number which adds to your number to make 10. Repeat for other numbers, working as quickly as possible.
MAIN TEACHING ACTIVITY	FINDING THE DIFFERENCE: Pin the A3 enlargement of 'Finding the difference' on the flip chart. Explain that pairs of numbers with a difference of 3 are to be joined and ask a child to find a pair. Once everyone understands what to do, ask the children to complete the sheet. When they have finished, challenge them to write pairs of numbers with a difference of, for example, 4, on the back of the sheet. Encourage them to work systematically, ordering their pairs: 4, 0; 5, 1....
DIFFERENTIATION	Less able: allow them to use number lines to help them if required. More able: encourage them to find number pairs with larger differences, such as 7 or 8.
PLENARY	Play 'Fast 10' again.

RESOURCES

Coins of all denominations in tubs; flip chart and pen; a copy of photocopiable page 36 (Money boxes) for each pair, plus an A3 enlargement: paper and pencils.

PREPARATION

Place tubs of coins so that all the children can have access to one. Make sure that each tub contains at least one 20p coin. Make the required photocopies and enlarge a copy of 'Money boxes' to A3.

LEARNING OUTCOMES

ORAL AND MENTAL STARTER
● **Know by heart: all pairs of numbers with a total of 10** (eg 3 + 7).

MAIN TEACHING ACTIVITY
● Recognise coins of different values. Work out how to pay an exact sum using smaller coins.
● Begin to recognise that more than two numbers can be added together.
● Put the larger number first and count on in ones, including beyond 10 (eg 7 + 5).

ORAL AND MENTAL STARTER
FAST 10: Repeat from Lesson 7. Encourage the children to count on in their heads to 10.

VOCABULARY
Money; coin; pence; price; cost; how much...?

MAIN TEACHING ACTIVITY

20P IN COINS: Ask all the children to sort out the coins in the tub on their table and to find the 20p coin. Ask: *How many pennies is this worth? Is it worth more than 10p? More than 50p?* Using their coins to help them, ask the children to find some ways of making 20p and record these on the flip chart: 20p = 10p + 5p + 2p + 2p + 1p. For each way, encourage the children to put out the coins and count up to 20p. Then challenge the children, in groups, to find more ways of making 20p. At the end of five minutes ask a child from each group to write one possible solution on the flip chart. For each method encourage the children to check by counting, using their coins.

Now ask them to work in pairs, taking turns to shut their eyes and choose three coins from the tub. Their partner totals the coins and they both record this by drawing the coins in the money boxes on the photocopiable sheet and writing the total underneath, including the 'p' for pence. Encourage them to use the strategy of 'putting the larger number first and counting on'.

DIFFERENTIATION

Less able: for the activity on the photocopiable sheet, limit the available coins to 1ps, 2ps and 5ps.
More able: encourage them to extend to totalling four coins.

PLENARY

Pin the A3 enlargement of 'Money boxes' onto the flip chart. Choose pairs of children to write one of their examples of three coins and the total onto the sheet. For each example ask the others to check by counting in their heads. Encourage them to count on from the larger number each time.

RESOURCES	Price labels for 5p, 6p, 7p... to 20p; coins; flip chart and pen; a copy of photocopiable page 36 (Money boxes) for each child.
LEARNING OUTCOMES	**ORAL AND MENTAL STARTER** ● **Know by heart: all pairs of numbers with a total of 10** (eg 3 + 7). **MAIN TEACHING ACTIVITY** ● Recognise coins of different values. ● Work out how to pay an exact sum using smaller coins.
ORAL AND MENTAL STARTER	Play 'Fast ten' from Lesson 7.
MAIN TEACHING ACTIVITY	EXACT AMOUNTS: Write an amount, up to 20p, on the flip chart, and ask the children to use their coins to make the exact amount. Write some solutions on the chart and discuss which uses the least coins. Repeat for other amounts. Now, working in groups, the children should turn over a price label, find coins to total that price, then compare to find which way used the least number of coins. They record their coins on photocopiable page 36 (Money boxes) and the group member who used least coins draws a star beside it. They continue until all the money boxes are full. The child with the most stars wins the game.
DIFFERENTIATION	Less able: use labels with lower prices. More able: challenge them to find all possible ways of making a total other than just using one pence coins.
PLENARY	WHICH COINS HAVE I?: Explain that you have three coins which can make totals of 5p, 7p and 8p... Ask: *Which coins do I have?*

RESOURCES

Coins to 10p; items to sell in a shop, such as small toys, with price labels from 1p to 10p; numeral cards 0 to 20 (pages 14 and 15); a copy of photocopiable page 102 (Giving change) for each pair plus an A3 enlargement of this sheet.

PREPARATION

Make the price labels and attach them to the items for the shop. Set up a class shop, where children can take turns to play the roles of shopkeeper and customer.

LEARNING OUTCOMES

ORAL AND MENTAL STARTER

● Begin to partition into '5 and a bit' when adding 6, 7, 8 or 9, then recombine (eg 6 + 8 = 5 + 1 + 5 + 3 = 10 + 4 = 14).

MAIN TEACHING ACTIVITY

● **Understand the operation of subtraction (as** 'how many more to make'**) and use the related vocabulary.**
● Recognise coins of different values. Find totals and change from up to 10p. Work out how to pay an exact sum using smaller coins.

VOCABULARY

How many more to make...?; price; cost; buy; sell; pay; change; how much...?.

ORAL AND MENTAL STARTER

PARTITIONING: Remind children of the strategy of partitioning larger numbers into '5 and a bit', then recombining to make 10, then counting on (see Lesson 9 of Unit 3, Term 1 on page 32). Give examples including 5 initially, such as: 5+7; 5+9. Then give examples such as 6+8; 7+6, where both numbers need to be made into '5 and a bit'. Ask the children to hold up numeral cards to show their responses.

MAIN TEACHING ACTIVITY

GIVING CHANGE: Explain that today's lesson is about shopping and giving change. Ask a child to be the customer, and give him or her a 5p coin. Show an item with a price tag of 2p and ask the child to swap the item for the 5p. Ask: *How much is this? How much money did she give? How much change should I give?* Encourage the children to count on in their heads from 2p to 5p to find the change, and ask another child to be the shopkeeper and choose coins to give the change. Encourage the shopkeeper to use the least number of coins. Repeat with other examples, extending to giving change from 10p. Pin the enlargement of 'Giving change' to the flip chart and, pointing to the first example, ask: *How much change will there be from 10p?* Ask a child to find the coins for the change and record this on the sheet.

　　Ask the children to work in pairs and, for each example on the sheet, take turns to give change from 10p, recording this on photocopiable page 102 (Giving change). Choose a small group of children to act as shopkeeper or customers in the class shop, and explain that they should take turns at buying and giving and checking change. Repeat this during the next week so that all the children have the experience of buying and giving and checking change.

DIFFERENTIATION

Less able: work with this group, encouraging them to count on to find the change.
More able: challenge the children to find the least number of coins for the change each time.

PLENARY

Choose pairs of children to write an answer on the A3 enlargement of the sheet. Ask the others to check that the change is correct.

LESSON 11

RESOURCES	Sets of price labels from 1p to 10p; coins; flip chart and pen; paper and pencils.
LEARNING OUTCOMES	**ORAL AND MENTAL STARTER** ● Describe and extend number sequences: **count on and back in ones from any small number, and in tens from and back to zero.** **MAIN TEACHING ACTIVITY** ● **Understand the operation of subtraction (as** 'how many more to make') **and use the related vocabulary.** ● Recognise coins of different values. Find totals and change from up to 10p. Work out how to pay an exact sum using smaller coins.
ORAL AND MENTAL STARTER	COUNTING: Count in ones to 20 and back to zero. Count around the class, forwards and back to zero. Count in tens to one hundred and back to zero.
MAIN TEACHING ACTIVITY	GIVING CHANGE: Repeat the **Main teaching activity** from Lesson 10, this time encouraging the children to choose the least number of coins. Suggest that they count up to 10p, from the cost of the item, using coins, such as '6p and 2p makes 8p and 2p makes 10p. The change is 4p.' Repeat this for different prices, and record on the flip chart (for spending 7p and giving a 10p coin): '7p + 2+ 1p = 10p. Change is 3p.' Repeat for other amounts. Pairs take turns to choose a price label, then count out the change for their partner, using the least number of coins. They record as you did on the flip chart.
DIFFERENTIATION	Less able: encourage them to count out the change, check to see if they can substitute a 2p coin for two 1p coins, then count the change again, counting up to 10p. More able: extend the prices beyond 10p, and the amount offered to 20p.
PLENARY	Ask pairs to show examples. Ask: *Have they used the least number of coins?*

LESSON 12

RESOURCES	Sets of price labels from 1p to 5p; coins; flip chart and pen; paper and pencils; labelled items from the class shop; number fans (page 17).
LEARNING OUTCOMES	**ORAL AND MENTAL STARTER** ● **Know by heart : all pairs of numbers with a total of 10** (eg 3 + 7). **MAIN TEACHING ACTIVITY** ● **Understand the operation of subtraction (as** 'how many more to make') **and use the related vocabulary.** ● Begin to recognise that more than two numbers can be added together. Recognise coins of different values. Find totals and change from up to 10p. Work out how to pay an exact sum using smaller coins.
ORAL AND MENTAL STARTER	FAST 10: Explain that whatever number you say, you want the children to hold up the fan blade which shows what to add to it to make 10. Ask: *How did you work that out?* so the children can explain their mental strategies.
MAIN TEACHING ACTIVITY	SHOPPING: Choose two items from the shop, each costing less than 5p. For 3p and 4p items, ask: *How much do these cost in total? (7p). What change will I get from 10p?* (3p). Ask two children to act the roles of shopkeeper and customer, and tender the 10p, then give the change. Ask the customer to check that the change is correct, by counting up from 7p: '7p and 2p is 9p and 1p is 10p.' Repeat for other amounts. Working in pairs, children take turns to take two price labels. Their partner totals them, then counts out the change.
DIFFERENTIATION	Less able: if they have difficulty in finding the total, encourage them to put out the coins for each amount, then count all these to find the total. They can put out more coins to make the total up to 10p, then say how much the change is. More able: suggest that they total four prices, and find the change from 20p.
PLENARY	Play 'Fast 10' again.

RESOURCES

Pencils and paper; flip chart and pen; number fans and number lines (pages 17 and 18).

LEARNING OUTCOMES

ORAL AND MENTAL STARTER

● **Know by heart: all pairs of numbers with a total of 10** (eg 3 + 7).

MAIN TEACHING ACTIVITY

● **Use mental strategies to solve simple problems** set in 'real life' or money contexts, **using counting, addition, subtraction, doubling and halving, explaining methods and reasoning orally.**

● Choose and use appropriate number operations and mental strategies to solve problems.

VOCABULARY

Pattern; puzzle; answer; right; wrong; how did you work it out...?; what could we try next?; count out; share out; left; left over; number sentence; sign; operation; how many...?

ORAL AND MENTAL STARTER

Play 'Fast 10' from Lesson 12.

MAIN TEACHING ACTIVITY

PROBLEMS: Explain that the purpose of the next three lessons is to solve problems. Begin: *I am thinking of a number, then I take away 3. The answer is 5. What is my number?* Ask the children to explain the strategies that they used to solve the problem.*Did everyone use the same strategy? Which was best? Why?* Repeat this by reading out some of the problems below, adapting them to suit your own needs. With complex problems (such as 2 or 10), it may help to write some information on the flip chart. Encourage the children to record in their own way on paper and to explain their methods and reasoning orally.
1. Paulo had 10 sweets. Nico ate four. How many has Paulo now?
2. In a game Jed scores 5, Mark 7 and Sam 4. Who scored most? Least? Who scored more than Jed? How many more? How many did Jed and Sam score in total? And Mark and Jed? And Jed, Mark and Sam?
3. My sister is six years old and my brother is two years younger. How old is my brother?
4. The ribbon is the same length as 10 straws. If I cut off a piece of ribbon as long as three straws, how long is the ribbon that is left?
5. I have added three numbers to total 10. What could my number be? (Challenge the children to write down, as addition sums, as many solutions as they can find in 5 minutes.)
6. I stuck a 5p, 10p and 2p stamp on a letter. How much was that altogether?
7. I have three coins which total 12p. What coins do I have? Find at least two answers.
8. Oranges are 7p each. How much do two cost? What coins can I use to pay for them?
9. I had 10p in my pocket. I spent 4p. How much have I left?
10. Jade has some coins in her purse. They are: three 5p coins, a 1p coin and two 2p coins. How much does she have altogether? Choose just three of these coins to make the largest/smallest possible total.
11. There are six cakes in the box. If I buy two boxes how many cakes will I have?
12. John rolled two dice and got double 4. What was his score?
13. Which costs more: two oranges at 6p each, or an apple at 5p and a banana at 8p?
14. I have 10p. How many 5p lollies can I buy?

DIFFERENTIATION

Less able: simplify the numbers in the problems.
More able: encourage them to work for about 5 minutes to make up some word problems for sums such as 9 – 2 = 7; 6 – 4 = 2; 8 + 6 = 14; then swap with a partner.

PLENARY

Discuss children's word problems. Ask individuals to explain how they would solve them.

LESSONS 14 AND 15

Repeat Lesson 13, choosing new problems from the list in the **Main teaching activity**.

Finding the difference

Join all numbers with a difference of 3.

Join pairs of numbers with a difference of 5.

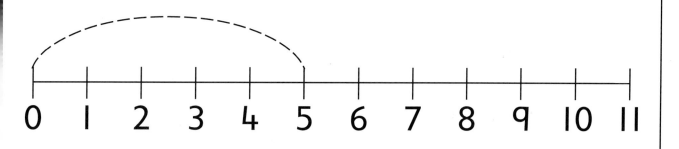

Giving change

Use 10p.
Draw the change.

6p

☐ p
change

5p

☐ p
change

7p

☐ p
change

3p

☐ p
change

qp

☐ p
change

102

UNITS 5-6

ORGANISATION (8 LESSONS)

	LEARNING OUTCOMES	ORAL AND MENTAL STARTER	MAIN TEACHING ACTIVITY	PLENARY
LESSON 1 +2	• Understand and use the vocabulary related to mass. • **Compare two masses by direct comparison**; extend to more than two. • Measure using uniform non-standard units (eg wooden cubes, plastic weights), or standard weights. • **Suggest suitable standard or uniform non-standard units and measuring equipment to estimate, then measure, a mass,** recording estimates and measurements as 'about as heavy as 20 cubes'.	FACT CARDS: Addition and subtraction facts to 5.	PARCEL COMPARE: Comparing the weights of parcels and checking using a balance.	Discussion of results.
LESSON 3	• Understand and use the vocabulary related to mass. • **Compare two masses by direct comparison**; extend to more than two. • Measure using uniform non-standard units (eg wooden cubes, plastic weights), or standard weights. • **Suggest suitable standard or uniform non-standard units and measuring equipment to estimate, then measure, a mass,** recording estimates and measurements as 'about as heavy as 20 cubes'.	DOUBLES: Doubling numbers to 10.	CHOOSING UNITS: Choosing suitable uniform non-standard units to balance parcels.	Discussion of results.
LESSON 4	• **Use mental strategies to solve simple problems** set in measurement contexts, **using counting, addition, subtraction, doubling and halving, explaining methods and reasoning orally.**	FACT CARDS: Addition and subtraction facts to 5.	PROBLEMS: Estimating weight and balancing, using non-standard units.	Discussion of solution strategies.
LESSON 5 +6	• **Use everyday language to describe features of familiar 2-D shapes,** including the circle, triangle, square, rectangle... referring to properties such as the shapes of flat faces, or the number of faces, or corners... or the number and types of sides. • Make and describe models, patterns and pictures using construction kits, everyday materials, Plasticine...	DOUBLES: Finding the doubles of numbers to 10.	SHAPE PICTURES AND PATTERNS: Making pictures and patterns with 2-D shapes.	Discussion of results.
LESSON 7	• Fold shapes in half, then make them into symmetrical patterns.	MAKE 10: Finding complements to make 10.	SYMMETRICAL PATTERNS: Folding and cutting to make symmetrical shapes and patterns.	Discussion of results.

cont...

LESSON 8			
● Solve simple mathematical problems or puzzles; recognise and predict from simple patterns and relationships. Suggest extensions by asking 'What if...?' or 'What could I try next?'. ● Investigate a general statement about familiar shapes by finding examples that satisfy it. ● Explain methods and reasoning orally.	FACT CARDS: Addition and subtraction facts to 5.	SHAPE PROBLEMS: Solving problems.	Explanation of solution strategies.

ORAL AND MENTAL SKILLS   Know by heart: all pairs of numbers with a total of 10 (eg 3 + 7); addition facts for all pairs of numbers with a total up to at least 5, and the corresponding subtraction facts; addition doubles fo all numbers to at least 5 (eg 4 + 4).

In Unit 5, Lessons 1, 4 and 5 are shown in detail. Lessons 2 and 3 are extensions of what has already been taught, and follow Lesson 1. In Unit 6, Lesson 6 is a continuation of Lesson 5, and is shown following Lesson 5. Lessons 7 and 8 are shown in full.

LESSON 1

RESOURCES

Copies of photocopiable pages 111 and 112 (Fact cards); flip chart and marker pen; parcels for balancing and weighing (see **Preparation**); non-standard units such as interlocking cubes, scoops of sand, marbles, beads, gravel, small pebbles...; a bucket or beamer balance for each group; paper and pencils; props for a class Post Office (optional).

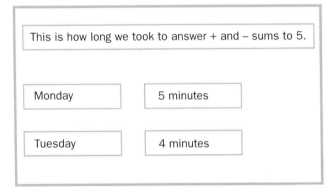

This is how long we took to answer + and – sums to 5.

Monday	5 minutes
Tuesday	4 minutes

PREPARATION

Enlarge each photocopiable sheet to A3; cut in two to make two A4 sheets; enlarge each of these to A3, then cut out each fact card. Select some of the cards for the **Oral and mental starter**. Make a 'time taken' chart to go on the class wall.

Prepare a set of about sixteen 'parcels' for weighing. These can be made by placing items in cardboard boxes, or by putting some sand into plastic bags, then sealing them. Include: two that are the same size and weight; two that are the same size and different weights; two which are different sizes but the same weight – all under 100g. Label the parcels with letters, so that the children can identify each parcel for recording. You may wish to set up a class post office so that children can role-play weighing parcels and paying for stamps.

LEARNING OUTCOMES

ORAL AND MENTAL STARTER
● **Know by heart:** addition facts for all pairs of numbers with a total up to at least 5, and the corresponding subtraction facts.

MAIN TEACHING ACTIVITY
● Understand and use the vocabulary related to mass.
● **Compare two masses by direct comparison**; extend to more than two.
● Measure using uniform non-standard units (eg wooden cubes, plastic weights), or standard weights.
● **Suggest suitable standard or uniform non-standard units and measuring equipment to estimate, then measure, a mass,** recording estimates and measurements as 'about as heavy as 20 cubes'.

VOCABULARY

Weigh; weighs; balances; heavy/light; heavier/lighter; heaviest/lightest; weight; balance; scales; guess; estimate; enough; not enough; too much; too little; too many; too few; nearly; roughly; about; close to; about the same as; just over; just under.

ORAL AND MENTAL STARTER

FACT CARDS: Explain that you will hold up a card for the children to read aloud with you, then ask for someone to give the answer. Tell the others that they should give the answer the 'thumbs up' if they agree, and 'thumbs down' if they do not. This will enable you to make a quick check of who did/did not know the answer. Keep the pace as fast as possible for this, and make a note of how long it took to work through the cards on the 'time taken' chart. This will give the children a target to aim to beat next time.

MAIN TEACHING ACTIVITY

PARCEL COMPARE: To check that they know what the vocabulary means, begin by asking a child to choose two parcels from the selection and compare their weights by hand. Ask: *Which is heavier/lighter?,* then place the parcels on the bucket balance and ask *Did you make a good guess? Which is heavier/lighter?* Discuss how to use the balance, and what happens to the pan with the heavier/lighter parcel in it. Repeat, asking other children to take a turn.

Ask the children to work in small groups, each with four parcels and a balance. Explain that they should first use their hands to compare the parcels and order them by weight, then check using the balance. They then record their results by writing down the letters on the parcels in order, from lightest to heaviest:

Lightest			**Heaviest**
Parcel C	Parcel A	Parcel D	Parcel B

DIFFERENTIATION

Less able: provide parcels where there is a clear difference in weight. Work with this group and check that they are comparing weight, rather than volume.
More able: provide parcels which are more difficult, including the parcels that look the same in volume but have different weights; and those that have different volumes but the same weight. When they have found the two with the same weight, suggest that they record these as 'having about the same weight'.

PLENARY

Ask the more able group to explain about their parcels. Discuss how it is the weight (what they feel, and see with the balance) rather than the volume or 'size' of the parcel which is being compared.

LESSON 2

Repeat Lesson 1, but in the **Oral and mental starter** try to beat the previous day's time. In the **Main teaching activity** take one parcel, and place it into a pan on the balance. Ask a child to add cubes until it balances. Repeat for a different parcel, but this time ask for an estimate first. On the flip chart, record the count of the measure (see figure).

I weighed parcel A		
I used	My estimate is	My measure is
Cubes	10 cubes	5 cubes
Marbles		

Ask the children to work in groups and give each group one parcel. Ask them to first estimate the weight, then balance the parcel on their balance, using the non-standard units provided (such as scoop and sand, marbles, interlocking cubes – 1g weights could be used here too). They record their answers as shown on the flip chart. Select a group to show their results and ask which units were most suitable for balancing their parcel, and why they thought this. Encourage the children to consider how many units they needed to use: *Did that produce a count which was too big? Did that unit allow you to be very accurate in your balancing?*

LESSON 3

RESOURCES	Non-standard units for balancing; selection of parcels; bucket and beamer balances; some 10g, 20g, 50g and 100g masses.
LEARNING OUTCOMES	**ORAL AND MENTAL STARTER** ● **Know by heart:** addition doubles of all numbers to at least 5 (eg 4 + 4). **MAIN TEACHING ACTIVITY** ● Understand and use the vocabulary related to mass. ● **Compare two masses by direct comparison;** extend to more than two. ● Measure using uniform non-standard units (eg wooden cubes, plastic weights), or standard weights. ● **Suggest suitable standard or uniform non-standard units and measuring equipment to estimate, then measure, a mass,** recording estimates and measurements as 'about as heavy as 20 cubes'.
ORAL AND MENTAL STARTER	DOUBLES: Ask the children to double numbers: *What is double 5/four add four/double 7…?*
MAIN TEACHING ACTIVITY	CHOOSING UNITS: Ask the children to decide which non-standard units to use to estimate, then balance, four or five parcels. They record this as they did in Lesson 2.
DIFFERENTIATION	Less able: ask the children to order their parcels first, from lightest to heaviest, then to order each non-standard unit in the same way. For each parcel ask them to explain why they chose that particular non-standard unit. More able: show them some 10g, 20g, 50g and 100g masses, explain that these are the units used for weighing items in shops, and ask them to choose suitable non-standard units to balance these, estimating first.
PLENARY	Ask a group to show their results and to explain why they chose the unit they used to balance each parcel.

LESSON 4

RESOURCES

Parcels for balancing and weighing; non-standard units such as interlocking cubes, scoops of sand, marbles, beads, gravel, small pebbles; 1g and 100g masses; bucket or beamer balances; Plasticine; margarine tubs; foam ball; quoit; classroom items suitable for weighing, such as pencils, paintbrushes, books; fact cards from photocopiable pages 111 and 112, paper and pencils.

PREPARATION

Choose from the activities below, and set up each table with the required items for the activity or activities you have selected for that group of children.

VOCABULARY

Weigh; weighs; balances; heavy/light; heavier/ lighter; heaviest/ lightest; weight; balance; scales; guess; estimate; enough; not enough; too much; too little; too many; too few; nearly; roughly; about; close to; about the same as; just over; just under.

LEARNING OUTCOMES

ORAL AND MENTAL STARTER
● **Know by heart:** addition facts for all pairs of numbers with a total up to at least 5, and the corresponding subtraction facts.

MAIN TEACHING ACTIVITY
● **Use mental strategies to solve simple problems** set in measurement contexts, **using counting, addition, subtraction, doubling and halving, explaining methods and reasoning orally.**

ORAL AND MENTAL STARTER

FACT CARDS: repeat the activity from Lesson 1, page xx, encouraging the children to beat their previous time.

MAIN TEACHING ACTIVITY

PROBLEMS: Ask the class questions such as: *A marble weighs the same as six cubes. How much will two marbles weigh? An orange weighs five cubes and a lemon four. How much do they weigh altogether?* For each question encourage the children to write a number sentence and explain how they solved the problem. Explain that you will read out a variety of practical problems about balancing which they should solve, working in small groups. Point out that they can use the apparatus which has been provided and ask them, each time, to make an estimate before they balance their parcel with the appropriate non-standard units. Tell them that they are to record their results in a simple table (such as the one on page 105).

1. How much sand is needed to balance this parcel? Ask the children to pour the sand until the parcel is balanced.
2. What weighs about the same as my shoe? Encourage the children to find objects in the classroom that will approximately balance their shoe.
3. How many scoops of sand are needed to balance four/five/10 marbles? Estimate first, then check with the balance.
4. Put a lighter object such as a foam ball in one pan of the balance, and a heavier object such as a quoit in the other. Children choose their non-standard units to add to the lighter object to make the two objects balance. This can be repeated with other non-standard units, and the children can then decide which unit is best to use for this, and why.
5. How much does a cube weigh? Let the children use 1g masses to estimate, then find the approximate weight of one cube.
6. In a group of four each child chooses a parcel, then puts some Plasticine into a margarine tub until it will balance the parcel. The tubs and parcels are muddled up and then, using only their hands, they try to match up the parcels with the tubs. They check by using the balance.
7. How much Plasticine will be needed to balance this parcel? What happens if you change the shape of the ball? Does it still balance the parcel? Ask the children to estimate first, then check using the balance.

DIFFERENTIATION

Less able: begin with problems 1 & 2, which will help children to understand about balance before they try number 3, where they use non-standard units.
More able: problem 7 is more challenging. Encourage the children to discuss with each other how they will solve these problems and to agree their strategies.

PLENARY

Choose a problem which most of the children have solved. Discuss their solutions, and the methods they chose to solve it.

RESOURCES

A set of numeral cards 0–20 for each child (pages 14 and 15); wallpaper or fabric samples with patterns containing recognisable 2-D shapes; straws; pipe cleaners; art straws; pre-cut sticky shapes; mosaic shape tiles; shape templates or tiles; adhesive; paint and brushes; sponge shapes; card; paper; flip chart and pen; a copy of photocopiable page 113 (2-D shape pictures) for each child, plus an A3 enlargement of it.

PREPARATION

If possible, wear a jumper that has clear 2-D shapes in it. Peg the wallpaper or fabric samples onto the flip chart. Find some tiles that are the same shapes as the displayed samples. Cut pieces of sponge to make shapes with triangular, square, rectangular, circular, star faces for printing. Make the required photocopies.

LEARNING OUTCOMES

ORAL AND MENTAL STARTER
● **Know by heart:** addition doubles of all numbers to at least 5 (eg 4 + 4).

MAIN TEACHING ACTIVITY

● **Use everyday language to describe features of familiar 2-D shapes**, including the circle, triangle, square, rectangle… referring to properties such as the shapes of flat faces, or the number of faces or corners… or the number and types of sides.

● Make and describe models, patterns and pictures using construction kits, everyday materials, Plasticine….

VOCABULARY

Flat; shape; circle; triangle; square; rectangle; star; side; corner; straight; curved; point; pointed; draw; pattern.

ORAL AND MENTAL STARTER

DOUBLES: Explain to the children that you are going to ask them some double facts and that they should hold up numeral cards to answer. Check that they all understand that when you ask the question they should find the appropriate numeral card and hold it in front of them, then, on a signal from you, turn their wrists to show you the card. Ask, for example: *What is …six add six? …double eight? …double 2? …10 add 10?*

MAIN TEACHING ACTIVITY

SHAPE PICTURES AND PATTERNS: Ask the children to look at the wallpaper or fabric samples. Ask them to take turns to come out, point to, describe and name a shape, then to find that shape amongst the shape tiles. If you are wearing clothing with printed shapes, ask the children to describe and name those shapes too. Pin the enlarged copy of '2-D shape pictures' to the flip chart. Ask individual children to describe what they can see and name the shapes used to make each item in the picture.

Then choose from the following activities, asking children to work individually in small cooperative groups so that they can share materials. Let the children try as many different activities as possible.

1. Use pre-cut sticky shapes to make some pictures, such as animals, flowers, trees or houses. Encourage the children to use their imaginations.
2. Use mosaic shape tiles to make a pattern or picture.
3. Draw around some shape tiles to make a picture, combining shapes. Colour them in.
4. Use paint and shape stencils to make a picture or pattern.
5. Use the sponges to print a pattern with paint.
6. Copy the pictures in the sheet '2-D shape pictures' using shape tiles, gummed shapes, or by drawing around shape tiles. Join name labels to the shapes.
7. Make a picture of a house and garage using straws or pipe cleaners stuck onto paper.

DIFFERENTIATION

Less able: provide ready-prepared materials to make pictures and patterns, as in 1 and 2 above. When they are confident with using these shapes, and can name the pieces, encourage them to try some of the other activities.

More able: activity 7 is more challenging. Encourage the children to plan their picture before they begin, by making a brief sketch, and to name the shapes that they intend to create by combining shapes.

PLENARY

Ask individuals to show their work and to describe the shapes that they have made. Encourage them to describe which shapes they have combined to make their pictures and patterns.

LESSON 6

Repeat Lesson 5, choosing different problems to challenge the children in the **Main teaching activity**.

LESSON 7

RESOURCES

A set of 'Make ten cards' from photocopiable page 114; scissors; paint; brushes; large sheets of paper; shape tiles which have a line of symmetry (such as squares; circles; rectangles; isosceles/equilateral triangles); time taken chart.

PREPARATION

Enlarge photocopiable page 114 (Make ten cards) to A3; cut the sheet in half and enlarge each half again to make two sheets of A3, then cut these out. This will make large cards for the children to read. Make a time taken chart similar to the one shown on page 104. Lay out the paints and brushes in an area used for painting.

LEARNING OUTCOMES

ORAL AND MENTAL STARTER
● **Know by heart all pairs of numbers with a total of 10** (eg 3 + 7).

MAIN TEACHING ACTIVITY
● Fold shapes in half, then make them into symmetrical patterns.

<table>
<tr><td>VOCABULARY</td></tr>
<tr><td>Pattern;
shape; draw.</td></tr>
</table>

ORAL AND MENTAL STARTER

MAKE 10: Explain that you will hold up a card for the children to read aloud with you. You will then ask for someone to give the answer and the others should give 'thumbs up' if they agree, and 'thumbs down' if they do not. This will allow you to check who did/did not know the answer. Keep the pace as fast as possible for this, and write how long it takes to work through the 'Make ten' cards on the 'time taken' chart. This will give the children a target they can aim to beat next time.

MAIN TEACHING ACTIVITY

SYMMETRICAL PATTERNS: Hold up a large rectangular sheet of paper, and ask what shape it is. Fold it in half and ask what shape it is now. Open it out, and show the fold line. Discuss how the two halves of the paper look the same. Fold the paper again, and cut out a half-butterfly shape.

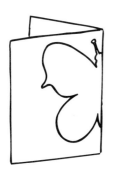

Ask: *What shape do you think we will have when the paper is opened up?* Open it and talk about how one half is a 'reflection' of the other.

Repeat, this time cutting a different shape, such as half a child. Ask the children to fold a large sheet of paper in two themselves, then to cut out a shape, being careful not to cut out the fold line. They might like to copy your butterfly shape. Ask them to open out the paper, then to make paint blots on one half of the paper, using different coloured paints to make an interesting pattern. They then fold the paper and press firmly across it. Finally they should open the paper out flat, and let it dry.

DIFFERENTIATION

Less able: decide whether to provide a template for them to draw around to make their shape.
More able: encourage them to make a repeating pattern on their shape. When they open out the paper, ask them to describe what they notice about their pattern.

PLENARY

Ask individual children to show their symmetrical shapes and describe what they see, focusing particularly upon the 'reflection' of one half of the pattern in the other.

RESOURCES

'Fuzzy felt' pieces; shape tiles; coloured gummed paper; straws or pipe cleaners; books with pictures of shapes; mosaic tiles; paper; adhesive.

LEARNING OUTCOMES

ORAL AND MENTAL STARTER
● **Know by heart: all pairs of numbers with a total of 10** (eg 3 + 7).

MAIN TEACHING ACTIVITY
● Solve simple mathematical problems or puzzles; recognise and predict from simple patterns and relationships. Suggest extensions by asking 'What if…?' or 'What could I try next?'.
● Investigate a general statement about familiar shapes by finding examples that satisfy it.
● Explain methods and reasoning orally.

VOCABULARY

Flat; shape; circle; triangle; square; rectangle; star; side; corner; straight; curved; point; pointed; pattern.

ORAL AND MENTAL STARTER

FACT CARDS: Repeat the activity from Lesson 1, page 104.

MAIN TEACHING ACTIVITY

SHAPE PROBLEMS: Say: *I am thinking of a shape. It has three straight sides. What is it?* (a triangle). Repeat this for other shapes, and for each one ask a child to choose the shape you have described from a selection and to explain why that shape is the right one. Tell the children that they will be asked to find ways of solving problems to do with shape and will have to explain what they did, and why, to others. Encourage them by asking 'What if…?' or 'What else could you try?' Offer the following problems, adapting them as necessary.
1. Use 'Fuzzy felt' pieces to make a picture or pattern.
2. Draw around some shape tiles on coloured gummed paper and combine shapes to make a picture.
3. Design your own picture using squares, rectangles, circles and triangles. Make it from straws or pipe cleaners stuck onto paper.
4. Choose a shape from a selection of shape tiles. Draw around it, cut it out, then try to fold the shape exactly in half. Repeat for other shapes to find which are symmetrical.

DIFFERENTIATION

Less able: activities 1 and 2 are easier. Encourage the children to try these first.
More able: encourage them to try activity 4, which is more challenging.

PLENARY

Ask individuals to explain their activity, what they did and how they solved their problem. Compare solutions with others who tackled the same activity.

Fact cards +

Enlarge these to A3 and cut them in two to make two A4 sheets.
Enlarge them again to A3 on card. Cut out each fact card.

$0 + 1$	$3 + 0$
$0 + 2$	$4 + 0$
$0 + 3$	$5 + 0$
$0 + 4$	$1 + 1$
$0 + 5$	$2 + 1$
$1 + 2$	$2 + 3$
$1 + 3$	$3 + 2$
$1 + 4$	$2 + 1$
$1 + 0$	$3 + 1$
$2 + 0$	$4 + 1$

Fact cards –

Enlarge these to A3 and cut them in two to make two A4 sheets.
Enlarge them again to A3 on card. Cut out each fact card.

5 – 0	4 – 4
5 – 1	3 – 0
5 – 2	3 – 1
5 – 3	3 – 2
5 – 4	3 – 3
5 – 5	2 – 0
4 – 0	2 – 1
4 – 1	2 – 2
4 – 2	1 – 0
4 – 3	1 – 1

2-D shape pictures

Use shapes to copy these pictures.
Join the labels to the shapes.

| rectangle | square | triangle | circle |

Make 10 cards

Enlarge these to A3 and cut them in two to make two A4 sheets. Enlarge them again to A3 on card. Cut out each fact card.

☐ + 0 = 10	0 + ☐ = 10
☐ + 1 = 10	1 + ☐ = 10
☐ + 2 = 10	2 + ☐ = 10
☐ + 3 = 10	3 + ☐ = 10
☐ + 4 = 10	4 + ☐ = 10
☐ + 5 = 10	5 + ☐ = 10
☐ + 6 = 10	6 + ☐ = 10
☐ + 7 = 10	7 + ☐ = 10
☐ + 8 = 10	8 + ☐ = 10
☐ + 9 = 10	9 + ☐ = 10
☐ + 10 = 10	10 + ☐ = 10

100 MATHS LESSONS ● YEAR 1 TERM 2

UNIT 7: Assess & Review

Choose from these activities. During the group activities, some children can be completing assessment worksheets 3A and 3B which assess the children's skills with reading, writing and ordering numbers, and subtraction, while others work with you on practical tasks. The specific assessment criteria for the assessment sheets can be found at the bottom of each sheet.

RESOURCES

A set of 0 to 10 numeral cards for each child (page 14); 'Make ten cards' from photocopiable page 114; pencils and paper; parcels; bucket balance; non-standard units such as cubes, marbles…; recording chart (see page 105); square, rectangular, triangular and circular shape tiles; a feely bag; interlocking cubes.

ORAL AND MENTAL WORK

ASSESSMENT

Do the children:
● **Know by heart: all pairs of numbers with a total of 10** (eg 3+7)**?**
● **Within the range 0 to 30, say the number that is 1 or 10 more or less than any given number?**
● **Count reliably at least 20 objects?**
NUMBER FACT: Hold up the 'Make ten' cards one at a time, and ask the children to show you their answer using their numeral cards. Check to see who has rapid recall of the facts, and who will need more practice.
COUNTING OBJECTS: Ask the children to count out some cubes. Say: *Count 15, and three more; how many now? Put four back; count how many you have now.* Check that the children count accurately and say how many each time.
MORE OR LESS: Say a number and ask the children to say the number that is 1 more or less. Repeat for 10 more or ten less than a given number. If children find this difficult use a number line or hundred square to help them.

GROUP ACTIVITIES

ASSESSMENT

Can the children:
● **Use everyday language to describe features of familiar 2-D shapes?**
● **Compare two masses by direct comparison?**
● **Suggest suitable standard or uniform non-standard units and measuring equipment to estimate, then measure, a mass?**
● **Use mental strategies to solve simple problems, using counting, addition, subtraction, doubling and halving, explaining methods and reasoning orally?**
2-D SHAPE: Ask children to take turns choosing a shape tile from a feely bag, holding the shape inside the bag. They describe the shape so that the others may guess what it is. Encourage them to describe the straight or curved sides, how many there are and how many corners it has. Check the children have grasped the main features of each shape.
BALANCING: Ask the children to compare two parcels for weight, say which is heavier/ lighter, then check by using a balance. Ask them to choose one parcel and decide which non-standard units to use to balance it, estimate how many units and check by balancing. They can record their results on a simple chart. (See page 105 for an example.) Encourage them to explain why they chose their particular units and to approximate their answer appropriately, using 'nearly' and 'a little more than…'
SOLVING PROBLEMS: Choose some problems from Unit 4, Lessons 13–15, page 100. For each problem ask children how they worked it out. Encourage them to use number facts that they know.

Assessment 3A

Put these numbers in order.

3 2 4 ☐ ☐ ☐   5 6 1 ☐ ☐ ☐

20 2 16 ☐ ☐ ☐

15 13 18 14 16 ☐ ☐ ☐ ☐ ☐

20 11 9 17 18 ☐ ☐ ☐ ☐ ☐

Write in the missing numbers.

4 5 ☐ 7

8 9 ☐ ☐ 12

20 19 ☐ ☐ ☐ 15

☐ 18 ☐ 16 ☐ 14

Write a number that is less.   16 ☐   12 ☐

Write a number that is more.   13 ☐   17 ☐

● Read, write and order numbers from 0 to at least 20; understand and use the vocabulary of comparing and ordering these numbers.

Assessment 3B

Join all numbers with a difference of 4.

Finish the sums.

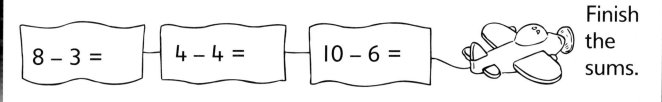

8 – 3 =   4 – 4 =   10 – 6 =

9 – 8 =   5 – 1 =   7 – 3 =

1 – 0 =   2 – 2 =   6 – 3 =

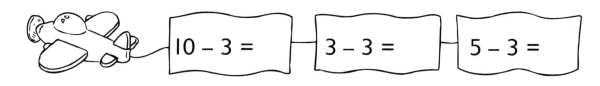

10 – 3 =   3 – 3 =   5 – 3 =

● Understand the operation of subtraction (as the result of 'take away' or 'difference') and use the related vocabulary.

UNIT 8

ORGANISATION (5 LESSONS)

	LEARNING OUTCOMES	ORAL AND MENTAL STARTER	MAIN TEACHING ACTIVITY	PLENARY
LESSON 1	● Know the number names and recite them in order to at least 20, from and back to zero. ● Describe and extend number sequences: **count on and back in ones from any small number, and in tens from and back to zero;** count on in twos from zero, then one, and begin to recognise odd or even numbers to about 20 as 'every other number'.	FAST 10: Complements to 10.	COUNTING PATTERNS: Counting in 1s, 2s and 10s. Recognising odd and even numbers.	ODD OR EVEN: Recognising odd and even numbers.
LESSON 2	● Know the number names and recite them in order to at least 20, from and back to zero. ● Describe and extend number sequences: **count on and back in ones from any small number, and in tens from and back to zero;** count on in twos from zero, then one, and begin to recognise odd or even numbers to about 20 as 'every other number'.	FAST 10: Complements to 10.	COUNTING PATTERNS: Counting in 1s, 2s and 10s. Recognising odd and even numbers.	Discussion of findings about counting patterns.
LESSON 3	● **Count reliably at least 20 objects.**	ODD OR EVEN: Recognising odd and even numbers.	UP TO 20: Counting out objects.	Discussion of children's work.
LESSON 4 +5	● Solve simple mathematical problems or puzzles; recognise and predict from simple patterns and relationships. Suggest extensions by asking 'What if...?' or 'What could I try next?' ● Investigate a general statement about familiar numbers by finding examples that satisfy it. ● Explain methods and reasoning orally.	ODD OR EVEN.	NUMBER PROBLEMS: Solving number problems which have more than	Explaining methods and reasoning orally.

ORAL AND MENTAL SKILLS   Know by heart: all pairs of numbers with a total of 10 (eg 3 + 7). Count on in twos from zero, then one, and begin to recognise odd or even numbers to about 20 as 'every other number'.

In Unit 8, Lessons 1 and 4 are shown in full. Lessons 2 and 3 are extensions of what has already been taught, and follow Lesson 1. Lesson 5 is an extension of Lesson 4, and follows it.

RESOURCES

Numeral cards 0 to 20 for each child (pages 14 and 15); washing line, pegs and large numeral cards 0 to 20; individual number lines (page 18); flip chart and pen; paper and pencils; an odd and an even card for each child (see **Preparation**, below).

PREPARATION

Divide the flip chart into two columns, one headed 'Odd numbers' and the other 'Even numbers'. Make a set of odd and even cards by marking a large 'O' on one side and a large 'E' on the other side of cards about the same size as the numeral cards.

LEARNING OUTCOMES

ORAL AND MENTAL STARTER
● **Know by heart: all pairs of numbers with a total of 10** (eg 3 + 7).

MAIN TEACHING ACTIVITY
● Know the number names and recite them in order to at least 20, from and back to zero.
● Describe and extend number sequences: **count on and back in ones from any small number, and in tens from and back to zero;** count on in twos from zero, then one, and begin to recognise odd or even numbers to about 20 as 'every other number'.

VOCABULARY

Number; zero, one, two, three,... to 20 and beyond; 10, 20,...to one hundred; count; count to; count up to; count on (from, to); count back (from, to); count in ones... twos... tens...; odd; even; every other; pattern; pair.

ORAL AND MENTAL STARTER

FAST 10: As before, ask the children to hold up the numeral card which, when added to the number you say, makes 10. So for '6', the children would hold up their '4' card. Encourage them to respond quickly, and move quickly on to the next number.

MAIN TEACHING ACTIVITY

COUNTING PATTERNS: Count together in ones from zero to 20 and back to zero. Count around the class, up to 20 and back again, until everyone has had two turns. Count on from 7, 8, 9... and back to zero. Extend the count beyond 20, to thirty, and repeat. Count in tens, from zero to one hundred, and back to zero. Count around the class, in tens. Repeat, counting in twos to 20, starting from zero, then from one. Explain that you want to 'collect' all the even numbers on the class washing line. Starting from zero, with zero pegged to the number line, say: *Count two; what comes next?* and ask a child to peg the '2' card on the line. Continue until all the even numbers have been pegged on the line. Remove these numbers and repeat, this time for the odd numbers, starting from one. Again remove all the cards from the line. Ask the children to count very slowly to 20, from zero. For each number they should show, (by holding up the 'O' side for odd, and the 'E' side for even) with their odd and even cards, whether they think it is odd or even. You will then write it in the appropriate column on the flip chart.

Working in pairs, using just one pack of 1 to 20 numeral cards, ask the children to shuffle the cards, and place the pack face down. They then take turns to pick up a card, and decide whether it is odd or even, place it in a line (either an 'odd' line or an 'even' line), spacing out the cards to leave room for those that have still to be placed. Tell them that if they are not sure whether the number is odd or even, they can count in twos with their partner to check. The object of the game is to make two lines of cards, in order, one odd from 1 to 19, and the other even from 2 to 20. They should both check that the cards are appropriately ordered. When they have finished the game, ask them to record the odd and even numbers to 20, writing the heading 'Odd numbers' with the odds listed below, then the evens under the heading 'Even numbers'.

DIFFERENTIATION

Less able: remind the children that they can use the flip chart odds and evens columns as an aid.
More able: encourage them to play the game as quickly as possible, using their mental image of a number line. Challenge them to extend their recording to numbers up to 30.

PLENARY

ODD OR EVEN: Explain that you will say numbers, and that you want the children to decide whether each number is odd or even .They can show this by holding up their 'O' card for odd, and their 'E' card for even, as before. Begin with smaller numbers, up to about 8, and for each number encourage the children to check with you by counting in twos up to the number, either from 1 or from zero.

RESOURCES	Large numeral cards 0 to 20; washing line and pegs; photocopiable page 122 (Counting patterns); an A3 enlargement of 'Counting patterns'.
LEARNING OUTCOMES	**ORAL AND MENTAL STARTER** ● **Know by heart all pairs of numbers with a total of 10** (eg 3 + 7). **MAIN TEACHING ACTIVITY** ● Know the number names and recite them in order to at least 20, from and back to zero. ● **Describe and extend number sequences:** count on and back in ones from any small number, and in tens from and back to zero; **count on in twos from zero, then one, and begin to recognise odd or even numbers to about 20 as 'every other number'.**
ORAL AND MENTAL STARTER	FAST 10: Repeat the activity from Lesson 1, page 118.
MAIN TEACHING ACTIVITY	COUNTING PATTERNS: Repeat the oral counting as in Lesson 1 of this unit, page 118. Ask children to take turns to choose and peg numeral cards onto the washing line, ordered from 0 to 20. Remove and shuffle the cards then ask individuals to take the top card and place it where they think it will go, leaving space for other 'missing' cards, before and after. Remove the cards. Now peg the '7' card on the line and ask the children to take turns to place the card before and after this, and so on, until the line is full. Provide each child with a copy of photocopiable page 122 and ask them to complete the counting patterns by writing in the missing numerals.
DIFFERENTIATION	Less able: work with this group, talking through each pattern on the photocopiable sheet. More able: challenge them to create their own missing number lines, to swap with a partner, complete, then check each other's work.
PLENARY	Use an A3 enlargement of 'Counting patterns' to discuss the results.

RESOURCES	Numeral cards 0 to 10, O and E cards; 4–9 dice; cubes.
LEARNING OUTCOMES	**ORAL AND MENTAL STARTER** ● Count on in twos from zero, then one, and begin to recognise odd or even numbers to about 20 as 'every other number'. **MAIN TEACHING ACTIVITY** ● **Count reliably at least 20 objects.**
ORAL AND MENTAL STARTER	ODD OR EVEN: Play this game from the Plenary session of Lesson 1, page 118.
MAIN TEACHING ACTIVITY	UP TO 20: Ask all the children to count out a given number of cubes. Say: *Count out 15, 17, 20,... cubes. Put one more.... Take away two.... How many are left?* Check that the children count accurately. Ask them to work in pairs, taking turns to throw two dice, add the score and count out that number of cubes. Partners check the totalling and counting.
DIFFERENTIATION	Less able: decide whether to limit the count by using two 1–6 dice. More able: encourage them to count by pointing, without touching, so that they remember which cubes have already been counted.
PLENARY	Repeat counting out given quantities of cubes from the **Main teaching activity**. Check that the children count accurately.

RESOURCES

1–6 dice; paper and pencils; flip chart and pen; dominoes.

PREPARATION

Make two columns on a flip chart sheet, labelled 'Ben' and 'Sam'.

LEARNING OUTCOMES

ORAL AND MENTAL STARTER

● Count on in twos from zero, then one, and begin to recognise odd or even numbers to about 20 as 'every other number'.

MAIN TEACHING ACTIVITY
● Solve simple mathematical problems or puzzles; recognise and predict from simple patterns and relationships. Suggest extensions by asking 'What if...?' or 'What could I try next?'
● Investigate a general statement about familiar numbers by finding examples that satisfy it.
● Explain methods and reasoning orally.

VOCABULARY

Pattern; puzzles; answer; right; wrong; how did you work it out...?; count out; share out; left; left over; number sentence; sign; operation.

ORAL AND MENTAL STARTER

ODD OR EVEN: Repeat this activity, from the Plenary session of Lesson 1 of this unit, page 118.

MAIN TEACHING ACTIVITY

NUMBER PROBLEMS: Explain that you want the children to solve some number problems which will have more than one solution. Ask: *Ben is two years older than Sam. How old could each of them be?* Ask for suggestions of how this could be solved, and write possible solutions on the flip chart. Encourage the children to explain how they have worked out their solutions and to look for a pattern by ordering their responses.

Ben	Sam
3	1
4	2
5	3

Choose from the following problems, encouraging the children, working individually, to find different solutions for them.
1. Which dominoes have a total of five spots? seven spots? ten spots?
2. How many different ways can you score 4 by rolling two dice? What about 6? What about 7?

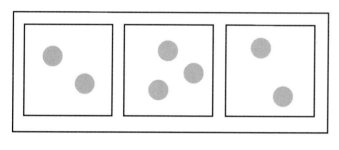

3. Write as many different ways as you can of making the number 10. (5+5; 1+9; 12–2...)
4. Investigate different ways of putting seven buttons into three boxes. Now try 10 buttons...
5. How many different ways can you score 9 by rolling three dice? What about 10? What about 12?
6. Using only the numerals 1, 2 and 3 and addition, make all the numbers to 10 (2 + 3 + 2 + 3 = 10, and so on).

DIFFERENTIATION

Less able: start with question 1. Encourage the children to sort out the dominoes, finding those which total 5. They can record by writing an addition sentence: 2 + 3 = 5.
More able: when the children have successfully tackled easier questions encourage them to try questions 5 and 6 which are more challenging.

PLENARY

Discuss the possible solutions to questions 1 and 2. Ask individual children to explain their methods and encourage them to look for patterns in their results. With the dominoes, for example, they could put the dominoes in an order, perhaps starting with the 0 and 5 domino, then 1 and 4, and so on.

LESSON 5

Repeat the activities for Lesson 4. In the **Main teaching activity** begin by asking: *How many different ways can you colour two squares using a red and a blue pen if each square must be just one colour?* (Red and blue; blue and red; red and red; blue and blue.)

Encourage the children to suggest different combinations, and to take turns to colour in the squares, drawn out on the flip chart. Suggest the extension: *What if there were three squares: how many ways then?* Ask the children to try this for themselves for about five minutes on paper and report back. Choose some more problems from Lesson 4 and ask the children to solve these.

Counting patterns

Continue the patterns.

| 2 | 4 | 6 | | | |

| 1 | 3 | 5 | | | |

| 6 | 8 | 10 | | | |

| 9 | 11 | 13 | | | |

| 20 | 18 | 16 | | | |

| 17 | 15 | 13 | | | |

| 7 | 8 | 9 | | | |

UNITS 9-10

ORGANISATION (10 LESSONS)

	LEARNING OUTCOMES	ORAL AND MENTAL STARTER	MAIN TEACHING ACTIVITY	PLENARY
LESSON 1	● **Read and write numerals from 0 to at least 20.** ● **Understand and use the vocabulary of comparing and ordering numbers,** including ordinal numbers to at least 20.	COUNTING PATTERNS.	ORDERING NUMBERS: Using ordinal numbers.	Ordinal numbers.
LESSON 2	● **Understand and use the vocabulary of comparing and ordering numbers,** including ordinal numbers to at least 20. ● **Compare two familiar numbers, say which is more or less, and give a number which lies between them.**	COUNTING OUT: Counting out a given quantity.	COMPARING NUMBERS: Using vocabulary such as larger, smaller,….	Discussion of the children's work.
LESSON 3	● **Understand and use the vocabulary of comparing and ordering numbers,** including ordinal numbers to at least 20. ● Use the = sign to represent equality.	COUNTING PATTERNS.	EQUALITIES: Understanding that 3 + 5 = 2 + 6.	Discussion of the children's work.
LESSON 4 +5	● **Understand the operation of addition, and use the related vocabulary.** Begin to use the + and = signs to record mental calculations in a number sentence, and to recognise the use of symbols such as ™ or D to stand for an unknown number. ● Use known number facts and place value to add or subtract a pair of numbers mentally within the range 0 to at least 10, then 0 to at least 20. ● Use patterns of similar calculations (eg 10 – 0 = 10, 10 – 1 = 9, 10 – 8 = 2…).	FACT CARDS: Rapid recall of addition and subtraction facts to 5.	USING SYMBOLS: Substituting numbers for symbols in addition and subtraction sentences.	Discussion of the children's work.
LESSON 6	● **Within the range 0 to 30, say the number that is 1 or 10 more or less than any given number.** ● **Understand the operation of addition, and use the related vocabulary.** ● Use known number facts and place value to add or subtract a pair of numbers mentally within the range 0 to at least 10, then 0 to at least 20. ● Put the larger number first and count on in ones, including beyond 10 (eg 7 + 5).	COUNTING OUT.	BEYOND 10: Adding or subtracting 10 from a number.	Discussion of the children's strategies.
LESSON 7	● **Understand the operation of addition, and of subtraction (as 'take away' or 'difference'), and use the related vocabulary.** ● Begin to recognise that addition can be done in any order.	10 MORE OR LESS: Saying the number that is 10 more or less than a given number.	TRIOS: Finding two addition and two subtraction sentences for three linked numbers, such as 3, 5, 8.	TRIOS: Discussion of the children's work.

cont…

LESSON 8	● **Understand the operation of addition, and use the related vocabulary.** ● Begin to understand that addition can be done in any order. ● Begin to recognise that more than two numbers can be added together.	TRIOS.	ADDING THREE NUMBERS: Finding combinations of three small numbers.	Discussion of the children's work.
LESSON 9 +10	● **Use mental strategies to solve simple problems** set in 'real life' or money contexts, **using counting, addition, subtraction, doubling and halving, explaining methods and reasoning orally.** ● Recognise coins of different values. ● Find totals and change from up to 20p. ● Work out how to pay an exact sum using smaller coins. ● Choose and use appropriate number operations and mental strategies to solve problems.	ADDING THREE NUMBERS: Finding combinations of three small numbers.	PROBLEMS: Solving addition, subtraction and money problems.	Discussion of the children's work.

ORAL AND MENTAL SKILLS   Count reliably at least 20 objects. Describe and extend number sequences: **count on and back in ones from any small number, and in tens from and back to zero;** count on in twos from zero, then one, and begin to recognise odd and even numbers to about 20 as 'every other number'. **Know by heart:** addition facts for all pairs of numbers with a total up to at least 5, and the corresponding subtraction facts. Use known number facts and place value to add or subtract a pair of numbers mentally within the range 0 to at least 10, then 0 to at least 20. Begin to recognise that more than two numbers can be added together. **Within the range 0 to 30, say the number that is 1 or 10 more or less than any given number.**

In Unit 9 Lessons 1, 2 and 4 are shown in full. Lessons 3 and 5 are extensions of what has already been taught and follow Lessons 2 and 4, as appropriate. In Unit 10 Lessons 6, 7 and 9 are shown in full detail. Lessons 8 and 10 are again extensions and follow Lessons 7 and 9.

RESOURCES

Large numeral cards 0 to 20; washing line and pegs; interlocking cubes; squared paper and coloured pencils.

LEARNING OUTCOMES

ORAL AND MENTAL STARTER
● Describe and extend number sequences: **count on and back in ones from any small number, and in tens from and back to zero.**

MAIN TEACHING ACTIVITY
● **Read and write numerals from 0 to at least 20.**
● **Understand and use the vocabulary of comparing and ordering numbers,** including ordinal numbers to at least 20.

ORAL AND MENTAL STARTER

COUNTING PATTERNS: Count forward from zero to 20, then back to zero, altogether first, then around the class. Next count together, starting from any small number, such as 3, 5, or 4... up to 20 and back to zero. Repeat, this time around the class, until everyone has had at least two turns.

VOCABULARY

First, second, third,...tenth, eleventh,.... to twentieth; last; last but one; before; after; next; between; half-way between; compare; order; size.

MAIN TEACHING ACTIVITY

ORDERING NUMBERS: Explain that you would like the children to take turns to peg a number from one to 20 on the washing line where they think it will fit in order. Ask a child to begin by pegging the number 10, and to explain why they have placed it in that particular position. Continue handing out other numbers, not in order, so that the position for each one has to be justified. Children may find that they need to rearrange the cards in order to make the complete number line. Then choose six children to line up, and number them, using ordinal names: first, second, third,… sixth. Ask questions such as: *Who is first? Last? Who is after the fourth? Before the second? The one before last?* Now ask the children to respond using ordinal numbers such as: *Where is Katy? And John?* Ask the children to sit at their tables, and to count out 10 interlocking cubes, of which only one is blue. Ask them to make a tower of cubes in which the blue one is seventh, then hold up their towers. Repeat this, asking for the blue one to be put in different places, such as: first; last; last but one; sixth…., checking each time that all the children are following the spoken instructions.

Working in pairs, and using squared paper, each child now draws a box around a line of 10 squares. One child colours one of these squares without his or her partner seeing, and tells what has been done, for example: 'I coloured the fifth square in green'. The partner does the same on his or her own sheet, then colours another square and says, for example, 'I coloured the second square blue'. When all 10 squares are coloured they compare to see if they have the same coloured pattern.

DIFFERENTIATION

Less able: work with this group, asking them to colour in specific squares, using ordinal numbers.

More able: offer some challenges: *What is the seventh letter of the alphabet? What is the fifth word on the fifth page of your reading book?* Ask them to try these, then make up and try out some challenges for each other.

PLENARY

Ask some children to line up again, as in the **Main teaching activity**, and ask questions such as: *Who is fifth? One before the fourth?* and so on.

LESSON 2

RESOURCES

20 cubes or counters for each child; a pack of 0 to 20 numeral cards for each pair (pages 14 and 15); flip chart and pen; pencils and paper.

LEARNING OUTCOMES

ORAL AND MENTAL STARTER
● **Count reliably at least 20 objects.**

MAIN TEACHING ACTIVITY
● **Understand and use the vocabulary of comparing and ordering numbers,** including ordinal numbers to at least 20.
● Compare two familiar numbers, say which is more or less, and give a number which lies between them.

ORAL AND MENTAL STARTER

COUNTING OUT: Ask children to count out fifteen cubes. Say: *Put out 1, 2, 5… more. How many now? Take away 1, 2, 4…* How many now? Repeat for other starting quantities.

MAIN TEACHING ACTIVITY

COMPARING NUMBERS: Ask some questions about pairs of numbers, writing them on the flip chart: *Which is more: 15 or 19? 18 or 13? Which is less: 13p or 8p?* Repeat this for other numbers, using the vocabulary: more, larger, bigger, greater, fewer, smaller and less.

VOCABULARY
More; bigger; larger; greater; fewer; smaller; less; most; biggest; largest; greatest; fewest; smallest; least.

Now try with three numbers, such as: *Which is most: 15, 17 or 13?* Repeat this using the vocabulary: most, biggest, largest, greatest, fewest, smallest and least. On the flip chart write: 3 ☐ 8. Ask: *What number can we write in the box so that the three numbers are in order?* Encourage the children to give different solutions.

Working in pairs, ask the children to take turns to draw two cards from the top of a pack of numeral cards, and place them in front of them, with the smaller on the left-hand side. They then need to decide what number they could put in between, so that the three numbers are in order. They record by writing their three numbers.

DIFFERENTIATION

Less able: limit the range of numbers to zero to 10.
More able: ask them to draw three cards and put these in order, then ask them to insert another number into the sequence. They may find that this is not possible for some sequences, for example 5, 6, 7, in which case they may put a number before and after to extend the sequence further, such as 3, 5, 6, 7, 10.

PLENARY

Discuss the children's ordered numbers. Ask for other possible solutions for each one.

RESOURCES	Numeral cards 0 to 10; flip chart and pen; pencils and paper.
LEARNING OUTCOMES	**ORAL AND MENTAL STARTER** ● Describe and extend number sequences: **count in tens from and back to zero.** **MAIN TEACHING ACTIVITY** ● **Understand and use the vocabulary of comparing and ordering numbers,** including ordinal numbers to at least 20. ● Use the = sign to represent equality.
ORAL AND MENTAL STARTER	COUNTING PATTERNS: Count in tens to and from one hundred. Count around the class, to and back from one hundred, giving everyone two turns. Start from 30, count three tens; count back five tens from 80…
MAIN TEACHING ACTIVITY	EQUALITIES: On the flip chart write the addition: 3 + 5 = and ask the children to give two numbers to go on the other side of the equals sign to make this true. They might suggest: 5 + 3; or 2 + 6… Discuss how both sides of the number sentence total the same amount and explain that the equals sign means that both sets of numbers have the same total. Repeat this for more pairs of numbers. Then ask the children to use their numeral cards to find pairs of numbers which have the same total. They record this as an addition sentence.
DIFFERENTIATION	Less able: limit the cards to 0 to 8. More able: extend the cards to 0 to 15.
PLENARY	Ask children to give examples of their number pairs. Ask if there are other pairs which would give the same total.

RESOURCES

Fact cards from photocopiable pages 111 and 112; a number fan for each child (page 17); flip chart and pen; pencils and paper; number lines; a copy for each child of photocopiable page 131 (Using symbols).

LEARNING OUTCOMES

ORAL AND MENTAL STARTER

● **Know by heart:** addition facts for all pairs of numbers with a total up to at least 5, and the corresponding subtraction facts.

MAIN TEACHING ACTIVITY
● **Understand the operation of addition, and use the related vocabulary.**
Begin to use the + and = signs to record mental calculations in a number sentence, and to recognise the use of symbols such as □ or △ to stand for an unknown number.
● Use known number facts and place value to add or subtract a pair of numbers mentally within the range 0 to at least 10, then 0 to at least 20.
● Use patterns of similar calculations (eg $10 - 0 = 10$, $10 - 1 = 9$, $10 - 2 = 8$...).

<table>
<tr><td>

VOCABULARY

Add; more; plus; make; sum; total; altogether; score; is the same as; equals; sign.

</td></tr>
</table>

ORAL AND MENTAL STARTER

FACT CARDS: Hold up the cards, in turn, and ask the children to show the answers with their number fans. Encourage them to work as quickly as possible, so that they rely upon rapid recall of the number facts.

MAIN TEACHING ACTIVITY

USING SYMBOLS: On the flip chart write: $2 + 3 = \square$. Ask: *What number will go in the box? What is 2 add 3?* Encourage the children to use their rapid recall of facts to respond quickly, using their number fans. Repeat this for other examples. Now write two symbols: $\square + \triangle = 5$. Ask: *What numbers could the square and triangle be?* Encourage the children to give a range of answers, and write them on the flip chart, ordering them so that they show a pattern:

$$5 + 0 = 5$$
$$4 + 1 = 5$$
$$3 + 2 = 5$$
$$2 + 3 = 5$$
$$1 + 4 = 5$$
$$0 + 5 = 5$$

Encourage the children to talk about the patterns that they can see: for example, one number decreases, whilst the other increases, by 1. Discuss how adding zero does not change the number to which it is added. Ask them to work individually to complete the addition patterns for: $\square + \triangle = 6$; $\square + \triangle = 7$. Encourage them to work through these as quickly as possible, using rapid recall of addition facts.

DIFFERENTIATION

Less able: ask the children to complete the addition patterns for $\square + \triangle = 3$ and $\square + \triangle = 4$.
More able: Ask them to try $\square + \triangle = 9$ and $\square + \triangle = 10$, doing them as quickly as possible.

PLENARY

Ask a more able child to write his or her results on the flip chart. Encourage the others to discuss the patterns that they see. Write ™ + D = 8, and ask the children to help you complete this as quickly as possible, using the patterns of similar calculations.

LESSON 5

Repeat the **Main teaching activity**, this time extending to totals of more than 10, such as $11 + 4 = \square$. Encourage the children to count on mentally from the larger number to solve this. Repeat for other examples. Write $\square + \triangle = 12$. Ask for suggestions of how this could be solved, if necessary reminding them of the previous day's work, and suggest that they use their number lines to help them. Provide photocopiable page 131 (Using symbols).
Less able children may benefit from completing more examples for totals to 10. Challenge more able children to work mentally, and to explain which strategies they used.

RESOURCES

Flip chart and pen; 20 cubes for each child; a hundred square for each child; a 4–9 dice for each pair of children; copies of photocopiable page 132 (Beyond 10).

PREPARATION

Make and photocopy a 1–100 number square for each child.

LEARNING OUTCOMES

ORAL AND MENTAL STARTER
● **Count reliably at least 20 objects.**

MAIN TEACHING ACTIVITY
● **Within the range 0 to 30, say the number that is 1 or 10 more or less than any given number.**
● **Understand the operation of addition, and use the related vocabulary.**
● Use known number facts and place value to add or subtract a pair of numbers mentally within the range 0 to at least 10, then 0 to at least 20.
● Put the larger number first and count on in ones, including beyond 10 (eg 7 + 5).

VOCABULARY

Add; more; plus; make; sum; total; altogether; score; is the same as; equals; sign.

ORAL AND MENTAL STARTER

Repeat 'Counting out' from Lesson 2, page 125.

MAIN TEACHING ACTIVITY

BEYOND 10: Ask some questions for 10 more or less than a number, eg: *What is 10 more than five? 10 less than sixteen? 10 less than nineteen?* If any children are unsure they may count on or back on a hundred square until they see the pattern. When they are confident with this, write on the flip chart: 10 + 5 = □ and ask what to write in the box. Extend this to adding any single digit to a 'teens' number *without* crossing the tens, eg: 11 + 4; 13 + 5. Encourage them to explain their mental strategies, such as using their knowledge of addition facts to 10: 'If I add one to four it is five, so eleven add four is fifteen'. Ask all the children to complete photocopiable page 132, working mentally.

DIFFERENTIATION

Less able: provide number lines and explain that they can use these to count on from the larger number if necessary.
More able: challenge the children to make up some more sums for each other to try.

PLENARY

Ask children to write a sum on the flip chart, then explain their mental strategy. Finish by asking more questions to do mentally, eg: *What is 12 add 7? How did you work it out?*

RESOURCES

Trio cards (photocopiable pages 133 and 134), one set between four children; flip chart and pen; pencils and paper

PREPARATION

Photocopy the Trio cards onto card and cut them out; one set per four children.

LEARNING OUTCOMES

ORAL AND MENTAL STARTER
● **Within the range 0 to 30, say the number that is 1 or 10 more or less than any given number.**

MAIN TEACHING ACTIVITY
● **Understand the operation of addition, and of subtraction (as 'take away' and 'difference') and use the related vocabulary.**
● Begin to understand that addition can be done in any order.

VOCABULARY

Add; more; plus; make; sum; total; altogether; subtract; take away; minus; leave; is the same as; equals; sign.

ORAL AND MENTAL STARTER

10 MORE OR LESS: Ask the children to count together: start at 3 and count on 10, in ones. Ask: What is 10 more than 3? Count back 10 from thirteen, and ask: What is 10 less than thirteen? Repeat this for other numbers, within the range zero to 20.

MAIN TEACHING ACTIVITY

TRIOS: Write on the flip chart: 5, 2, 3. Ask the children to use these three numbers to make some addition and subtraction 'sums' with the answers. If they need help to get started, write: 2 + 3 = 5. Encourage them to find all four facts: 2 + 3 = 5; 3 + 2 = 5; 5 – 2 = 3; 5 – 3 = 2. Point out that addition can be done in any order. Encourage the children to respond to sentences such as: *The difference between 5 and 3 is 2.* Repeat this for other numbers, such as 9, 5, 4 (give teen number examples such as 11, 4, 15).

Ask the children to work in groups of four, taking turns to turn over a trio card. Each child gives one fact, different from the others, so that all four facts are collected each time. The child who turns over the card writes down the four facts on paper.

DIFFERENTIATION

Less able: decide whether to sort out the cards with facts up to 5, then encourage them to use rapid recall to find the solutions.
More able: challenge them to make up some trio facts for each other, with the largest number being a 'teens' number, such as 6, 12, 18.

PLENARY

TRIOS: Give trios of numbers, such as 4, 5, 9, or 5, 3, 8 and challenge the children to take turns to write a fact on the flip chart.

LESSON 8

RESOURCES	Trio cards from photocopiable pages 133 and 134; flip chart and pen; three 1-6 dice for each pair of children.
LEARNING OUTCOMES	**ORAL AND MENTAL STARTER** ● Use known number facts and place value to add or subtract a pair of numbers mentally within the range 0 to at least 10, then 0 to at least 20. **MAIN TEACHING ACTIVITY** ● Understand the operation of addition, and use the related vocabulary. ● Begin to understand that addition can be done in any order. ● Begin to recognise that more than two numbers can be added together.
ORAL AND MENTAL STARTER	TRIOS: Give three trio numbers, eg: 6, 4, 10; 5, 3, 8; 12, 7, 19. Ask the children to say the four related addition and subtraction facts. Check that the subtraction sentences are correctly stated (8 – 3, not 3 – 8).
MAIN TEACHING ACTIVITY	ADDING THREE NUMBERS: Write an addition with three numbers on the flip chart: 5 + 2 + 6 = ; and ask the children for suggestions of how to solve this. Now write: 7 + 6 = 13; or, adding the 5 and 6 first, 11 + 2 = 13; or, adding the 2 and 6 first, 8 + 5 = 13. Discuss how, for addition, the order in which the numbers are added does not matter. Working in pairs, ask them to throw all three dice and add the scores. One child then writes an addition sum, which his or her partner checks.
DIFFERENTIATION	Less able: provide numeral cards so that the children can have the numbers in front of them in their preferred order for adding. Decide whether to simplify one or two dice by using 1, 1, 2, 2, 3, 3. More able: decide whether to substitute one dice for a 4-9 one.
PLENARY	Ask children to write some of their sums on the flip chart and to explain the mental strategies which they used.

RESOURCES

Numeral cards 0 to 20 (pages 14 and 15); coins; paper and pencils.

LEARNING OUTCOMES

ORAL AND MENTAL STARTER

● Begin to recognise that more than two numbers can be added together.

MAIN TEACHING ACTIVITY

● **Use mental strategies to solve simple problems** set in 'real life', money or measurement contexts, **using counting, addition, subtraction, doubling and halving, explaining methods and reasoning orally.**

● Recognise coins of different values.

● Find totals and change from up to 20p.

● Work out how to pay an exact sum using smaller coins.

● Choose and use appropriate number operations and mental strategies to solve problems.

VOCABULARY

Pattern; puzzle; answer; right; correct; wrong; what could we try next?; how did you work it out?; number sentence; sign; operation; symbol; money; coin; penny; pence; pound; price; cost; buy; sell; spend; spent; pay; change; dear; costs more; cheap; costs less; cheaper; costs the same as; how much…?; how many….?; total.

ORAL AND MENTAL STARTER

ADDING THREE NUMBERS: Ask the children to add three numbers, mentally, holding up a numeral card to show the answer. For example: 5 + 4 + 6; 2 + 7 + 9; 3 + 4 + 5.

MAIN TEACHING ACTIVITY

PROBLEMS: Say that you will be reading out some money or number problems which you want the children to work out. You also want them to explain how they solved them. For the money problems, encourage them to work mentally whenever possible; otherwise they can use the coins, and record in their own way. Choose some of the following problems.

Money: 1. How much altogether is 6p and 3p? **2.** My pencil cost 7p. I paid for it and was given no change. Which coins might I have used? **3.** How much more is 10p than 4p? **4.** How much altogether is 5p + 2p + 3p? **5.** How much more is 6p + 4p than 5p + 1p? **6.** Mark spent 3p on a lolly and 5p on a chew. How much change did he get from 10p? **7.** I had 15p, then spent 6p. How much do I have left? **8.** Which coins make 13p, 17p, 19p? For each one, use as few coins as possible. **9.** Which is cheaper: two cakes at 8p each; or a lolly at 4p, a mint at 5p and a chew at 6p?

Addition and subtraction: 10. I think of a number and add 3. The answer is 13. What is my number? **11.** If I roll double 4 on my dice, what is my score? **12.** If I roll 5 and 6 on my dice, what is my score? **13.** The farmer's three hens laid five eggs, three eggs and four eggs last week. How many did they lay altogether? **14.** Jeni ate half of the biscuits in this box of 10. How many are left? **15.** I have three more cakes than pies. If I have seven pies, how many cakes do I have? **16.** In the shop we bought four oranges, three apples and six pears. How many pieces of fruit did we buy in total? **17.** I scored 5; Ahmed scored 9; Chelsea scored 3. Who scored the most? How much did we score in total? How much more did Ahmed score than Chelsea? **18.** Maresh had four conkers, Jon had twice as many. How many did Jon have? How many did they have altogether? They decided to share them and have half each; how many do they each have now?

DIFFERENTIATION

Less able: start with questions 1–3 and 10–11.
More able: try them with questions 8–9 and 17–18. Explain any unfamiliar vocabulary.

PLENARY

Discuss solutions to the problems, including the mental strategies used.

LESSON 10

Repeat Lesson 9, using problems you have not already used. Challenge all the children to make up word problems for number sentences such as 12 + 5 = 17 or 15 – 4 = 11. In the Plenary session, ask them to give examples of their own word problems.

Using symbols

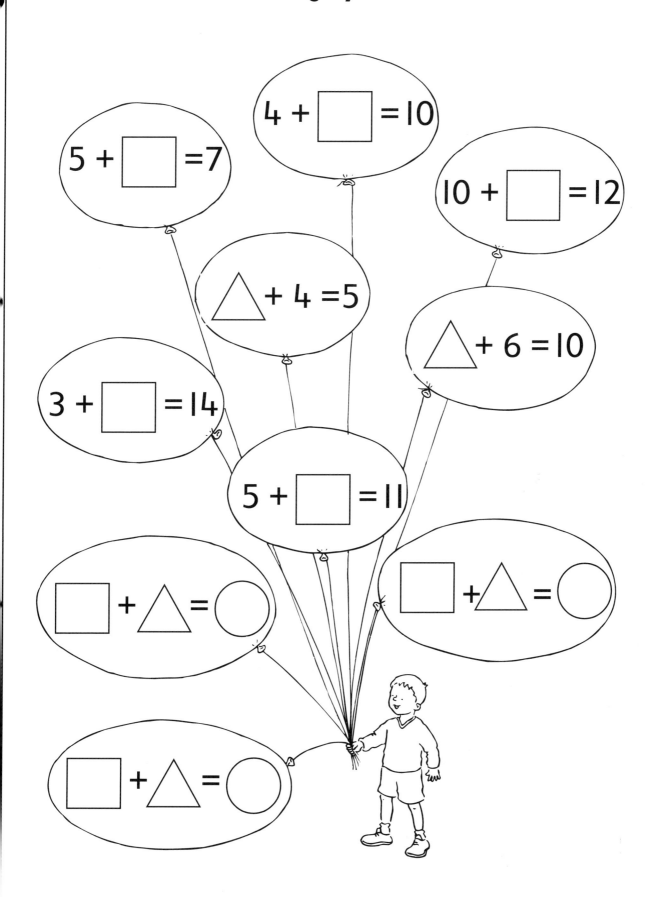

$5 + \square = 7$

$4 + \square = 10$

$10 + \square = 12$

$\triangle + 4 = 5$

$\triangle + 6 = 10$

$3 + \square = 14$

$5 + \square = 11$

$\square + \triangle = \bigcirc$

$\square + \triangle = \bigcirc$

$\square + \triangle = \bigcirc$

Finish these sums.

Beyond 10

Finish these sums.

$10 + 5 = \boxed{}$ $15 - 10 = \boxed{}$

$18 - 10 = \boxed{}$ $8 + \boxed{} = 18$

$\boxed{} + 10 = 19$ $19 - \boxed{} = 10$

$\boxed{} + 10 = 20$ $\boxed{} - 10 = 10$

$11 + 4 = \boxed{}$ $15 - \boxed{} = 11$

$12 + 6 = \boxed{}$ $\boxed{} - 6 = 12$

$13 + \boxed{} = 15$ $15 - \boxed{} = 13$

$14 + 4 = \boxed{}$ $18 - \boxed{} = 14$

$\boxed{} + 5 = 20$ $\boxed{} - 5 = 15$

$12 + \boxed{} = 19$ $19 - 7 = \boxed{}$

Trio cards 6 to 10

Photocopy these onto card and cut them out.

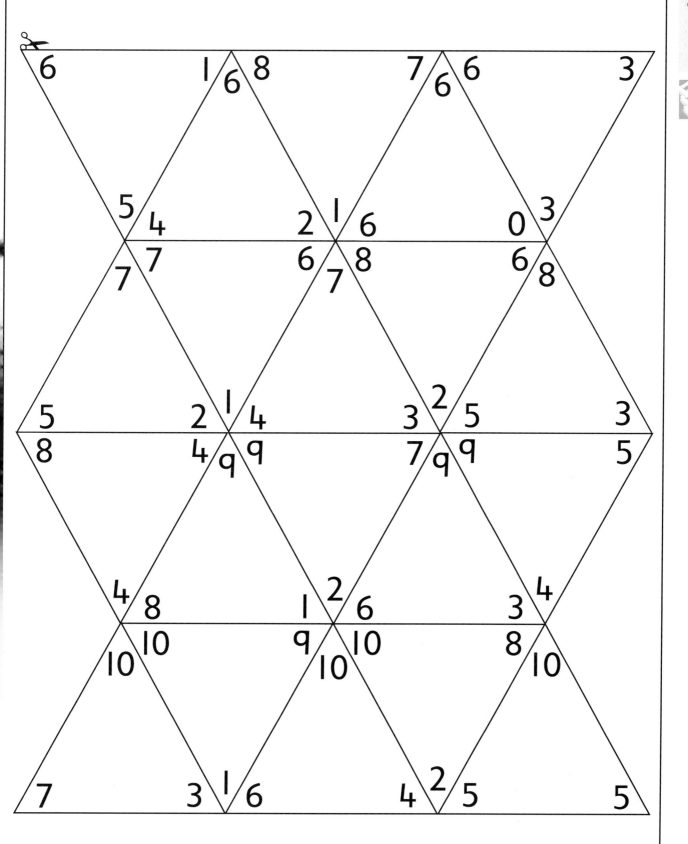

Trio cards 11 to14

Photocopy these onto card and cut them out.

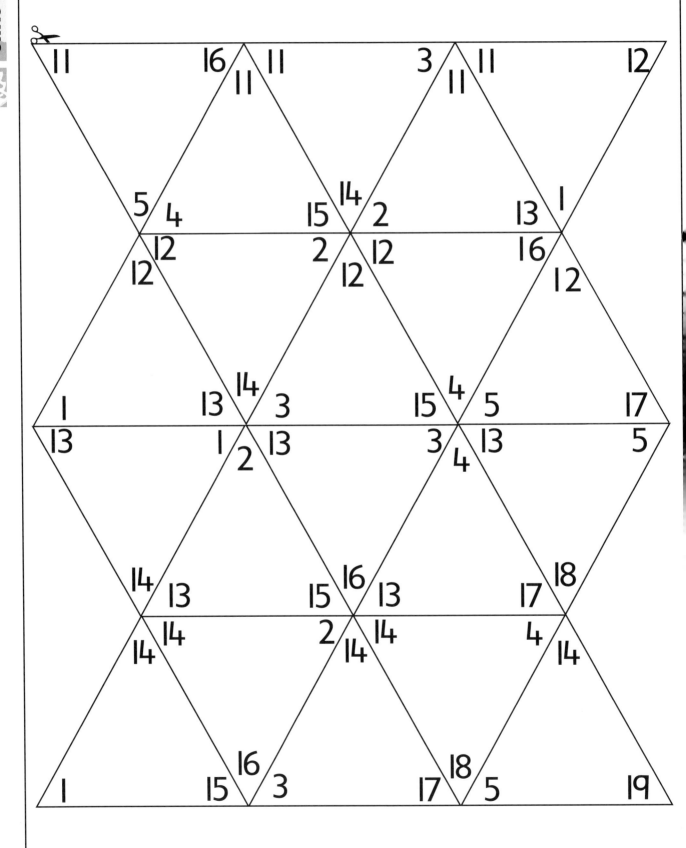

UNITS 11-12

ORGANISATION (10 LESSONS)

	LEARNING OUTCOMES	ORAL AND MENTAL STARTER	MAIN TEACHING ACTIVITY	PLENARY
LESSON 1	● Solve a given problem by sorting, classifying and organising information in simple ways, such as: using objects or pictures. Discuss and explain results.	TRIOS: Finding addition and subtraction facts for three linked numbers such as 5, 4, 9.	ALL ABOUT US: Finding out about interests, likes and dislikes; voting; recording using objects or pictures.	Sorting by one criterion.
LESSON 2	● Solve a given problem by sorting, classifying and organising information in simple ways, such as: using objects or pictures; in a list. Discuss and explain results.	TRIOS.	SORTING: Sorting collections and recording using pictures.	Sorting by one criterion.
LESSON 3	● Solve a given problem by sorting, classifying and organising information in simple ways, such as: using objects or pictures; in a list. ● Discuss and explain results.	TRIOS.	PROBLEMS: Solving problems and recording the results using lists and pictures.	Sorting by one criterion.
LESSON 4 +5	● Understand and use the vocabulary related to time. ● Order familiar events in time. ● Read the time to the hour or half hour on analogue clocks. ● Know the days of the week and the seasons of the year.	TRIOS. TELLING THE TIME.	TELLING THE TIME: Telling the time to the hour and half hour. ORDERING EVENTS: Using time vocabulary; putting events in order.	Using time vocabulary; putting events in order. Discussion of the children's work.
LESSON 6	● Understand and use the vocabulary related to time. ● Order familiar events in time. ● Know the days of the week and the seasons of the year. ● Read the time to the hour or half hour on analogue clocks.	TELLING THE TIME.	ALL ABOUT ME: Recording time information about themselves.	Discussion of the children's work.
LESSON 7 + 8 + 9 +10	● Understand and use the vocabulary related to length and mass. **Compare two lengths or masses by direct comparison;** extend to more than two. Measure using uniform non-standard units (eg straws, wooden cubes, plastic weights) or standard units (eg metre sticks). ● **Suggest suitable standard or uniform non-standard units and measuring equipment to estimate, then measure, a length or mass,** recording estimates and measurements as 'about as heavy as 20 cubes'. ● **Use mental strategies to solve simple problems** set in measurement contexts, **using counting, addition, subtraction, doubling and halving, explaining methods and reasoning orally.**	ADDITION AND SUBTRACTION FACTS: Answering mental calculation questions by holding up numeral cards.	PROBLEMS: Solving length and mass problems.	Discussion of the children's work.

In Unit 11 Lessons 1 and 4 are shown in full. Lessons 2, 3 and 5 are extensions of what has already been taught. In Unit 12 Lesson 6 is an extension of what has already been taught. Lessons 7–10 are set up as a 'circus' of activities.

RESOURCES

Interlocking cubes; flip chart and pen; pencils and large sheets of paper.

PREPARATION

Place interlocking cubes on each table so that all the children can reach them easily. Prepare large sheets of paper for each table, labelled with columns for favourite pets, such as 'Dog'; 'Cat'; 'Bird'; 'Fish'. Prepare flip chart sheets with columns headed with favourite crisp flavours and favourite school activities.

LEARNING OUTCOMES

ORAL AND MENTAL STARTER
● Begin to know addition facts for all pairs of numbers with a total up to at least 10, and the corresponding subtraction facts.

MAIN TEACHING ACTIVITY
● Solve a given problem by sorting, classifying and organising information in simple ways, such as: using objects or pictures.
● Discuss and explain results.

VOCABULARY
Count; sort; vote.

ORAL AND MENTAL STARTER

TRIOS: Give the children a set of three numbers, such as 3, 4, and 7 and ask for four number facts about the set: $3 + 4 = 7$; $4 + 3 = 7$; $7 - 3 = 4$; $7 - 4 = 3$. Repeat this for other number trios. Write each set of answers on the flip chart, so that the children can check easily which 'sums' are still needed.

MAIN TEACHING ACTIVITY

ALL ABOUT US: Explain to the children that they will be solving problems about themselves, their interests, likes and dislikes. Ask: *What is your favourite flavour of crisps?* Collect some suggestions, write these on the flip chart, as labels, then ask children to vote by holding up their hands. Ask one child to collect the votes for plain crisps by making a tower of cubes to match the number of votes, and place this under the label on the ledge of the flip chart. Repeat this for the other flavours. Ask: *How many people voted? How do we know? Which is the favourite flavour? Which is more/less popular than...? Which one did fewest people like?* Encourage the children to use the towers of cubes to help them to respond. Repeat for another problem, such as: *Which is your favourite school activity?*

Ask children to work in small groups for about five minutes, to find out: 'Which is our favourite pet?' Within each group they should work together, deciding where to place their individual cube on the labelled sheet of paper. Then ask the groups to contribute their towers of cubes to the class graph, set up on the flip chart as before. Ask similar questions, such as: Which pet did most/fewest children vote for?

DIFFERENTIATION

Differentiate the questioning when the cube graphs have been made.
Less able: ask questions such as: *How many? Which is the most/least popular?*
More able: ask questions such as: *Which are more/less popular than....? How many liked both ... and ...?*

PLENARY

Sort the children into lines by a given criterion, such as colour of shoes or colour of hair. Ask them to look at each line, and to guess how you sorted them. Ask questions such as: *Which is most/least popular? How many have ...? How many more have .... than ....?*

LESSON 2

RESOURCES	Interlocking cubes; flip chart sheet prepared with cube colour labels (see illustration below) and similar large sheets for groups; equally-sized squares of coloured sticky paper to match the cube colours.
LEARNING OUTCOMES	**ORAL AND MENTAL STARTER** ● Begin to know addition facts for all pairs of numbers with a total up to at least 10, and the corresponding subtraction facts. **MAIN TEACHING ACTIVITY** ● Solve a given problem by sorting, classifying and organising information in simple ways, such as: using objects or pictures; in a list. ● Discuss and explain results.
ORAL AND MENTAL STARTER	TRIOS: Repeat this activity from Lesson 1, page 136.
MAIN TEACHING ACTIVITY	SORTING: Ask the children to help you sort a set of different coloured interlocking cubes by colour. When they have done this, ask how many of each colour there are, and record this in a list. Ask one child to stick enough red squares in the red column on the flip chart sheet to represent the red cubes, making sure that the squares just touch. Repeat for the other colours. Ask questions, as in Lesson 1. Ask the children, working in groups, to sort the cubes on their table, make a list, then make their own graph using sticky coloured squares on paper.
DIFFERENTIATION	Differentiate the questioning when the cube graphs have been made. Less able: ask questions such as: *How many? Which colour has the most/least?* More able: ask questions such as: *Which colour has more/fewer than....? How many more/fewer ... than ...?*
PLENARY	Repeat the Plenary session of Lesson 1, page 136, sorting the children for a different criterion.

Colour of cubes	How many
Red	5
Blue	6
Green	3
Yellow	4

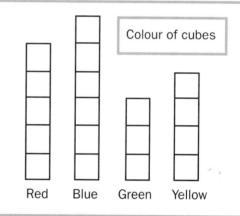

Colour of cubes

Red Blue Green Yellow

LESSON 3

RESOURCES	Interlocking cubes; pencils and paper; flip chart and pen.
LEARNING OUTCOMES	**ORAL AND MENTAL STARTER** ● Begin to know addition facts for all pairs of numbers with a total up to at least 10, and the corresponding subtraction facts. **MAIN TEACHING ACTIVITY** ● Solve a given problem by sorting, classifying and organising information in simple ways, such as: using objects or pictures; in a list. ● Discuss and explain results.
ORAL AND MENTAL STARTER	TRIOS: Repeat this activity from Lesson 1, page 136.
MAIN TEACHING ACTIVITY	PROBLEMS: Set the first problem: *How many cubes can you hold in your hand?* Ask for suggestions about how to find out, and how to organise the information. Working in groups, children collect the data and organise it in a table, then make a graph, as in Lesson 2. Ask questions such as: *Who can hold the most/least cubes? Who can hold one more/fewer cubes than ...? How many more/fewer cubes than ...can you hold?* Repeat this for other questions such as: *How many letters do you have in your first name? How many pages in your reading book? How many brothers and sisters do you have?*
DIFFERENTIATION	Differentiate the questioning when the graphs have been made. Less able: ask questions such as: *How many? Who has the most/least?* More able: ask questions such as: *Who has more/fewer than....? How many more/fewer does ... have than ...?*
PLENARY	Repeat the Plenary session of Lesson 1, page 136, sorting the children for another different criterion.

 **LESSON 4**

RESOURCES

Teaching clock; card clocks from page 81 (Term 1); copies of page 141 ('My day'); an A3 enlargement of 'My day'; flip chart and pen; pencils and paper; flash cards with words for days of the week, seasons, weekend, night, day; copies of page 142 ('When is this?').

PREPARATION

Make the required photocopies and flash cards. Prepare the children's clock faces.

LEARNING OUTCOMES

ORAL AND MENTAL STARTER
● Begin to know addition facts for all pairs of numbers with a total up to at least 10, and the corresponding subtraction facts.

MAIN TEACHING ACTIVITY
● Understand and use the vocabulary related to time.
● Order familiar events in time.
● Read the time to the hour or half hour on analogue clocks.
● Know the days of the week and the seasons of the year.

VOCABULARY

Time; hour; o'clock; half past; clock; watch; hands.

ORAL AND MENTAL STARTER

TRIOS: repeat this activity from Lesson 1, page 136.

MAIN TEACHING ACTIVITY

TELLING THE TIME: Ask the children to set the hands on their card clock faces to the times you say, such as: *Show me 8 o'clock; 10 o'clock; one hour after 3 o'clock; two hours before 5 o'clock.* Use the teaching clock to show the children half past three. Discuss how the hour hand is halfway between the 3 and the 4, and the minute hand points to the 6. Show more half hour times and ask the children to say them. Discuss what time it is when the children get up in the morning, have breakfast, start school and so on, setting the teaching clock to these times. Ask them to set their clocks to half hour times that you say.

Give each child a copy of 'My day' (photocopiable page 141) to complete.

DIFFERENTIATION

Less able: work with these children, asking them to set their clocks to each time on the sheet, say the time, then look at the pictures and decide what happens at that time of day. More able: on the back of the sheet, ask them to draw or stamp more clock faces and write some times for things that they do at home.

PLENARY

Pin the A3 copy of 'My day' to the flip chart. Ask individual children to join a clock to each picture with the pen, then explain why they have matched them. When everything has been joined up, ask the children to order the times and events from the earliest to the latest.

LESSON 5

For the **Oral and mental starter**, reprise 'Telling the time' (the **Main teaching activity** from Lesson 4). For the **Main teaching activity**, go on to ORDERING EVENTS: Recite the days of the week in order. Ask questions, eg *What day is before Monday; after Saturday; tomorrow; yesterday; in two days' time; how long will it be till…?* Ask which season it is and how you can tell. Ask the children to name and describe each season. Talk about plans the children have, using words such as *evening, morning, night, weekend.* For each question, ask a child to choose a flashcard. Provide copies of page 142; ask the children to decide which picture belongs to which word. Work with less able children, discussing what each picture shows and what comes first, next and so on. Ask more able children to draw different pictures showing what they do on weekdays and at weekends. In the **Plenary**, discuss the solutions to the problems on the sheet. Ask the children to explain their thinking.

LESSON 5

RESOURCES	Teaching clock; flash cards with words for days of the week, seasons, weekend, night, day; copies of photocopiable page 142 (When is this?).
LEARNING OUTCOMES	**ORAL AND MENTAL STARTER** ● Read the time to the hour and the half hour on analogue clocks. **MAIN TEACHING ACTIVITY** ● Understand and use the vocabulary related to time. Order familiar events in time. Know the days of the week and the seasons of the year. ● Read the time to the hour or half hour on analogue clocks.
ORAL AND MENTAL STARTER	TELLING THE TIME: Set the teaching clock to o'clock and half hour times and ask the children to say what time it is. Ask questions, eg *What is the time two hours after... three hours before...?; How did you work it out?*
MAIN TEACHING ACTIVITY	ORDERING EVENTS: Recite the days of the week in order. Ask questions, eg *What day is before Monday...after Saturday... tomorrow... yesterday... in two days time.. how long will it be till... ?* Ask which season it is and how you can tell, then ask the children to name and describe each season. Talk about any plans the children have, using vocabulary such as: evening, morning, night, weekend,.... For each question ask a child to choose the relevant flashcard. Provide copies of page 142 and ask the children to decide which picture belongs to which word.
DIFFERENTIATION	Less able: work with this group, discussing what each picture shows and what comes first, next.... More able: encourage them to draw some pictures, in order, to show the difference between what they do on weekdays and at weekends.
PLENARY	Discuss the pictures and how they should be joined. Ask the children to explain their thinking.

LESSON 6

RESOURCES	Copies of photocopiable page 143 (All about me); an A3 enlargement of 'All about me'; flip chart and pen; teaching clock.
LEARNING OUTCOMES	**Oral and mental starter** ● Read the time to the hour or half hour on analogue clocks. **Main teaching activity** ● Understand and use the vocabulary related to time. Order familiar events in time. Know the days of the week and the seasons of the year.
ORAL AND MENTAL STARTER	TELLING THE TIME: Repeat this activity from Lesson 5, above.
MAIN TEACHING ACTIVITY	ALL ABOUT ME: Pin the enlarged photocopiable to the flip chart. Ask the children to read the questions. Discuss what they might write as their responses. Talk about their age, how many days in a week, how many hours in the day. Then ask the children to complete the sheets. Remind them that they will have different answers, because everyone is different.
DIFFERENTIATION	Less able: work with this group, helping children to write their answers. More able: challenge them to think of more details about themselves which involve time.
PLENARY	Ask the more able group for their questions and answers about themselves which involve time.

LESSON 7 + 8 + 9 +10

RESOURCES

Numeral cards 0 to 20 (pages 14 and 15); metre sticks; canes; ribbons; string; straws; cubes; balances; beanbags; marbles; sand; scoops; Roamer; paper and pencils.

PREPARATION

Set up the activities listed below as a circuit, so that over four days the children can experience a range of activities.

LEARNING OUTCOMES

ORAL AND MENTAL STARTER

●Use known number facts and place value to add or subtract a pair of numbers mentally within the range 0 to at least 10, then 0 to at least 20.

MAIN TEACHING ACTIVITY

● Understand and use the vocabulary related to length and mass.
● **Compare two lengths, or masses by direct comparison;** extend to more than two.
● Measure using uniform non-standard units (eg straws, wooden cubes, plastic weights) or standard units (eg metre sticks).
● **Suggest suitable standard or uniform non-standard units and measuring equipment to estimate, then measure, a length or mass,** recording estimates and measurements as 'about as heavy as 20 cubes'.
● **Use mental strategies to solve problems** set in measurement contexts, **using counting, addition, subtraction, doubling and halving, explaining methods and reasoning orally.**

VOCABULARY

Length; width; height; depth; long; short; tall; high; low; wide; narrow; deep; shallow; thick; thin; longer; shorter; taller; higher; longest; shortest; tallest; highest; far; near; close; metre; ruler; metre stick; weigh; weighs; balances; heavy/light; heavier/ lighter; heaviest/ lightest; weight; balance; scales; o'clock; half past; measure; size; compare; guess; estimate; enough; not enough; too much; too little; too many; too few; nearly; roughly; close to; about the same as; just over; just under.

ORAL AND MENTAL STARTER

ADDITION AND SUBTRACTION FACTS: Ask questions such as 5 + 9; 12 – 3; 3 + 5 + 7. Ask the children to show the answers using numeral cards. Ask individuals how they did it.

MAIN TEACHING ACTIVITY

PROBLEMS: For each lesson, choose from these mental maths questions. Ask the children to write a number sentence for each one, using + (or –) and =. Ask how they worked it out. **1.** My pencil is as long as eight cubes. John's is as long as six cubes. Which one is longer? How much longer? **2.** One ribbon is as long as 10 straws. The other one is as long as five straws. How much ribbon is there altogether? **3.** The corridor is 12 metres long and the hall is 20 metres long. The hall is longer than the corridor. How much longer? **4.** Four bricks balance an apple. Five bricks balance a pear. The apple and pear are put on the scales together. How many bricks will balance them? **5.** The orange and banana are on the scales together, balanced by 15 bricks. I take off the apple and seven bricks, so that the banana is balanced. How heavy is the banana? **6.** It is 5 o'clock. What time will it be two hours from now? What time was it four hours ago? If you had a snack at 3 o'clock, how long ago was that? If you go to bed at 8 o'clock, how many hours until bedtime?

Say that over the next four lessons, you would like the children to solve some measuring problems. They will need to find ways of solving the problems, and to explain what they did and why. Encourage them by asking *What if...?* or *What else could you try?* Choose from these problems. **1.** Choose three ribbons and order them by length or width. Choose non-standard units to measure them. Draw pictures to show the results. **2.** Choose two ribbons. Mark a strip of paper to show which ribbon has the greater length. **3.** Use string to find out which of three non-straight lines is the longest. **4.** Estimate, then check using non-standard units, how far up the wall you can reach. Draw a picture to show your results. Explain why you chose those units. **5.** Throw a beanbag from a mark on the floor for about 1 metre. Check with the metre stick. Now try for 2 metres. **6.** Put some objects on the floor, well spaced out. Estimate how many steps a Roamer will take to reach the first object from a mark on the floor. Check the estimate. Try again as accurately as possible. Repeat for the other objects. Draw a picture to show the results. **7.** How much does your shoe weigh? Choose a non-standard unit and estimate, then measure. **8.** Which is heavier, your shoe or a pencil case? Devise a way to find out. Record your results. **9.** What would you weigh in cubes? Estimate, then check by weighing. Were cubes a good choice? Why/ why not? **10.** What in the classroom do you think weighs about the same as three scoops of sand? Find some objects and check by weighing them. Make a list of results. **11.** Put a book in one bucket of the balance, and a different book in the other bucket. Do they balance? Decide how many cubes to place in which bucket to make them balance. Draw a picture to show the results. **12.** Put five marbles in one bucket of the balance. How many scoops of sand do you think will balance them? Estimate, then check. How many do you think will balance 10 marbles? Estimate, then check. Make a list to show the results.

DIFFERENTIATION

Less able: ask the children to start with questions 1 and 2, then 7 and 8.
More able: questions 5 and 6, and 11 and 12, are more challenging.

PLENARY

Choose a problem which some children have solved; discuss their solutions and methods.

My day

Join the pictures to the clocks to show the time that these things happen.

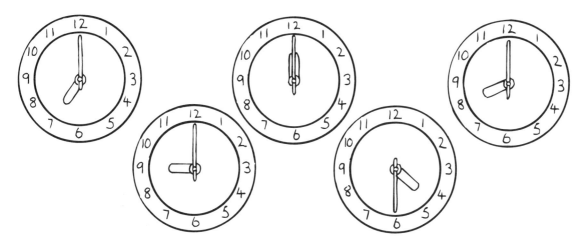

When is this?

Join each label to its picture.

day

night

summer

autumn

spring

winter

All about me

My name is _____

I am _____ years old.

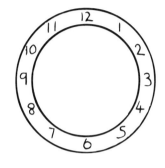

I get up in the morning at:

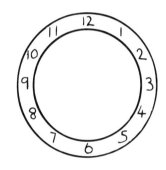

This is when I go to bed.

On Sunday I will _____

_____

On Monday I will _____

_____

Every day I _____

At night I _____

UNIT 13: Assess & Review

Choose from these activities. During the group activities, some of the children can be completing assessment worksheets 4A and 4B, which assess their skills with comparing and ordering numbers, addition and subtraction, and solving simple problems, while others work with you on practical tasks. The specific assessment criteria for the assessment sheets can be found at the bottom of each sheet.

RESOURCES

A set of numeral cards (page 14) and at least 20 cubes or counters for each child; enlargements of 'Make ten' cards (page 114); a bucket balance; parcels of different weights; a range of non-standard units such as cubes, marbles, sand and scoops.

ORAL AND MENTAL STARTER

ASSESSMENT

Do the children:
● **Know by heart: all pairs of numbers with a total of 10?**
● **Count on and back in ones from any small number, and in tens from and back to zero?**
● **Within the range 0 to 30, say the number that is 1 or 10 more or less than any given number?**
NUMBER FACTS: Hold up 'Make ten' cards, one at a time, and ask the children to hold up the appropriate numeral card to show the answer. Work as quickly as possible, keeping things moving at a brisk pace. Check to see who responds confidently, and who needs more practice with remembering these facts.
COUNTING: Count aloud together, first in ones from zero to 20, then back to zero, then from any small number and back to zero. Repeat for counting in tens from and back to zero. Check to see who is confident, and who needs more practice with remembering the number names in order.
MORE OR LESS: Ask children to say the number that is 1 more or less than the number you say. Repeat for 10 more or less. Ask: *What is 1 more than 20, 18, 21, 29? What is 1 less than 20, 15, 30? What is 10 more than 4, 18? What is ten less than 30, 20, 27?*

GROUP ACTIVITIES

ASSESSMENT

Can the children:
● **Count reliably at least 20 objects?**
● **Compare two masses by direct comparison?**
● **Suggest suitable standard or uniform non-standard units and measuring equipment to estimate, then measure, a mass?**
● **Use mental strategies to solve simple problems using counting, addition, subtraction, doubling and halving, explaining methods and reasoning orally?**
COUNTING OUT: Ask children to take a handful of cubes and count them. Ask: *How many have you? Put them in a circle, how many now?* Next, ask the children to count out, for example, 20 cubes, and say: *How many are there? Take away 3, 4, 7,... how many now? Add 4, 6, 9,... now how many?* Check that the children count accurately, no matter how the cubes are arranged in front of them.
WEIGHING: Ask children to take two parcels and compare their weights using their hands, then check their estimates using a balance. Decide whether to extend this to ordering more than two parcels. Ask children to suggest which units should be used to estimate, then weigh, different parcels. They should explain their reasoning, then estimate and check, by weighing, the actual weight of some parcels. Check that the children make reasonable estimates and count the units accurately.
PROBLEM SOLVING: Choose some word problems from Units 11 and 12, Lessons 7–10. For each question, ask the children which strategy they used to solve the problem.

Assessment 4A

Write numbers that are less. 16

Write numbers that are more. 12

Finish these add walls.

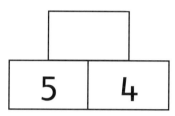 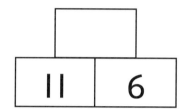 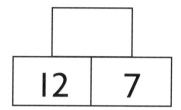

Finish these take away walls.

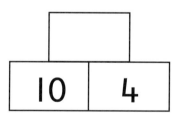 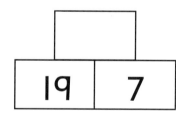 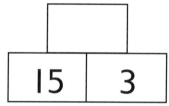

Finish these difference walls.

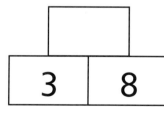 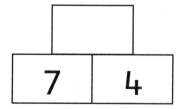 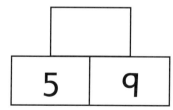

● Read, write and order numbers from 0 to at least 20; understand and use the vocabulary of comparing and ordering these numbers.
● Understand the operation of addition, and of subtraction as 'take away' or difference', and use the related vocabulary.

Assessment 4B

  How much in total? $\boxed{}$ p

Who scored more? _____

How many more? $\boxed{}$

Jon   Mark

How many sweets altogether? $\boxed{}$

How many eggs are there in total? $\boxed{}$

How many more in basket B than basket A? $\boxed{}$

● Use mental strategies to solve simple problems using counting, addition, subtraction, doubling and halving, explaining methods and reasoning orally.

TERM 3

This term's work reinforces that of Term 2 and develops knowledge, skills and understanding with counting in ones, tens, twos, fives and threes. Children continue to develop their skills in comparing and ordering two familiar numbers. Mental strategies for adding to at least 20, using known facts and place value, and bridging through 10 and 20 are taught. Using symbols to stand for unknown numbers is also taught. Children are encouraged to use coins to total and give change to 20p and to solve problems using mental strategies. The concept of capacity is taught, including estimating and measuring with standard and non-standard units. Children should develop their understanding of position, direction and movement and of making patterns using shapes. They make lists and tables to solve data problems.

ENLARGE THIS SHEET TO A3 AND USE IT AS YOUR MEDIUM-TERM PLANNING GRID.

Oral and mental skills: Describe and extend number sequences: **count on and back in ones from any small number, and in tens from and back to zero;** count on in twos from zero, then one, and begin to recognise odd or even numbers to about 20 as 'every other number'; count in steps of 5 from zero to 20 or more, then back again; begin to count on in steps of 3 from zero. Use known number facts and place value to add a pair of numbers mentally within the range 0 at least 10, then 0 to at least 20. Begin to bridge through 10, when adding a single-digit number. Begin to know what each digit in a two-digit number represents. Partition a 'teens' number and begin to partition larger two-digit numbers into a multiple of 10 and ones (TU). **Within the range 0 to 30, say the number that is 1 or 10 more or less than any given number. Know by heart: all pairs of numbers with a total of 10** (eg 3 + 7); addition doubles of all numbers to at least 5 (eg 4 + 4). Identify near doubles, using doubles already known (eg 6 + 5). Begin to know: addition facts for all pairs of numbers with a total up to at least 10, and the corresponding subtraction facts.

UNIT	TOPIC	OBJECTIVES: CHILDREN WILL BE TAUGHT TO...
1	Counting and properties of numbers	● **Count reliably at least 20 objects.** Describe and extend number sequences: **count on and back in ones from any small number, and in tens from and back to zero;** count on in twos from zero, then one, and begin to recognise odd or even numbers to about 20 as 'every other number'; count in steps of 5 from zero to 20 or more, then back again; begin to count in steps of 3 from zero.
2–4	Place value and ordering Understanding + and – Mental calculation strategies (+ and –) Money and 'real life' problems Making decisions	● **Understand and use the vocabulary of comparing and ordering numbers,** including ordinal numbers to at least 20. Use the = sign to represent equality. Compare two familiar numbers, say which is more or less, and give a number which lies between them. **Order numbers to at least 20,** and position them on a number track. ● **Understand the operation of addition, and of subtraction (as 'take away' or 'difference), and use the related vocabulary.** Begin to use the – and = signs to record mental calculations in a number sentence, and to recognise the use of symbols such as □ or △ to stand for an unknown number. Begin to recognise that more than two numbers can be added together. ● Use known number facts and place value to add or subtract a pair of numbers mentally within the range 0 to at least 10, then 0 to at least 20. Begin to bridge through 10, and later 20, when adding a single-digit number. ● **Use mental strategies to solve simple problems** set in 'real life' or money contexts, **using counting, addition, subtraction, doubling and halving, explaining methods and reasoning orally.** Recognise coins of different values. Find totals and change from up to 20p. Work out how to pay an exact sum using smaller coins. ● Choose and use appropriate number operations and mental strategies to solve problems.
5–6	Measures, including problems Shape and space Reasoning about shapes	● Understand and use the vocabulary related to capacity. **Compare two capacities by direct comparison;** extend to more than two. Measure using uniform non-standard units (eg yoghurt pots) or standard units (eg litre jugs). **Suggest suitable standard or uniform non-standard units and measuring equipment to estimate, then measure, a capacity,** recording estimates and measurements as 'about 3 beakers full'. **Use mental strategies to solve simple problems** set in measurement contexts, **using counting, addition, subtraction, doubling and halving, explaining methods and reasoning orally.** ● Use everyday language to describe position, direction and movement. Talk about things that turn. Make whole turns and half turns. Use one or more shapes to make, describe and continue repeating patterns.... ● Solve simple mathematical problems or puzzles; recognise and predict from simple patterns and relationships. Suggest extensions by asking 'What if...?' or 'What could I try next?' Investigate a general statement about familiar shapes by finding examples that satisfy it. Explain methods and reasoning orally.
7	Assess and review	● **Know by heart: all pairs of numbers with a total of 10** (eg 3 + 7). **Count on and back in ones from any small number, and in tens from and back to zero. Count reliably at least 20 objects. Compare two capacities by direct comparison. Suggest suitable standard or uniform non-standard units and measuring equipment to estimate, then measure, a capacity. Read, write and order numbers from 0 to at least 20; understand and use the vocabulary of comparing and ordering these numbers. Understand the operation of addition and of subtraction (as 'take away' or 'difference') and use the related vocabulary. Use mental strategies to solve simple problems using counting, addition, subtraction, doubling and halving, explaining methods and reasoning orally.**

Oral and mental skills: Describe and extend number sequences: **count on and back in ones from any small number, and in tens from and back to zero;** count on in twos from zero, then one, and begin to recognise odd or even numbers to about 20 as 'every other number'; count in steps of 5 from zero to about 20 or more, then back again; begin to count on in steps of 3 from zero. **Know by heart: all pairs of numbers with a total of 10** (eg 3 + 7); addition doubles for all pairs of numbers with a total up to at least 5. Begin to know addition facts for all pairs of numbers with a total up to at least 10, and the corresponding subtraction facts. Identify near doubles, using doubles already known (eg 6 + 5). Begin to bridge through 10, and later 20, when adding a single-digit number. Read the time to the hour or half hour on analogue clocks.

UNIT	TOPIC	OBJECTIVES: CHILDREN WILL BE TAUGHT TO...
8	Counting and properties of numbers Reasoning about numbers	● Describe and extend number sequences: **count on and back in ones from any small number, and in tens from and back to zero;** count on in twos from zero, then one, and begin to recognise odd or even numbers to about 20 as 'every other number'; count in steps of 5 from zero to about 20 or more, then back again; begin to count on in steps of 3 from zero. ● Solve simple mathematical problems or puzzles, recognise and predict from simple patterns and relationships. Suggest extensions by asking 'What if...?' or 'What could I try next?' Investigate a general statement about familiar numbers by finding examples that satisfy it. Explain methods and reasoning orally.
9–11	Place value, ordering, estimating Understanding + and – Mental calculation strategies (+ and –) Money and 'real life' problems Making decisions	● Begin to know what each digit in a two-digit number represents. Partition a 'teens' number and begin to partition larger two-digit numbers into a multiple of 10 and ones (TU). **Understand and use the vocabulary of comparing and ordering numbers,** including ordinal numbers to at least 20. Use the = sign to represent equality. Compare two familiar numbers, say which is more or less, and give a number which lies between them. **Within the range 0 to 30, say the number that is 1 or 10 more or less than any given number. Order numbers to at least 20,** and position them on a number track. Understand and use the vocabulary of estimation. Give a sensible estimate of a number of objects that can be checked by counting (eg up to about 30 objects). ● **Understand the operation of addition, and of subtraction (as 'take away' or 'difference' and 'how many more to make'), and use the related vocabulary.** ● Use known number facts and place value to add or subtract a pair of numbers mentally with the range 0 to at least 10, then 0 to at least 20. Begin to bridge through 10, and later 20, when adding a single-digit number. ● **Use mental strategies to solve simple problems** set in 'real life' or money contexts, **using counting, addition, subtraction, doubling and halving, explaining methods and reasoning orally.** Recognise coins of different values. Find totals and change from up to 20p. Work out how to pay an exact sum using smaller coins. ● Choose and use appropriate number operations and mental strategies to solve problems.
12–13	Measures, and time, including problems Organising and using data	● Understand and use the vocabulary related to capacity. **Compare two capacities by direct comparison;** extend to more than two. Measure using uniform non-standard units (eg yoghurt pots) or standard units (litre jugs). **Suggest suitable standard or uniform non-standard units and measuring equipment to estimate, then measure, a capacity,** recording estimates and measurements as 'about 3 beakers full'. Understand and use the vocabulary related to time. Order familiar events in time. Know the days of the week and the seasons of the year. Read the time to the hour or half hour on analogue clocks. **Use mental strategies to solve simple problems** set in measurement contexts, **using counting, addition, subtraction, doubling and halving, explaining methods and reasoning orally.** ● Solve a given problem by sorting, classifying and organising information in simple ways, such as: using objects or pictures; in a list or simple table. Discuss and explain results.
14	Assess and review	● Count on and back in ones from small number, and in tens from and back to zero. **Within the range 0 to 30, say the number that is 1 or 10 more or less than any given number. Read, write and order numbers from 0 to at least 20; understand and use the vocabulary of comparing and ordering numbers. Understand the operation of addition, and of subtraction (as 'take away' or 'difference'), and use the related vocabulary. Use mental strategies to solve simple problems,** set in 'real life', money and measurement contexts, **using counting, addition, subtraction, doubling and halving, explaining methods and reasoning orally.**

UNIT 1

ORGANISATION (3 LESSONS)

	LEARNING OUTCOMES	ORAL AND MENTAL STARTER	MAIN TEACHING ACTIVITY	PLENARY
LESSON 1	● **Count reliably at least 20 objects.**	ADDITION BEYOND 10: Adding 'teen' and single-digit numbers, without crossing the tens.	COUNTING OBJECTS BEYOND 10.	COUNTING SOUNDS.
LESSON 2	● **Count reliably at least 20 objects.**	ADDITION BEYOND 10.	HOW MANY?: Counting pictures of between 10 and 20 objects.	Discussion of the children's work.
LESSON 3	● Describe and extend number sequences: **count on and back in ones from any small number, and in tens from and back to zero;** count on in twos from zero, then one, and begin to recognise odd or even numbers to about 20 as 'every other number'; count in steps of 5 from zero to 20 or more, then back again; begin to count on in steps of 3 from zero.	ADDITION BEYOND 10.	COUNTING PATTERNS: Counting in ones, tens, twos, fives and threes.	Discussion of the children's work.

ORAL AND MENTAL SKILLS   Use known number facts and place value to add a pair of numbers mentally within the range 0 to at least 10, then 0 to at least 20.

In Unit 1, Lesson 1 is shown in full. Lessons 2 and 3 are extensions of what has already been taught and follow on from Lesson 1.

RESOURCES

Cards made from photocopiable page 152 (Addition beyond 10); a set of 0 to 20 numeral cards for each child (pages 14 and 15); items for counting, such as interlocking cubes, buttons, pennies or straws; a tambourine.

PREPARATION

Enlarge the photocopiable page 152 (Addition beyond 10) onto A3 card. Cut out the cards to make a teaching set.

LEARNING OUTCOMES

ORAL AND MENTAL STARTER
● Use known number facts and place value to add a pair of numbers mentally within the range 0 to at least 10, then 0 to at least 20.

MAIN TEACHING ACTIVITY
● **Count reliably at least 20 objects.**

ORAL AND MENTAL STARTER

ADDITION BEYOND 10: Hold up a card, and ask the children to work out the answer

---

VOCABULARY
Zero, one, two,....20; none; how many...?

mentally, then show you the answer by holding up a numeral card. Ask: *How did you work it out?* Encourage the children to use strategies such as counting on from the larger number; partitioning into '5 and a bit' then recombining; and using known number facts and place value, such as: *if* 3 + 5 = 8, *then* 13 + 5 = 18.

MAIN TEACHING ACTIVITY

COUNTING OBJECTS BEYOND 10: Ask the children to work with a partner, as they will need 20 fingers between them! Explain that you will say a number, and you want them to hold up their hands together, using their combined fingers to show that number. Say: *Hold up twelve fingers. How did you do that?* Some may have each held up two lots of six; others may have had a 10 and a two. Compare their responses, and agree that for each way there are still twelve fingers. Repeat for other numbers, between 10 and 20.

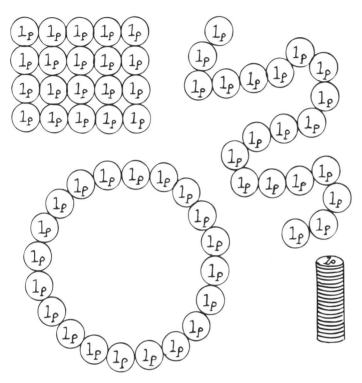

Now ask the children, working with their partners, to count out 20 items. After counting them out, they should spread them out and count them again; then put them into a line, or stack them, or make a circle arrangement, or an array, and count them again without touching. Each time the children count the objects they should agree that, whatever the arrangement, there are still 20. Ask them to repeat this for other quantities. Encourage the children to count by pointing, rather than touching, but they need to remember which have been counted, and recognise which ones they still need to count. Finally, working individually, ask each child to take a handful of items and count how many. Say: *Who has more than fifteen? Fewer than twelve?...* Repeat for other handfuls of counting items.

DIFFERENTIATION

Less able: decide whether to reduce the size of the count to between 10 and fifteen. Check that they count each item just once, and encourage them, if they find this difficult, to synchronise touching, counting and moving each item so that they can check which have and which have not been counted.
More able: decide whether to extend the count to more than 20. Encourage them to count by pointing, not touching, and to remember which they have counted.

PLENARY

COUNTING SOUNDS: Hide a tambourine from view, explain that you will tap the tambourine, and ask the children to count the number of taps.

LESSON 2

RESOURCES	Addition beyond 10 cards (photocopiable page 152); a copy of photocopiable page 153 (How many?) for each child; one A3 enlargement of 'How many'; pencils; flip chart and pen; flip chart sheet with at least 20 simple pictures or spots drawn on; paper and Blu-Tack to hide some of them, so the quantity on view can be changed.
LEARNING OUTCOMES	**ORAL AND MENTAL STARTER** ● Use known number facts and place value to add a pair of numbers mentally within the range 0 to at least 10, then 0 to at least 20. **MAIN TEACHING ACTIVITY** ● **Count reliably at least 20 objects**
ORAL AND MENTAL STARTER	ADDITION BEYOND 10: Repeat this activity from Lesson 1 on page 151.
MAIN TEACHING ACTIVITY	HOW MANY?: Cover some of the pictures on the flip chart so that only fifteen are visible. Ask: *How many can you see?* and invite a child to count them by touching. Repeat by asking them all to shut their eyes while you move the paper so that a different quantity can be seen. Give each child the sheet 'How many?' and ask them to count and write the quantities onto the sheet.
DIFFERENTIATION	Less able: work with this group, encouraging them to use counting strategies of touching and counting. They may find it helpful to make a light pencil mark on the pictures they have counted so that they can see which are left to count. More able: Ask them to draw pictures or spots for each other, with more than 20 objects.
PLENARY	Use the A3 enlargement of 'How many?' to check how many are in each set.

LESSON 3

RESOURCES	Addition beyond 10 cards (photocopiable page 152), a copy of photocopiable page 154 (Patterns) for each child and an A3 enlargement; class number line.
LEARNING OUTCOMES	**ORAL AND MENTAL STARTER** ● Use known number facts and place value to add a pair of numbers mentally within the range 0 to at least 10, then 0 to at least 20. **MAIN TEACHING ACTIVITY** ● Describe and extend number sequences: **count on and back in ones from any small number, and in tens from and back to zero;** count on in twos from zero, then one, and begin to recognise odd or even numbers to about 20 as 'every other number'; count in steps of 5 from zero to 20 or more, then back again; begin to count on in steps of 3 from zero.
ORAL AND MENTAL STARTER	ADDITION BEYOND 10: Repeat from Lesson 1 on page 151.
MAIN TEACHING ACTIVITY	COUNTING PATTERNS: Count together in ones from zero to 20 and beyond, and back to zero, then from any small number. Say: *Count from 7 to 10/... back from 8 to 4/... . How many did you count?* Count in tens from zero and back to one hundred. Count in twos, from zero, then one. Ask, for individual numbers: *Is it odd? Even? How do you know?* Count in fives from zero to 20, then back again. Count forwards in threes from zero. Give each child a copy of 'Patterns' and ask them to fill in the missing numbers.
DIFFERENTIATION	Less able: if they find this challenging, suggest that the children use the class number line to help them. More able: ask them to write the pattern of fives, starting at zero, to thirty, on the back of their sheet. If they are not sure, suggest that they use the number line to help them.
PLENARY	Use the A3 enlargement and discuss the children's answers.

Addition beyond 10

Enlarge this sheet to A3 onto card and cut out the addition cards.

11 + 4	12 + 5	13 + 7
11 + 5	12 + 6	14 + 4
11 + 6	12 + 7	14 + 5
11 + 7	12 + 8	14 + 6
11 + 8	13 + 4	15 + 4
11 + 9	13 + 5	15 + 5
12 + 4	13 + 6	16 + 4

UNIT 1

Name

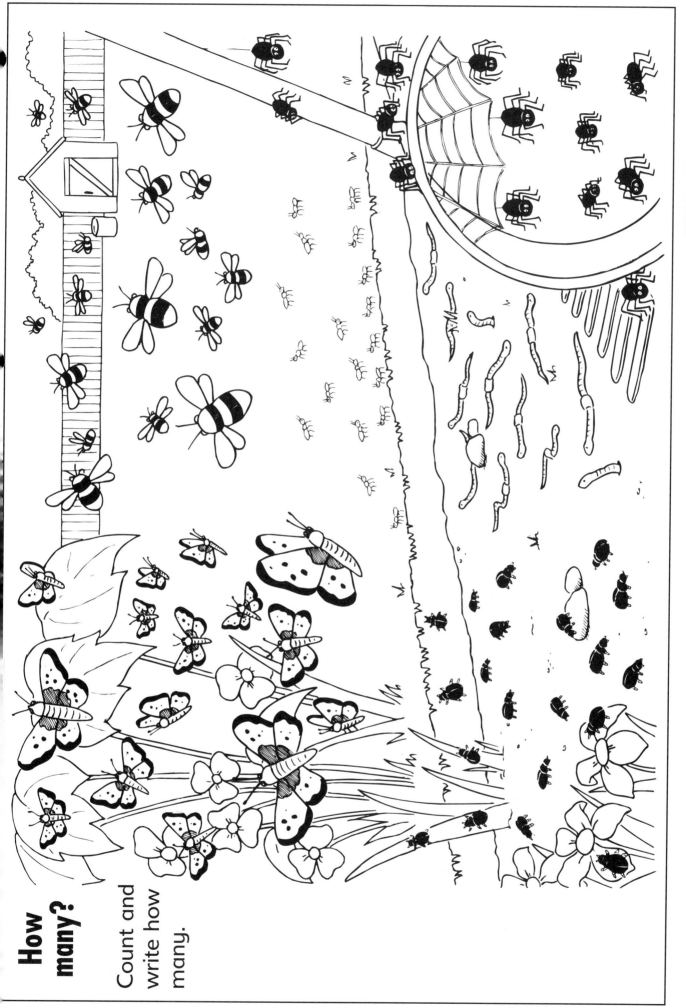

How many?

Count and write how many.

Patterns

Finish the counting patterns.

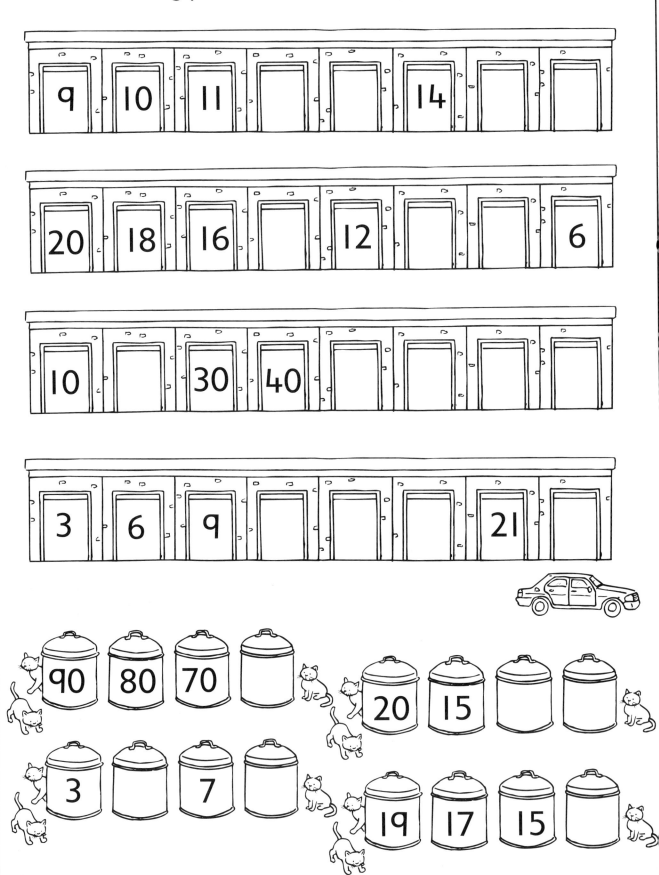

UNITS 2-4

ORGANISATION (15 LESSONS)

	LEARNING OUTCOMES	ORAL AND MENTAL STARTER	MAIN TEACHING ACTIVITY	PLENARY
LESSON 1 +2	● **Understand and use the vocabulary of comparing and ordering numbers,** including ordinal numbers to at least 20. ● Use the = sign to represent equality. ● Compare two familiar numbers, say which is more or less, and give a number which lies between them.	TEENS: Recognising teen numbers as a 10 and units.	MORE AND LESS: Ordering numbers.	WHAT GOES IN THE BOX? Ordering numbers.
LESSON 3	● **Order numbers to at least 20,** and position them on a number track.	10 MORE, 10 LESS: Saying the number which is 10 more/less than a given number.	RACE DAY: Using ordinal number.	Discussion of the children's work.
LESSON 4	● **Order numbers to at least 20,** and position them on a number track.	10 MORE, 10 LESS.	ORDERING NUMBERS: Using ordinal number.	Checking children's work together.
LESSON 5 +6	● **Understand the operation of addition, and use the related vocabulary.** ● Begin to recognise that more than two numbers can be added together. ● Use known number facts and place value to add a pair of numbers mentally within the range 0 to at least 10, then 0 to at least 20.	ADDITION AND SUBTRACTION TO 10: Developing rapid recall of all addition and subtraction facts to 10.	DIFFERENT TOTALS: Adding three numbers mentally.	Discussion of the children's work.
LESSON 7	● **Understand the operation of addition, and use the related vocabulary.** ● Begin to bridge through 10, and later 20, when adding a single-digit number.	ADDITION AND SUBTRACTION TO 10.	BRIDGING 10: Adding two numbers mentally using two stages.	Discussion of the children's work.
LESSON 8	● **Understand the operation of addition, and use the related vocabulary.** ● Begin to bridge through 10, and later 20, when adding a single-digit number. ● Work out how to pay an exact sum using smaller coins.	ADDITION AND SUBTRACTION TO 10.	BRIDGING 10: Adding two prices mentally using two stages, and stating which coins to use to pay for the two items.	Discussion of the children's work.
LESSON 9	● **Understand the operation of addition, and use the related vocabulary.** ● Begin to bridge through 10, and later 20, when adding a single-digit number. ● Recognise coins of different values. Find totals and change from up to 20p. Work out how to pay an exact sum using smaller coins.	10 MORE, 10 LESS.	TOTALS AND CHANGE: Totalling two prices which bridge 10, then finding the change from 20p.	Discussion of the children's work.

cont...

LESSON 10	● Understand the operation of addition, and use the related vocabulary. ● Begin to bridge through 10, and later 20, when adding a single-digit number.	TEENS.	TOTALS: Finding a number of solutions for adding two numbers to make a given total.	Discussion of the children's work.
LESSON 11	● **Understand the operation of addition, and use the related vocabulary.** ● Begin to bridge through 10, and later 20, when adding a single-digit number.	TEENS.	ADDING: Finding solutions for additions which bridge 10.	Discussion of the children's work.
LESSON 12 +13	● **Understand the operation of subtraction (as 'take away') and use the related vocabulary.** ● Begin to use – and = signs to record mental calculations in a number sentence, and to recognise the use of symbols such as □ or △ to stand for unknown numbers. ● Use known number facts and place value to add or subtract a pair of numbers mentally within the range 0 to at least 10, then 0 to at least 20.	ADDITION AND SUBTRACTION TO 10.	SUBTRACTING: Finding solutions for subtraction from 'teen' numbers, without crossing 10.	Addition and subtraction to 10.
LESSON 14 +15	● **Use mental strategies to solve simple problems** set in 'real life' or money contexts, **using counting, addition, subtraction, doubling and halving, explaining methods and reasoning orally.** ● Recognise coins of different values. Find totals and change from up to 20p. Work out how to pay an exact sum using smaller coins. ● Choose and use appropriate number operations and mental strategies to solve problems.	COUNTING: Reciting counting patterns.	PROBLEMS: Solving addition and subtraction problems in 'real life' and money contexts.	Discussion of the children's work.

ORAL AND MENTAL SKILLS   Begin to know what each digit in a two-digit number represents. Partition a 'teens' number and begin to partition larger two-digit numbers into a multiple of 10 and ones (TU). **Within the range 0 to 30, say the number that is 1 or 10 more or less than any given number.** Begin to know addition facts for all pairs of numbers with a total up to at least 10, and the corresponding subtraction facts. Describe and extend number sequences: **count on and back in ones from any small number, and in tens from and back to zero;** count in twos from zero, then one, and begin to recognise odd or even numbers to about 20 as 'every other number'; count in steps of 5 from zero to 20 or more, then back again; begin to count on in steps of 3 from zero.

Lessons 1, 3, 5, 7, 10, 11, 12 and 14 are shown in full. Other lessons are extensions of what has already been taught, and follow in number order.

RESOURCES
Arrow cards for each child (photocopiable page 68); flip chart and pen; a set of numeral cards 10 to 20 for each child (pages 14 and 15); photocopiable page 165 (Missing numbers); an A3 enlargement of 'Missing numbers'; class number line.

LEARNING OUTCOMES
ORAL AND MENTAL STARTER
● Begin to know what each digit in a two-digit number represents. Partition a 'teens' number and begin to partition larger two-digit numbers into a multiple of 10 and ones (TU).

MAIN TEACHING ACTIVITY

● **Understand and use the vocabulary of comparing and ordering numbers,** including ordinal numbers to at least 20. Use the = sign to represent equality. Compare two familiar numbers, say which is more or less, and give a number which lies between them.

<table>
<tr><td>

VOCABULARY

The same number as; as many as; equal to; more; larger; bigger; greater; fewer; smaller; less; most; biggest; largest; greatest; fewest; smallest; least; compare; order; size.

</td></tr>
</table>

ORAL AND MENTAL STARTER

TEENS: Ask the children to use their Arrow cards to make the numbers that you say: *Show me: 12; 1 more than 13; 1 less than 17; the number that is 2 more than 15...* For each response, ask how many tens, how many units. Write the numbers on the flip chart like this: 18 = 1 ten and 8 units.

MAIN TEACHING ACTIVITY

MORE AND LESS: Ask questions such as: *Which is more, 15p or 20p? Which is less, 12p or 17p?* Ask the children to think of two numbers between 13 and 19. On the flip chart write their responses, then ask a child to rewrite the numbers so that they are in numerical order. Repeat this for other pairs of numbers.

Now ask the children to work in pairs. They shuffle two sets of numeral cards 10–20, and place them face down. They each take five cards and lay these out in the order that they come off the stack of cards. They then, in turn, take the next card off the stack and decide whether they will substitute it for one of their cards. Unwanted cards are placed on a discard pile. The object of the game is to be the first player to end up with cards which have lowest to highest number, left to right. Encourage the children to play the game three or four times.

DIFFERENTIATION

Less able: limit the children to just three cards initially until they are confident with playing the game.

More able: extend to a line of six cards. This makes the game more challenging.

PLENARY

WHAT GOES IN THE BOX?: Write 12 ☐ 18 on the flip chart. Ask: *What number could go in the box?* Children should find all the solutions.

LESSON 2

Repeat Lesson 1. Make comparisons of numbers as in the **Main teaching activity**, then provide copies of 'Missing numbers' for the children to fill in. Encourage less able children to use the class number line for help. More able children can go on to make up some missing number examples and swap these with a friend.

LESSON 3

RESOURCES

A copy of photocopiable page 166 (Race day) for each child, plus an A3 enlargement of this page; flash cards of ordinal number names (first, second,... twentieth) printed on cards (possibly from the NNS *Mathematics Vocabulary* CD-ROM); flip chart and pen.

PREPARATION

Enlarge 'Race day' to A3 size and colour in the pictures so that each child is easy to identify. Prepare flash cards with the ordinal number names from first to twentieth.

LEARNING OUTCOMES
ORAL AND MENTAL STARTER
● **Within the range 0 to 30, say the number that is 1 or 10 more or less than any given number.**

MAIN TEACHING ACTIVITY
● **Order numbers to at least 20,** and position them on a number track.

VOCABULARY

First, second, third,…tenth, eleventh,… twentieth; last; last but one; before; after; next; between; half-way between.

ORAL AND MENTAL STARTER

10 MORE, 10 LESS: Explain to the children that you will say a number and will ask them for the number that is 10 more or less than it. Say: *What is 10 more than 3, 5, 10…? What is 10 less than 20, 15…?*

MAIN TEACHING ACTIVITY

RACE DAY: Pin the enlargement of 'Race day' to the flip chart, with the questions at the bottom covered. Ask the class to look at the picture and ask: *Who is first? Who is last? Who is next to last? Which child is fifth/sixth…? Who is half way between the first and the last?* Give out the flash cards for first to fifth, and ask these five children to stand at the front. Encourage the others to put these children in order, for example: 'Ruth, stand between Henry and Jeni because Henry is first, Ruth is second and Jeni is third'.

Read together the questions on the 'Race day' sheet, then ask the children to write in the answers to these questions on their own copies.

DIFFERENTIATION

Less able: work with this group, helping them to recognise the written vocabulary of ordinal numbers.
More able: when they have finished the photocopiable sheet, ask the children to shuffle the flash cards for all ordinal numbers to twentieth, and then set them out in order.

PLENARY

Discuss the answers to the questions on 'Race day'. Ask individual children to write in answers on the A3 enlargement.

RESOURCES	Jars with one, two,… to 20 objects in them; flip chart and pen. For each child: a copy of a sheet of paper with eight empty number tracks, four with 10, and four with 20 spaces (these can be made using *Draw* on a computer), numeral cards 1 to 20.
LEARNING OUTCOMES	**ORAL AND MENTAL STARTER** ● **Within the range 0 to 30, say the number that is 1 or 10 more or less than any given number.** **MAIN TEACHING ACTIVITY** ● **Order numbers to at least 20,** and position them on a number track.
ORAL AND MENTAL STARTER	10 MORE, 10 LESS: Repeat this activity from Lesson 3, page 157.
MAIN TEACHING ACTIVITY	ORDERING NUMBERS: Ask children to take turns to order the jars so that they are ordered from the one containing 1 to the one containing 20. Ask: *Which is first, last,….* On the flip chart draw a number track, write 1 in box 1, and 10 in box 10 (see figure on page 159). Ask: *Where will these numbers go: 4, 7, 3, 8?* Ask children to take turns to write them into the boxes, in the correct places. Encourage them to count the 'missing numbers' to check. Provide everyone with blank number tracks and ask them to take four numbers at random from the 1 to 10 numeral cards, then write these numbers on the tracks, then repeat to make three more patterns. They then use all the cards 1 to 20, drawing five cards each time and writing each in its space on the track.
DIFFERENTIATION	Less able: decide whether to limit the children to patterns for 1 to 10. More able: decide whether to ask them to use 1 to 20 to make patterns.
PLENARY	Ask individual children to write one of their results on the flip chart. Ask the others to check if they agree.

I									10

LESSON 5 +6

RESOURCES

A copy of photocopiable 167 (Addition 6 to 10 cards); a set of numeral cards 0 to 10 (photocopiable page 14) for each child; flip chart and marker pen; pencil and paper.

PREPARATION

Enlarge photocopiable page 167 to A3, cut to make two A4 sheets, and enlarge again to A3 onto card. Cut out the individual cards to make flash cards.

LEARNING OUTCOMES

ORAL AND MENTAL STARTER
● Begin to know addition facts for all pairs of numbers with a total up to at least 10, and the corresponding subtraction facts.

MAIN TEACHING ACTIVITY
● **Understand the operation of addition, and use the related vocabulary.**
● Begin to recognise that more than two numbers can be added together.
● Use known number facts and place value to add a pair of numbers mentally within the range 0 to at least 10, then 0 to at least 20.

VOCABULARY

Add; more; plus; make; sum; total; altogether; score; is the same as; equals; sign.

ORAL AND MENTAL STARTER

ADDITION AND SUBTRACTION TO 10: Explain that you will hold up flash cards with addition sums on them; they will work mentally to find the answer and hold up a numeral card to answer. Ask a number of children how they worked out each answer.

Ask them some similar oral subtraction questions, such as 10 – 6; 7 – 3… and ask children how they worked out the answer.

MAIN TEACHING ACTIVITY

DIFFERENT TOTALS: Write 1, 2, 3, and 4 on the flip chart. Ask a child to choose three of these numbers and write them as an addition sum, for example 1 + 2 + 3 =● (6). Ask the children to total these in their heads, and ask which strategies they used. Then challenge another child to choose three more of the numbers and write them on the flip chart as an addition sum. Repeat this, then increase the size of the numbers to 2, 3, 4, 5 and start again.

Ask the children to choose four of their numeral cards at random, then find as many addition sums as they can using three of these numbers each time. Ask them to work mentally, and to record by writing addition sentences.

DIFFERENTIATION

Less able: limit the card range to 1 to 6.
More able: use cards 3 to 10.

PLENARY

Ask individual children to write up their four numbers and some of their solutions on the flip chart. Ask the others to work these out mentally. Discuss the mental strategies that they used.

LESSON 6

Repeat Lesson 5, but during the **Main teaching activity**, ask the children to find three numbers which add up to 11. They record their totals as addition sums.

LESSON 7

RESOURCES
A set of Addition 6–10 flash cards (photocopiable page 167); a set of numeral cards 0–10 for each child; flip chart and pen; one 4–9 dice for each child; paper and pencils.

PREPARATION
Prepare the 4-9 dice and flash cards, if you do not have these resources already available.

LEARNING OUTCOMES

ORAL AND MENTAL STARTER
● Begin to know addition facts for all pairs of numbers with a total up to at least 10, and the corresponding subtraction facts.

MAIN TEACHING ACTIVITY
● **Understand the operation of addition, and use the related vocabulary.**
● Begin to bridge through 10, and later 20, when adding a single-digit number.

VOCABULARY
Add; more; plus; make; sum; total; altogether; score; is the same as; equals; sign.

ORAL AND MENTAL STARTER
ADDITION AND SUBTRACTION TO 10: Repeat this activity from Lesson 5, page 159.

MAIN TEACHING ACTIVITY
BRIDGING 10: Write 6 + 7 = on the flip chart. *Is the answer more or less than 10?* Say that the best way to work out sums like this is to do two mental steps. Write 6 + 4 + 3 = on the flip chart. Ask the children to say what you have done; encourage them to see that 7 has been 'partitioned' into 3 and 4 so that 10 can be made (6 + 4). Now write: 10 + 3 = 13. Repeat for other examples, asking the children to explain their two mental steps.

Ask the children to work in pairs, tossing two dice each time, writing a sum, then working mentally, using two steps, to find the answer. Ask them to complete 10 sums.

DIFFERENTIATION
Less able: work with this group, encouraging them to explain each step of the calculation, until they are confident with the strategy.
More able: time them. Can they complete 15 questions in 10 minutes?

PLENARY
Ask a pair to write one of their sums on the flip chart; challenge the others to find the answer quickly, and explain how they worked it out. Repeat this for other examples.

LESSON 8

RESOURCES	Sets of price labels for 1p to 9p; coins; flip chart and pen paper and pencils.
LEARNING OUTCOMES	**ORAL AND MENTAL STARTER** ● Begin to know addition facts for all pairs of numbers with a total up to at le[...] 10, and the corresponding subtraction facts. **MAIN TEACHING ACTIVITY** ● **Understand the operation of addition, and use the related vocabulary.** ● Begin to bridge through 10, and later 20, when adding a single-digit numbe[...] ● Work out how to pay an exact sum using smaller coins.
ORAL AND MENTAL STARTER	ADDITION AND SUBTRACTION TO 10: Repeat this activity from Lesson 5, p.159
MAIN TEACHING ACTIVITY	Repeat 'Bridging 10' from Lesson 7, using prices. For example, write 6p + 9p on the flip chart and ask the children to work this out using two mental steps then write the answer and which coins they would use to pay it. Now ask them working in pairs, to take two price labels each time, work out the total, write [...] sum, then write which coins they would use to pay it.
DIFFERENTIATION	Less able: encourage them to check their calculations using the coins. More able: ask them to work out the change from 20p for each sum.
PLENARY	Ask one pair to write one of their sums on the board and explain how they worked it out. Encourage the others to check the answer mentally.

RESOURCES	Photocopiable page 168 (Totals and change); coins; flip chart and pen; pencils and paper.
LEARNING OUTCOMES	**ORAL AND MENTAL STARTER** ● **Within the range 0 to 30, say the number that is 1 or 10 more or less than any given number.** **MAIN TEACHING ACTIVITY** ● **Understand the operation of addition, and use the related vocabulary.** Begin to bridge through 10, and later 20, when adding a single-digit number. ● Recognise coins of different values. Find totals and change from up to 20p. Work out how to pay an exact sum using smaller coins.
ORAL AND MENTAL STARTER	10 MORE, 10 LESS: Repeat this activity from Lesson 3, page 157.
MAIN TEACHING ACTIVITY	TOTALS AND CHANGE: Ask the children to use the strategy of bridging 10 using two mental stages in order to find totals and change. Write on the flip chart: 8p + 6p, then ask what the total is and what the change from 20p will be. Provide each child with a copy of 'Totals and change' and ask them to complete the questions.
DIFFERENTIATION	Less able: encourage them to use coins to check their totals and the change. More able: use the least possible number of coins to give the change.
PLENARY	Discuss the more able group's responses, and ask the other children to check if they have used the least number of coins possible each time.

RESOURCES
A set of 0–20 numeral cards for each pair of children; pencils and paper; flip chart and pen.

PREPARATION
Write the numerals 1 to 20 on a flip chart sheet.

LEARNING OUTCOMES

ORAL AND MENTAL STARTER
● Begin to know what each digit in a two-digit number represents. Partition a 'teens' number and begin to partition larger two-digit numbers into a multiple of 10 and ones (TU).

MAIN TEACHING ACTIVITY
● **Understand the operation of addition, and use the related vocabulary.**
● Begin to bridge through 10, and later 20, when adding a single-digit number.

ORAL AND MENTAL STARTER
TEENS: Repeat this activity from Lesson 1, on page 156.

MAIN TEACHING ACTIVITY
TOTALS: Show the children the flip chart page with the numerals written on it. Ask: *Which two numbers will total 13?* Ask for suggestions, and encourage children to find as many as possible: 3 + 10; 4 + 9; 5 + 8; 6 + 7. Discuss how they added these mentally. Ask for suggestions for another total, such as 15.

Now ask the children, working in pairs, and using their numeral cards and mental strategies, to find as many combinations of two numerals to total 17 as they can in about 10 minutes. They record these as addition sentences.

DIFFERENTIATION
Less able: encourage the children to work as a group, finding solutions together.
More able: suggest that they extend the activity by making up some similar sums of their own, adding three numbers to make given totals.

VOCABULARY

Add; more; plus; make; sum; total; altogether; score; is the same as; equals; sign.

PLENARY

Discuss some of the answers. Encourage the children to explain the strategies they used.

RESOURCES

A set of Arrow cards for each child (photocopiable page 68); flip chart and pen; ready-prepared sheets of sums (see **Preparation**) pencils and paper.

PREPARATION

Either prepare some written questions of the type: $9 + 4 = \square$; $9 + \square = 13$; $\square + 4 = 13$, or find appropriate examples from your school resources. These questions should be differentiated for the more and less able children by difficulty. For the more able include some of the $\square + \triangle = \diamond$ type where they provide their own numbers.

LEARNING OUTCOMES

ORAL AND MENTAL STARTER

● Begin to know what each digit in a two-digit number represents. Partition a 'teens' number and begin to partition larger two-digit numbers into a multiple of 10 and ones (TU).

MAIN TEACHING ACTIVITY

● **Understand the operation of addition, and use the related vocabulary.**
● Begin to bridge through 10, and later 20, when adding a single-digit number.

VOCABULARY

Add; more; plus; make; sum; total; altogether; score; is the same as; equals; sign.

ORAL AND MENTAL STARTER

TEENS: Repeat this activity from Lesson 1, page 156.

MAIN TEACHING ACTIVITY

ADDING: Write $8 + 4 = \square$ on the flip chart, and ask the children to work out the answer mentally. Ask how they did this. Now write $8 + \square = 12$ and ask what the answer is, and how they worked this out. Repeat for $\square + 4 = 12$. Ask: *What is the link between these questions?* and encourage the children to explain. Now write $\square + \triangle = \diamond$ and ask for some suggestions for numbers to complete this.

Provide the prepared sheets of questions, and set a time limit of about 10 minutes.

DIFFERENTIATION

Less able: suggest that they think about number trios as they work. *Can you see the pattern?*

More able: challenge them to make up some questions of their own using $\square + \triangle = \diamond$, with two numbers written in but not the third. They should then swap these and solve them.

PLENARY

Discuss the work that the more able group has done as a challenge. Ask these children to give some examples and explain how they worked them out.

RESOURCES

A set of Addition 6 to 10 cards (photocopiable page 167); individual number lines 0–20 (page 18); sheets of subtraction sums of the variety $15 - 3 = \square$; $12 - \square = 9$; $\square - 5 = 14$.

PREPARATION

Find a source of written subtraction sums, differentiating according to children's needs. Make sure that the less able begin with examples that use numbers less than 10.

LEARNING OUTCOMES

ORAL AND MENTAL STARTER

● Begin to know addition facts for all pairs of numbers with a total up to at least 10, and the corresponding subtraction facts.

MAIN TEACHING ACTIVITY

● **Understand the operation of subtraction (as 'take away'), and use the related vocabulary.**

● Begin to use the − and = signs to record mental calculations in a number sentence, and to recognise the use of symbols such as □ or △ to stand for an unknown number.

● Use known number facts and place value to add or subtract a pair of numbers mentally within the range 0 to at least 10, then 0 to at least 20.

VOCABULARY
How many more to make…?; subtract; take away; minus; leave; how many are left/ left over?; How many are gone?; How much less is …?; How much fewer is … than …?; difference between; is the same as; equals; sign.

ORAL AND MENTAL STARTER

ADDITION AND SUBTRACTION TO 10: Repeat this activity from Lesson 5, page 159.

MAIN TEACHING ACTIVITY

SUBTRACTING: Write on the flip chart 15 − 3 = □ and ask children to solve this using their number line. Now write 15 − □ = 12, and ask for the answer. Repeat for □ − 3 = 12. Ask children to look at these three sums and say what they notice.

Now ask the children, individually, to complete the sheets of written subtraction sums from school resources.

DIFFERENTIATION

Less able: provide examples initially which involve numbers less than 10.

More able: challenge them to find as many answers as they can to □ − △ = 13.

PLENARY

Repeat 'Addition and subtraction to 10' from the **Oral and mental starter** of this lesson.

LESSON 13

Repeat Lesson 12, using different examples in the **Main teaching activity**, and encouraging children to use the number facts to 10 that they already know to help them subtract: for example, if 8 − 3 = 5, then 18 − 3 = 15.

In pairs, ask the children to sort a set of 0 to 20 numeral cards into two piles, one of 0 to 10, the other 11 to 20. Ask them to take turns to take one card from each pile and to write a subtraction sum. The child who draws the card completes the sum, deciding whether to use a number line or to work mentally, the partner checks the sum. For the less able, decide whether to limit this to just drawing two numeral cards from the 0 to 10 set. Challenge the more able to work mentally.

RESOURCES

Pencils and paper; number lines.

LEARNING OUTCOMES

ORAL AND MENTAL STARTER

● Describe and extend number sequences: **count on and back in ones from any small number and in tens from and back to zero;** count in twos from zero then one, and begin to recognise odd or even numbers to about 20 as 'every other number'; count in steps of 5 from zero to 20 or more, then back again; begin to count on in steps of 3 from zero.

MAIN TEACHING ACTIVITY

● **Use mental strategies to solve simple problems** set in 'real life' or money contexts, **using counting, addition, subtraction, doubling and halving, explaining methods and reasoning orally.**

● Recognise coins of different values. Find totals and change from up to 20p. Work out how to pay an exact sum using smaller coins.
● Choose and use appropriate number operations and mental strategies to solve problems.

VOCABULARY

Answer; right; wrong; What could we try next?; How did you work it out?; count out; share out; left; left over; number sentence; sign; operation; money; coin; penny; pence; pound; price; cost; buy; sell; spend; spent; pay; change; dear; costs more; cheap; costs less; cheaper; costs the same as; how much…?; how many…?; total.

ORAL AND MENTAL STARTER

COUNTING: Count in steps of 1 from zero, to 30 and back, then from any small number. Count in tens from zero to 100 and back. Count in twos from zero, then from one. Ask: *Is … odd/even?* Count in fives from zero to 20 or more and back again. Count in steps of 3 from zero.

MAIN TEACHING ACTIVITY

PROBLEMS: Explain that the purpose of the next two lessons is to find a solution to some problems. Begin by asking: *I am thinking of a number, then I subtract 3. The answer is 10. What is my number?* Ask the children to explain the strategies that they used to solve the problem. Compare strategies: *Did everyone use the same one? Which was best? Why?* Repeat this for other questions, choosing from the list below, and adapting these to make new problems as needed. Encourage the children to record in their own way and to explain their methods and reasoning orally.

1. I am thinking of two numbers which total 10. What might these numbers be? (Find at least three answers.)
2. I am thinking of two numbers which have a difference of 3. Which might these numbers be? (Find at least three answers.)
3. I am thinking of two numbers. One is five more than the other. What might these numbers be? (Find at least three answers.)
4. Polly has three coins which total 14p. Which coins does she have?
5. There are three marbles in one box, four in the next box, and five in the third. How many marbles are there altogether?
6. Jon ate three toffees, two chews and six mints. How many sweets did he eat altogether?
7. Rosie had 20p. She spent 8p. How much does she have left?
8. Mark buys a cake for 6p and some chocolate for 8p. How much does he spend? How much change does he get from 20p?
9. Sheena buys two cakes at 6p each. How much does that cost? Which two coins could she use to pay for the cakes?
10. Which costs more: two cakes at 5p each or a biscuit at 3p and an apple at 9p?
11. Half of the chocolates in this box of 12 are gone. How many are left?
12. How can I pay exactly 13p? Think of three different ways. Which way uses the least number of coins?

DIFFERENTIATION

Less able: for questions 1-3, encourage the children to work mentally.
More able: for question 1, extend to totals greater than 10.

PLENARY

Discuss the word problems which the children invented. Ask individuals to explain how they would solve them.

LESSON 15

Repeat Lesson 14, choosing different questions for the **Main teaching activity**.

Missing numbers

Write numbers that will fit in the gaps.

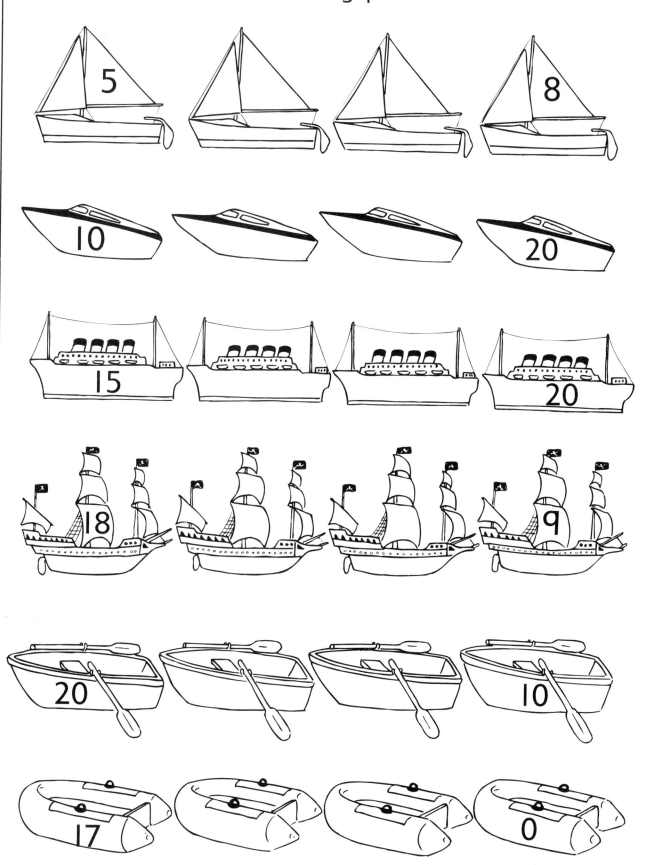

Race day

UNIT 2-4

Who is first? _____

Who is last? _____

Who is between the second and the fourth child? _____

Where is Ann?_____

Addition 6 to 10

Enlarge this sheet to A3 size on card, then cut up to make a set of addition cards.

✂

6 + 0	7 + 0	8 + 2
6 + 1	7 + 1	0 + 8
6 + 2	7 + 2	1 + 8
6 + 3	7 + 3	2 + 8
6 + 4	0 + 7	9 + 0
0 + 6	1 + 7	9 + 1
1 + 6	2 + 7	0 + 9
2 + 6	3 + 7	1 + 9
3 + 6	8 + 0	10 + 0
4 + 6	8 + 1	0 + 10

Name

Totals and change

Write the total.
Write the change from 20p.

Total	Change
p	p
p	p
p	p
p	p
p	p
p	p

UNITS 5-6

ORGANISATION (8 LESSONS)

	LEARNING OUTCOMES	ORAL AND MENTAL STARTER	MAIN TEACHING ACTIVITY	PLENARY
LESSON 1	• Understand and use the vocabulary related to capacity. **• Compare two capacities by direct comparison;** extend to more than two.	BRIDGING 10: Adding using two mental stages.	COMPARING CAPACITIES: Comparing by pouring; ordering containers by capacity.	Discussion of the children's work.
LESSON 2	• Understand and use the vocabulary related to capacity. Measure using uniform non-standard units (eg yoghurt pots) or standard units (eg litre jugs). **• Suggest suitable standard or uniform non-standard units and measuring equipment to estimate, then measure, a capacity,** recording estimates and measurements as 'about 3 beakers full'.	MAKE 10: Finding complements to 10.	MEASURING CAPACITIES: estimating and measuring using non-standard and standard units.	Discussion of the children's work.
LESSON 3	**• Use mental strategies to solve simple problems** set in measurement contexts, **using counting, addition, subtraction, doubling and halving, explaining methods and reasoning orally.**	BRIDGING 10.	PROBLEMS: Solving measurement problems using mental strategies.	Discussion of the children's work.
LESSON 4	• Use everyday language to describe position, direction and movement. • Talk about things that turn. Make whole turns and half turns. • Use one or more shapes to make, describe and continue repeating patterns...	BRIDGING 10.	POSITION, DIRECTION AND MOVEMENT: Developing understanding of the vocabulary through PE.	Discussion of the children's sequences of movements.
LESSON 5 +6	• Use everyday language to describe position, direction and movement. Talk about things that turn. Make whole turns and half turns.	DOUBLES AND NEAR DOUBLES: Developing rapid recall of doubles; mental calculation of near doubles.	POSITION, DIRECTION AND MOVEMENT: Developing vocabulary and understanding.	Discussion of journeys and movement.
LESSON 7	• Use one or more shapes to make, describe and continue repeating patterns...	BRIDGING 10.	REPEATING PATTERNS: Describing and making straight line patterns.	Discussion of the patterns.
LESSON 8	• Solve simple mathematical problems or puzzles; recognise and predict from simple patterns and relationships. Suggest extensions by asking 'What if...?' or 'What could I try next?'. • Investigate a general statement about familiar shapes by finding examples that satisfy it. • Explain methods and reasoning orally.	DOUBLES AND NEAR DOUBLES.	SHAPE PROBLEMS: Finding solutions to problems.	Discussion of solutions and strategies used.

Oral and mental skills   Begin to bridge through 10, when adding a single-digit number. Know by heart: **all pairs of numbers with a total of 10** (eg 3 + 7); addition doubles of all numbers to at least 5 (eg 4 + 4). Identify near doubles, using doubles already known (eg 6 + 5).

In Unit 5, Lessons 1, 2, 4 and 5 are shown in full. All others, including the three lessons in Unit 6, are extensions of what has already been taught, and are shown in numerical order.

RESOURCES

A set of numeral cards 0–20 (pages 14 and 15) for each child; flip chart and pen; containers of various shapes and sizes including cups, jugs, shampoo bottles; materials to fill these such as water, sand, rice, lentils; trays.

PREPARATION

Put a selection of containers in your teaching space, as well as a filling material, such as sand or water. For each group of children provide some containers and filling material. A tray on each table will help to contain any spilled material.

LEARNING OUTCOMES

ORAL AND MENTAL STARTER

● Begin to bridge through 10 when adding a single-digit number.

MAIN TEACHING ACTIVITY

● Understand and use the vocabulary related to capacity.
● **Compare two capacities by direct comparison;** extend to more than two.

VOCABULARY

Full; half full; empty; holds; container.

ORAL AND MENTAL STARTER

BRIDGING 10: Remind children of the strategy for adding two numbers whose answer will cross 10: $6 + 8 = 6 + 4 + 4 = 10 + 4 = 14$. Ask further similar questions, each child holds up a numeral card in response. After each question ask children how they worked it out: $5 + 9$; $4 + 8$; $9 + 7$….

MAIN TEACHING ACTIVITY

COMPARING CAPACITIES: Choose two differently-sized and shaped containers and ask: *Which do you think will hold more? How shall we find out?* Ask a child to fill one container, then pour from that to the other. Ask: *Which one holds more? How do we know?* Encourage the children to explain, using vocabulary such as full, half full, and holds. On the flip chart record the results, for example:
● The shampoo bottle holds more than the cup.
　Now put another container with these two and ask: *Which holds most/least?* Encourage the children to suggest how to find out, then check by filling and pouring. On the flip chart record:
● The shampoo bottle holds most.
● The teapot holds more than the cup.
● The cup holds least.
　Ask the children, in their groups, to choose two containers and find which holds more and which holds less. When they have done this, they can choose three or more containers and order them from 'holds most' to 'holds least'.

DIFFERENTIATION

Less able: encourage them to concentrate on two containers and order these, before adding one more.
More able: encourage them to order five containers by capacity.

PLENARY

Ask a group of children to explain their results. Encourage them to use the vocabulary of capacity while doing so.

RESOURCES

Number fan for each child (page 17); a set of 'Make ten cards' from photocopiable page 114; flip chart and pen; recording sheets; containers of various shapes and sizes including cups, jugs, shampoo bottles, buckets, bowls; filling materials such as water, sand, rice, lentils; egg cups, yoghurt pots, teapots, scoops and spoons.

PREPARATION

Put a jug of water and some identical cups in your teaching space. Prepare a recording sheet on the flip chart with columns for estimates and measures. Make some similar recording sheets for the children to use, one for each group. Leave one jug on each table.

How much does the jug hold?		
I used	I guessed	I counted
cups	5 cups	6 cups
yoghurt pots		

LEARNING OUTCOMES

ORAL AND MENTAL STARTER
● **Know by heart all pairs of numbers with a total of 10** (eg 3 + 7).

MAIN TEACHING ACTIVITY
● Understand and use the vocabulary related to capacity.
Measure using uniform non-standard units (eg yoghurt pots) or standard units (eg litre jugs).
● **Suggest suitable standard or uniform non-standard units and measuring equipment to estimate, then measure, a capacity,** recording estimates and measurements as 'about 3 beakers full'.

VOCABULARY

Full; half full; empty; holds; container.

ORAL AND MENTAL STARTER

MAKE 10: Explain that you will hold up a card with a number sentence on it which totals 10, but has one number missing; ask the children to hold up the blade of their fan which has the missing number on it. Encourage them to work as quickly as possible, so that they have to recall these number facts rapidly.

MAIN TEACHING ACTIVITY

MEASURING CAPACITIES: Hold the jug of water and ask: *How many cups do you think this jug will fill?* On the flip chart write in the estimate, then ask a child to fill some cups. Discuss what 'full' means: filling a bucket with sand means filling it to the brim; but filling a cup with tea means filling it so that it can still be carried safely. Write on the flip chart the results of the pouring.

Explain that, in their groups, you would like the children to find out how much their jug holds. Ask them to estimate, then check using cups, yoghurt pots and so on, and to record both estimate and measure on the recording sheet.

DIFFERENTIATION

Less able: ensure that the count of how many cups the jug will fill is well within the children's counting range.
More able: provide a larger container, such as a bucket, and a selection of measuring devices, including egg cups, bottles, yoghurt pots, beach buckets. Ask the children to decide which containers they would like to use, and ask for reasons for their choice.

PLENARY

Discuss children's results. Ask questions such as: *What could be measured using egg cups, cups, teapots, teaspoons...*

RESOURCES	Photocopiable page 175 (How much will it hold?); A3 enlargement of 'How much will it hold?'; flip chart and pen; numeral cards 0 to 20.
LEARNING OUTCOMES	**ORAL AND MENTAL STARTER** ● Begin to bridge through 10 when adding a single-digit number. **MAIN TEACHING ACTIVITY** ● **Use mental strategies to solve simple problems** set in measurement contexts, **using counting, addition, subtraction, doubling and halving, explaining methods and reasoning orally.**
ORAL AND MENTAL STARTER	BRIDGING 10: Repeat this activity from Lesson 1, page 156.
MAIN TEACHING ACTIVITY	PROBLEMS: Ask: *A full jug holds six cups; how much do two full jugs hold?* Ask children to explain how they worked it out, and write the answer as a number sentence: 6 + 6 = 12. Repeat for other problems, such as: *This jug holds five cups, and that one holds seven cups. How many cupfuls altogether?* Show the enlargement of 'How much will it hold?' and ask children to answer the questions on their own copies, writing a number sentence using + or − and =.
DIFFERENTIATION	Less able: work with this group, explaining each question. More able: challenge the children to write their own capacity question for the sum 9 + 8 = 17.
PLENARY	Discuss children's answers, asking for the mental strategies used.

RESOURCES
A set of numeral cards 0 to 20 (pages 14 and 15) for each child; PE apparatus such as ropes, benches, climbing frame and mats; time and space in the school hall!

PREPARATION
You will need to organise a PE session of about 30 minutes for the main teaching activity.

VOCABULARY

Position; over; under; underneath; above; below; top; bottom; side; on; in; outside; inside; around; in front; behind; front; back; before; after; beside; next to; opposite; apart; between; middle; edge; centre; corner; direction; journey; left; right; up; down; forwards; backwards; sideways; across; next to; close; far; along; through; to; from; towards; away from; movement; slide; roll; turn; whole turn; half turn; stretch; bend.

LEARNING OUTCOMES

ORAL AND MENTAL STARTER
Begin to bridge through 10 when adding a single-digit number.

MAIN TEACHING ACTIVITY
● Use everyday language to describe position, direction and movement. Talk about things that turn. Make whole turns and half turns.
● Use one or more shapes to make, describe and continue repeating patterns...

ORAL AND MENTAL STARTER

BRIDGING 10: Repeat this activity from Lesson 1, page 170.

MAIN TEACHING ACTIVITY

POSITION, DIRECTION AND MOVEMENT: During the PE 'warm up', ask the children to run around, then on a signal from you:
● stand in front of, behind, beside, opposite a partner;
● change direction and move forwards, backwards, sideways;
● change direction and turn right or left;
● stand still, facing towards the door, away from the window.
When the PE apparatus is in place, ask the children to follow your direction instructions, such as: *Move upwards, downwards, towards the window, away from the door, across the wall bars, through the gaps in the wall bars, along the top of the bench.* Ask the children to take turns to give instructions to their partners, using the language of direction.

For movement, ask them to: slide down the bench, roll over on the mat, turn towards the window, move in a straight line, move in a circle, turn on the spot, make a full turn, make a half turn to the right, two whole turns to your left, and so on.

Encourage individual children to demonstrate their moves and the other children to describe what they saw, using the vocabulary of position, direction and movement.

DIFFERENTIATION

Less able: if they find the vocabulary difficult to understand, demonstrate the position, direction or movements to them so that they make sense of the movement and language. More able: challenge them to make up a sequence of movements which involve position, direction and movement, then to demonstrate it and explain, using the correct vocabulary, what is happening.

PLENARY

Ask more able children to demonstrate their sequence and to explain what is happening.

RESOURCES

Scissors; teaching clock; book; cube; sheets of paper; a large picture showing items which are easy to distinguish (perhaps from a mathematics scheme 'big book'); shape tiles; Roamer; basket containing 3-D shapes including cubes, cuboids, pyramids, cylinders, cones, spheres, and items such as balls and boxes; shape tiles; dolls house and furniture; paper and pencils; flip chart; a set of numeral cards 0 to 20 for each child (pages 14 and 15).

PREPARATION

Pin the 'big book' picture to the flip chart.

LEARNING OUTCOMES

ORAL AND MENTAL STARTER
● **Know by heart:** addition doubles of all numbers to at least 5 (eg 4 + 4).
● Identify near doubles, using doubles already known (eg 6 + 5).

MAIN TEACHING ACTIVITY
● Use everyday language to describe position, direction and movement.
● Talk about things that turn. Make whole turns and half turns.

ORAL AND MENTAL STARTER

DOUBLES AND NEAR DOUBLES: Ask the children to hold up the appropriate numeral card to answer doubles and near doubles questions, such as: *What is double 4; 6 + 5; 3 + 3; 6 + 7...?* Discuss how children worked out the near doubles.

MAIN TEACHING ACTIVITY

POSITION, DIRECTION AND MOVEMENT: Ask the children questions related to things in the classroom, such as:
● *Name something which is above the sink, behind the cupboard, between the window and the door,....*
● *Where is the .... in this picture? (above the ...; below the ...; next to ...).*
● *Where is the cube on this sheet of paper? (in the middle, near the edge, at the top ...).*
Talk about things that turn about a point (spinning tops, taps, windmills, wheels, door handles, clock hands). Set the teaching clock to 5 o'clock and ask the children what time it shows. Then move the minute hand through a complete turn, and ask what time it is now. Move the hands through a half turn, and ask again what time the clock shows.

Talk about things that turn about a line (doors, book pages) and look at some examples. Explain to the children that there are a range of activities that they will be asked to do over this and the next lesson. Allocate each group to an activity chosen from this list.
1. Arrange the furniture in the dolls house. Talk about what you have done to others in your group. ('I put the cooker beside the fridge; the book on the table...').
2. Program Roamer to move from its spot on the floor to the cupboard, the door,...
3. Sort objects in the basket into: those that roll; those that slide; those that both roll and slide. Make a list of the results.
4. Find objects in the classroom that will roll, that will slide and that will both roll and slide. Make a list of the results.

VOCABULARY

Position; over; under; underneath; above; below; top; bottom; side; on; in; outside; inside; around; in front; behind; front; back; before; after; beside; next to; opposite; apart; between; middle; edge; centre; corner; direction; journey; left; right; up; down; forwards; backwards; sideways; across; next to; close; far; along; through; to; from; towards; away from; movement; slide; roll; turn; whole turn; half turn; stretch; bend.

DIFFERENTIATION

Less able: start with activity 1. Work with them as they carry out your instructions. Each time a piece of furniture is placed, ask them to explain what they have done.
More able: with activity 2, encourage them to record their instructions for moving Roamer so that others can follow them.

PLENARY

Talk about the journeys children make on their way home, describing left or right turns.

LESSON 6

Repeat Lesson 5. In the **Main teaching activity** ensure that children get a chance to do the activities they did not try in the previous lesson.

RESOURCES	Numeral cards 0 to 20 (pages 14 and 15); shape tiles; books.
LEARNING OUTCOMES	**ORAL AND MENTAL STARTER** ● Begin to bridge through 10 when adding a single-digit number. **MAIN TEACHING ACTIVITY** ● Use one or more shapes to make, describe and continue repeating patterns...
ORAL AND MENTAL STARTER	BRIDGING 10: Repeat this activity from Lesson 1, page 170.
MAIN TEACHING ACTIVITY	REPEATING PATTERNS: Make a repeating pattern with triangles and circles. Ask the children to describe what they see and to say what the next shape would be, and the next. Make a repeating pattern with three different tiles, such as circle, triangle, square, circle, triangle, square... and ask what the next shape would be. In pairs, one child makes a secret repeating pattern from a set of three shape tiles (using a book as a screen). The pattern is described to the partner, who then tries to make the same pattern. They compare to check that they have the same pattern, then swap roles.
DIFFERENTIATION	Less able: decide whether to limit the children to using just two different shape tiles to make their pattern. More able: suggest that they make more complex patterns, including using two of the same shape next to each other, but in different orientations.
PLENARY	Discuss some of the shape patterns made. Encourage children to describe them using the language of position, direction and movement.

RESOURCES	Numeral cards 0 to 10 (page 14); photocopiable page 176 (Shape problems); an A3 enlargement of page 176; shape tiles; assorted 3-D shapes; card; paper; scissors; coloured crayons; pencils; flip chart, pen.
LEARNING OUTCOMES	**ORAL AND MENTAL STARTER** ● **Know by heart:** addition doubles of all numbers to at least 5. ● Identify near doubles, using doubles already known (eg 6 + 5). **MAIN TEACHING ACTIVITY** ● Solve simple mathematical problems or puzzles; recognise and predict from simple patterns and relationships. Suggest extensions by asking 'What if...?' or 'What could I try next?'. Investigate a general statement about familiar shapes by finding examples that satisfy it. Explain methods and reasoning orally.
ORAL AND MENTAL STARTER	DOUBLES AND NEAR DOUBLES: Repeat the activity from Lesson 5, p173.
MAIN TEACHING ACTIVITY	SHAPE PROBLEMS: Pin the A3 copy of 'Shape problems' to the flip chart, and explain the problems. Remind the children that shapes can be turned to make them fit into spaces. Encourage everyone to try the problems.
DIFFERENTIATION	Less able: provide shape tiles so they do not have to cut out their own. More able: encourage them to make up their own shape problem, write it on the back of the sheet, then swap with a partner to try out.
PLENARY	Discuss the results. Encourage the children to talk about what they tried, and to suggest to each other what they could try next.

How much will it hold?

The jug fills 5 cups.
How many cups will 2 jugs fill? _____

 Holds 9 cups    Holds 6 cups

How many cups will they fill in total? _____

The bucket holds 16 litres of water.
How much water is there in each bowl? _____

 Holds 20 cups    Holds 15 cups

How much more does the bottle hold than the jug? _____

Name

Shape problems

Cut out these shapes.

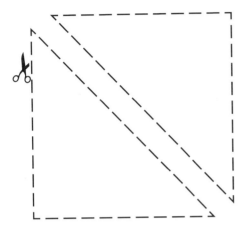

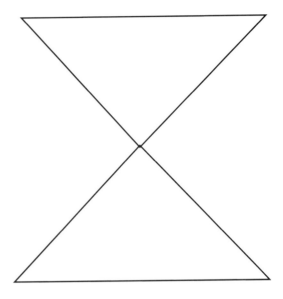

Make these shapes.

Cut out these shapes.

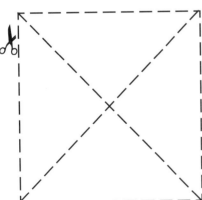

Make some new shapes with the four triangles.
Sketch your shapes on the back of this sheet.

UNIT 7: Assess & Review

ASSESSMENT AND REVIEW

Choose from these activities. During the group activities, some of the children can complete assessment worksheets 5A and 5B which assess their skills in ordering numbers to 20, addition and subtraction, and solving problems using mental strategies, while others work with you on practical tasks. The specific assessment criteria for the assessment sheets can be found at the bottom of each sheet.

RESOURCES

A number fan for each child (page 17); a set of 'Make ten cards' from photocopiable page 114; objects for counting such as cubes, straws, buttons...; washing line and pegs; numeral cards 0 to 20 (pages 14 and 15); a range of containers.

ORAL AND MENTAL STARTER

ASSESSMENT

Do the children:

● **Know by heart all pairs of numbers with a total of 10?**
● **Within the range 0 to 30, say the number that is 1 or 10 more or less than any given number?**

NUMBER FACTS: Hold up the 'Make ten' cards, one at a time, and ask children to give answers by showing a blade of their number fan. Encourage the children to respond quickly. Check to see who knows all the facts, and who needs more practice.

MORE OR LESS: Repeat the **Oral and mental starter**, Lesson 3, Units 2 to 4, including some examples for 1 more and 1 less.

GROUP ACTIVITIES

ASSESSMENT

Can the children:

● **Count reliably at least 20 objects?**
● **Compare two capacities by direct comparison?**
● **Suggest suitable standard or uniform non-standard units and measuring equipment to estimate, then measure, a capacity?**

COUNTING OBJECTS: Ask the children to count out a given number of objects. Then ask them to arrange them in a circle, rectangular array, straight line,... and to say, without recounting them, how many there are after each arrangement. Check that they conserve the quantity.

CAPACITY: Ask children to choose two containers, say which they think will hold more, then check by pouring. When they are confident with this decide whether to ask them to order three containers for capacity. Ask them to choose units to estimate, then measure, the capacity of a particular container. Check that they refer to the measure as, for example 'about 3 cupfuls'. Ask the children what units they would use to measure a cup, a teapot, a bucket or a shampoo bottle. Ask them to explain their choice and check that it is reasonable.

Assessment 5A

Write three numbers greater than 15.

Write three numbers less than 15.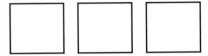

Write the answers to these sums.

9 + 6 = ☐   19 − ☐ = 5

☐ − 6 = 9   17 + 4 = ☐

12 + 8 = ☐   13 + 8 = ☐

☐ − 8 = 12   19 + 8 = ☐

☐ + 5 = 19   14 + 9 = ☐

● Read, write and order numbers from 0 to at least 20; understand and use the vocabulary of comparing and ordering these numbers.
● Understand the operation of addition and of subtraction (as 'take away' or 'difference'), and use the related vocabulary.

Assessment 5B

The classroom is about 14 canes long.
The hall is about 18 canes long.
How much longer is the hall?

□ canes

Sarah has 20p.
She buys a lolly for 9p and a chew for 5p.
How much does she spend?

□ p

How much change does she have? □ p

Johal has 12 marbles.
He gives half to Bina.
How many marbles has Bina? □

Peter has 19 conkers.
Mark has 12 conkers.

Who has more? _____

How many more? □

● Use mental strategies to solve simple problems using counting, addition, subtraction, doubling and halving, explaining methods and reasoning orally.

UNIT 8

ORGANISATION (5 LESSONS)

	LEARNING OUTCOMES	ORAL & MENTAL STARTER	MAIN TEACHING ACTIVITY	PLENARY
LESSON 1	● Describe and extend number sequences: **count on and back in ones from any small number, and in tens from and back to zero.**	MAKE 10: Finding the complements to 10.	COUNTING: Exploring counting patterns for ones and tens.	Discussion of the children's work.
LESSON 2	● Describe and extend number sequences: count in twos from zero, then one, and begin to recognise odd or even numbers to about 20 as 'every other number'; count in steps of 5 from zero to 20 or more, then back again; begin to count on in steps of 3 from zero.	COUNTING IN ONES AND TENS: Counting practice.	COUNTING IN TWOS, FIVES AND THREES: Exploring counting patterns.	Discussion of the children's work.
LESSON 3	● Describe and extend number sequences: **count on and back in ones from any small number, and in tens from and back to zero;** count in twos from zero, then one, and begin to recognise odd or even numbers to about 20 as 'every other number'; count in steps of 5 from zero to 20 or more, then back again; begin to count on in steps of 3 from zero.	COUNTING: Practising counting in ones, twos, threes, fives and tens.	CREATING NUMBER PATTERNS: Searching for number patterns.	Discussion of the patterns that children produced.
LESSON 4 +5	● Solve simple mathematical problems or puzzles, recognise and predict from simple patterns and relationships. Suggest extensions by asking 'What if...?' or 'What could I try next?'. ● Investigate a general statement about familiar numbers by finding examples that satisfy it. ● Explain methods and reasoning orally.	COUNTING.	REASONING ABOUT NUMBERS: Solving problems and puzzles; investigating general statements about numbers.	Discussion of the children's solutions.

In Unit 8, Lessons 1, 2, and 4 are shown in full. Lessons 3 and 5 are extensions of what has already been taught and are shown in numerical order.

RESOURCES

For each child: a number fan (page 17), a hundred square (photocopiable page 89), some prepared number line strips (see below); a set of 'Make ten cards' from photocopiable page 114; flip chart and pen; paper and pencils.

PREPARATION

Make and copy a few number lines with gaps for children to write in the missing numbers. The Number lines sheet (page 18) could be used or adapted for this. Depending on the children's ability (see 'Differentiation'), you could include number sequences such as:

● 9   10   11   ☐   ☐   ☐   ☐   16   17
● 20   19   18   ☐   ☐   15   14   ☐   ☐   ☐   10   9
● 3   13   23   ☐   ☐   ☐   ☐   ☐   ☐   93
● 95   85   75   ☐   ☐   ☐   ☐   ☐   ☐   ☐

VOCABULARY

Number, zero, one, two, three...to 20 and beyond; zero, 10, 20,....to one hundred; count; count up to; count on (from/to); count back (from/to); count in ones, tens...; more; less; how many times; pattern; pair.

LEARNING OUTCOMES

ORAL AND MENTAL STARTER

Know by heart: **all pairs of numbers with a total of 10** (eg 3 + 7).

MAIN TEACHING ACTIVITY

● Describe and extend number sequences: **count on and back in ones from any small number, and in tens from and back to zero.**

ORAL AND MENTAL STARTER

MAKE 10: Hold up a card and ask children to show complements to 10 as quickly as possible with their number fan.

MAIN TEACHING ACTIVITY

COUNTING: Count around the class in ones, from and back to zero, then from any small number. On the flip chart, write: 11, 10, 9, 8, and ask: *What is the next number in this pattern? And the next?* Invite a child to write in the missing numbers. Count around the class, starting at 5. Ask: *Who will say eleven? Fifteen?* Count back from 10 to 6 and ask: *How many did you count?* Now count in tens from zero to one hundred and back again. Ask the children to use their hundred square to answer questions such as:
● *Count on from 30; from 3, from 7.*
● *Count back in tens from 80, from 63, from 56.*
● *Count in tens from zero until I say stop. I will count the tens on my fingers. How many tens did you count?*
● *Count on from 30 for 6 tens; back from 90 for 5 tens.*
● *Show me the tens with your fingers as you count: 3 tens from 50; back 5 tens from 80.*
● *Count around the circle from Nandi; who will say 90?*
● *Describe this pattern: 80, 70, 60, 50 What are the next three numbers?*
Give each child some incomplete number lines (see 'Preparation'). Ask them to fill in the missing numbers. Point out that they can use their hundred squares to help them with numbers larger than 30.

DIFFERENTIATION

Less able: decide whether to limit the work to patterns which count in ones.
More able: challenge them to write the tens pattern on a sheet of paper, starting from 95 and counting backwards.

PLENARY

Discuss the children's work. Write the incomplete number lines on the board and ask individual children to come up and complete them.

RESOURCES

Flip chart and pen; a copy of photocopiable page 184 (Number tracks) for each child; an A3 enlargement of 'Number tracks'; pencils and paper.

PREPARATION

Make an A3 enlargement of 'Number tracks'.

LEARNING OUTCOMES

ORAL AND MENTAL STARTER

● Describe and extend number sequences: **count on and back in ones from any small number, and in tens from and back to zero.**

MAIN TEACHING ACTIVITY

● Describe and extend number sequences: count in twos from zero, then one, and begin to recognise odd or even numbers to about 20 as 'every other number'; count in steps of 5 from zero to 20 or more, then back again; begin to count on in steps of 3 from zero.

VOCABULARY

Number, zero, one, two, three... to 20 and beyond; zero, 10, 20,....to one hundred; count; count up to; count on (from, to); count back (from, to); count in ones, twos..., tens...; more; less; odd; even; every other; how many times; pattern; pair.

ORAL AND MENTAL STARTER

COUNTING IN ONES AND TENS: Choose from the counting activities in the **Main teaching activity** of Lesson 1. Encourage the children to count quickly and accurately.

MAIN TEACHING ACTIVITY

COUNTING IN TWOS, FIVES AND THREES: Count in twos from zero to about 20, then back again. Count in twos starting from 1. Ask: *0, 2, 4, 6, 8... what comes next? 15, 13, 11, ... what comes next?* Each time write the pattern on the flip chart and invite a child to put in the next two or three numbers. Ask: *Are these odd/even numbers? How do you know?* Provide each child with a number line and ask them to use it to help them answer some questions: *Hop in steps of five from zero to at least 20 and back again along the line. Zero, five, 10, fifteen... what comes next? 25, 20, fifteen... what comes next?*

Write the patterns on the flip chart and ask a child to write in the next two numbers in the pattern. *Hop in steps of three along the number line. What comes next: three, six, nine...?* Ask the children to finish the number patterns on photocopiable page 184 (Number tracks).

DIFFERENTIATION

Less able: decide whether to ask them to just complete the patterns for twos.
More able: encourage the children to extend their patterns beyond those on the sheet by writing in more numbers.

PLENARY

Pin the A3 enlargement of 'Number tracks' to the flip chart. Ask individual children to complete a pattern and explain how they worked it out.

RESOURCES	Squared paper; pencils and paper; flip chart and pen; hundred squares (page 89).
LEARNING OUTCOMES	**ORAL AND MENTAL STARTER/MAIN TEACHING ACTIVITY** ● Describe and extend number sequences: **count on and back in ones from any small number, and in tens from and back to zero;** count in twos from zero, then one, and begin to recognise odd or even numbers to about 20 as 'every other number'; count in steps of 5 from zero to 20 or more, then back again; begin to count on in steps of 3 from zero.
ORAL AND MENTAL STARTER	COUNTING: practise counting in ones, twos, threes, fives and tens.
MAIN TEACHING ACTIVITY	CREATING NUMBER PATTERNS: Ask the children to help you to write a number pattern on the flip chart which includes the number 4. Ask for different ideas. (2, 4, 6, 8...; 1, 2, 3, 4...; 4, 14, 24,...). The children can use their hundred squares to help them. Then ask the children to make up patterns which include the number 6, or 9..; which only has even/odd numbers in it; which does not have any tens.... They write their patterns on the squared paper.
DIFFERENTIATION	Less able: suggest that the children look at patterns with numbers to 20 to begin with. More able: encourage the children to extend their patterns using numbers to one hundred.
PLENARY	Ask for examples of patterns. Children can write their patterns on the flip chart. Encourage the children to compare and check the patterns.

RESOURCES

Coins; paper and pencils; flip chart and pen.

LEARNING OUTCOMES

ORAL AND MENTAL STARTER

● Describe and extend number sequences: **count on and back in ones from any small number, and in tens from and back to zero;** count in twos from zero, then one, and begin to recognise odd or even numbers to about 20 as 'every other number'; count in steps of 5 from zero to 20 or more, then back again; begin to count on in steps of 3 from zero.

MAIN TEACHING ACTIVITY

● Solve simple mathematical problems or puzzles, recognise and predict from simple patterns and relationships. Suggest extensions by asking 'What if...?' or 'What could I try next?'.
● Investigate a general statement about familiar numbers by finding examples that satisfy it.
● Explain methods and reasoning orally.

VOCABULARY

Pattern; puzzle; answer; right; wrong; What could we try next?; How did you work it out?; count out; share out; left; left over; number sentence; sign; operation.

ORAL AND MENTAL STARTER

COUNTING: Repeat this activity from Lesson 3, page 182.

MAIN TEACHING ACTIVITY

REASONING ABOUT NUMBERS: Say: *I can make six by adding two numbers. How can I do this?* Encourage the children to make suggestions, and record these on the flip chart, with the number sentences ordered:

$0 + 6 = 6$
$1 + 5 = 6$
$2 + 4 = 6$
$3 + 3 = 6$

Explain that you will set some challenges and that you would like the children to find ways of solving these. Questions 1 to 4 encourage the investigation of general statements; questions 5 to 8 encourage the solving of puzzles and problems. Choose from the following:

1. I can pay for anything from 1p to 5p if I have two 2p coins and one 1p coin (eg 3p = 1p + 2p).
2. When I add 10 to a number the units stay the same (eg 3 + 10 = 13).
3. I can add numbers in any order and the answer is the same (eg 3 + 10 = 10 + 3).
4. I can make four different numbers with two different digits (eg with 2 and 3: 22, 23, 32 and 33).
5. (See figure below.) Put 1, 2, or 3 in each circle so that each side adds up to 5. You can use each number as often as you like. Find different ways of doing this.
6. Write as many different ways as you can of making the number 20.
7. John has three more felt pens than Tom. How many could each boy have?
8. Mark adds three numbers and makes a total of 15. What could the three numbers be?

DIFFERENTIATION

Less able: ask the children to begin with question 1, then try 2 and 5.
More able: Questions 7 and 8 are more challenging.

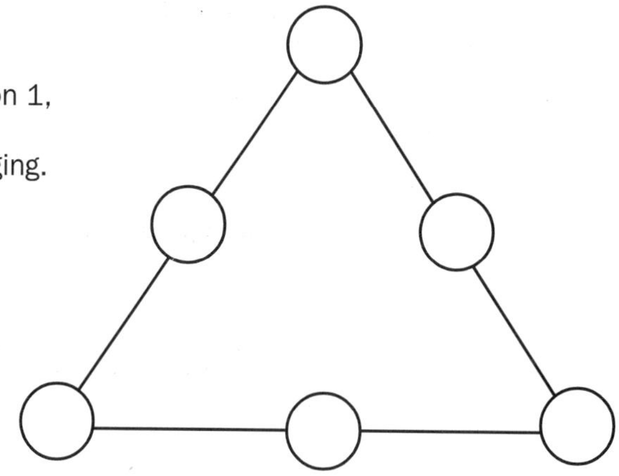

PLENARY

Discuss the strategies that children used to solve the problems.

LESSON 5

Repeat Lesson 4, choosing different questions from the **Main teaching activity**.

Name

Number tracks

Write in the missing numbers.

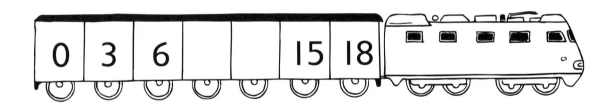

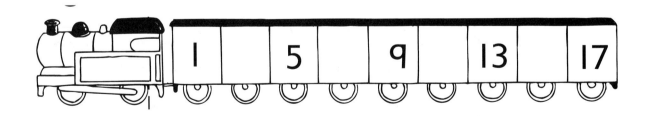

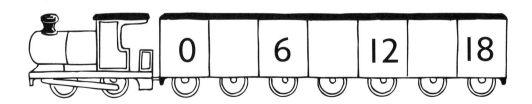

UNITS 9–11

ORGANISATION (15 LESSONS)

	LEARNING OUTCOMES	ORAL & MENTAL STARTER	MAIN TEACHING ACTIVITY	PLENARY
LESSON 1 +2	• Begin to know what each digit in a two-digit number represents. Partition a 'teens' number and begin to partition larger two-digit numbers into a multiple of 10 and ones (TU). • **Understand and use the vocabulary of comparing and ordering numbers,** including ordinal numbers to at least 20. • Use the = sign to represent equality. • Compare two familiar numbers, say which is more or less, and give a number which lies between them.	COUNT IN ONES AND TENS: Practising counting in ones and tens.	TENS AND UNITS: Using arrow cards and a paper abacus to show tens and units; comparing and ordering two-digit numbers.	Discussion of the children's work; searching for a pattern.
LESSON 3	• Understand and use the vocabulary of estimation. • Give a sensible estimate of a number of objects that can be checked by counting (eg up to about 30 objects).	BRIDGING THROUGH 10:Using two stages to add mentally.	ESTIMATING: Estimating and counting how many in sets of between 15 and 30 objects; using the vocabulary of estimation.	Checking results.
LESSON 4 +5	• **Within the range 0 to 30, say the number that is 1 or 10 more or less than any given number.** • **Order numbers to at least 20,** and position them on a number track.	COUNTING IN ONES AND TENS.	ORDERING NUMBERS: Saying one and 10 more and less than a number; ordering randomly-chosen numbers on.	OUT OF ORDER: Challenging all the children to put numerals in order.
LESSON 6 +7	• **Understand the operation of addition, and of subtraction (as 'take away', 'difference',** and 'how many more to make') **and use the related vocabulary.** • Use known number facts and place value to add or subtract a pair of numbers mentally within the range 0 to at least 10, then 0 to at least 20.	ADDITION TO 10: Rapid recall of number facts.	ADDING AND SUBTRACTING: Using known number facts to 10 to add or subtract a single-digit number to or from a 'teens' number, without crossing 10 or 20.	Discussion of the children's work.
LESSON 8 +9	• **Understand the operation of addition, and use the related vocabulary.** • Begin to bridge through 10, and later 20, when adding a single-digit number.	ADDITION TO 10.	BRIDGING 10 AND 20: Using two steps to add, bridging 10 or 20.	Discussion of the children's work.
LESSON 10	• **Understand the operation of addition, and use the related vocabulary.** • Use known number facts and place value to add a pair of numbers mentally within the range 0 to at least 10, then 0 to at least 20.	COUNTING IN FIVES AND THREES: Counting patterns.	ADDING TO TEENS: Adding a 'teen' number to a single-digit number, using mental methods without crossing the tens.	Discussion of the children's work.

cont...

cont...

LESSON 11 +12	• Recognise coins of different values. • Find totals and change from up to 20p. • Work out how to pay an exact sum using smaller coins.	COUNTING IN FIVES AND THREES.	BUYING AND SELLING: Totalling prices and giving change in practical activities using mental strategies.	Using specific examples of totalling and giving change, discussing strategies used.
LESSON 13 +14	• **Use mental strategies to solve simple problems** set in 'real life' or money contexts, **using counting, addition, subtraction, doubling and halving, explaining methods and reasoning orally.** • Choose and use appropriate number operations and mental strategies to solve problems.	DOUBLING AND HALVING: Identifying near doubles, and halves, from doubles already known.	REAL LIFE AND MONEY PROBLEMS: Solving problems using mental strategies. Presented orally to groups.	Discussion of the solutions to problems, and the mental strategies used.
LESSON 15	• **Use mental strategies to solve simple problems** set in 'real life' or money contexts, **using counting, addition, subtraction, doubling and halving, explaining methods and reasoning orally.** • Choose and use appropriate number operations and mental strategies to solve problems.	DOUBLING AND HALVING: Identifying near doubles, and halves, from doubles already known.	REAL LIFE AND MONEY PROBLEMS: Solving problems using mental strategies. Presented in writing.	Discussion of the solutions to problems, and the mental strategies used.

ORAL AND MENTAL SKILLS   Describe and extend number sequences: **count on and back in ones from any small number, and in tens from and back to zero;** count in steps of 5 from zero to 20 or more, then back again; begin to count on in steps of 3 from zero. Begin to bridge through 10 when adding a single-digit number. Begin to know addition facts for all pairs of numbers with a total up to at least 10, and the corresponding subtraction facts. **Know by heart:** addition doubles of all numbers to at least 5 (eg 4 + 4). Identify near doubles, using doubles already known (eg 6 + 5).

In Unit 9, Lessons 1, 3 and 4 are shown in full. Lessons 2 and 5 are extensions of what has already been taught and follow Lessons 1 and 4, respectively. In Unit 10, Lessons 6, 8 and 10 are shown in full, as are Lessons 11 and 13 in Unit 11. All other lessons are shown in numerical order.

RESOURCES

Set of Arrow cards for each child (photocopiable page 68); paper abacus for each child (see page 59); counters; flip chart and pen; copies of photocopiable page 195 (Comparing numbers) and an A3 enlargement of this; counting stick (see Introduction, page 9); pencils and paper.

PREPARATION

Make the required photocopies and an A3 enlargement of 'Comparing numbers' for Lesson 2.

LEARNING OUTCOMES

ORAL AND MENTAL STARTER
● Describe and extend number sequences: **count on and back in ones from any small number, and in tens from and back to zero.**

MAIN TEACHING ACTIVITY
● Begin to know what each digit in a two-digit number represents. Partition a 'teens' number and begin to partition larger two-digit numbers into a multiple of 10 and ones (TU).
● **Understand and use the vocabulary of comparing and ordering numbers,** including ordinal numbers to at least 20.
● Use the = sign to represent equality.
● Compare two familiar numbers, say which is more or less, and give a number which lies between them.

VOCABULARY

Units; ones; tens; exchange; digit; 'teens' number; the same number as; as many as; equal to.

COUNT IN ONES AND TENS: Point to one end of the counting stick. Name it zero and the other end 10, then count along the stick forwards and backwards. Point to any space on the stick and ask: *What number is that?* Then label one end 3 and the other 13, and repeat. Repeat for other numbers. Finally name one end zero and the other end 100, and count forwards and backwards in tens. Point to any space and ask: *What number is that?*

MAIN TEACHING ACTIVITY

TENS AND UNITS: Ask the children to spread out their Arrow cards so that they have the tens and the units cards in order. Remind them of how they can put two cards together to make a two-digit number:

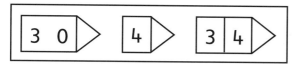

Ask the children to show you 17, 14, 19... and to say how many tens and how many units. Extend to larger two-digit numbers such as 23, 25, 32, 34,... and ask each time how many tens and how many units. Write on the flip chart: 34 = ☐ tens and ☐ units and invite a child to write in how many tens and units. Repeat for other numbers. Then reverse the process, by writing 2 tens and 7 units = ☐, and repeat for other numbers. Say: *Tell me a number between 14 and 19; between 23 and 28; between 32 and 36.* Ask the children to place counters onto their paper abacus to represent the numbers that you say: 12; 16; 19; 20; 25; 34; 38; 40; 42... Each time ask: *How many tens? How many units?*

Using just four counters on their abacus each time, the children should make all possible numbers between 4 and 40 and record them in order (4; 13; 22; 31; 40); then repeat with five counters (5; 14; 23; 32; 41; 50); then with six counters. (6; 15; 24; 33; 42; 51; 60).

DIFFERENTIATION

Less able: ask them to begin with just two counters (2; 11; 20), then 3 (3; 12; 21; 30) before they tackle four counters.
More able: challenge them to use seven counters, even eight. Can they see a pattern?

PLENARY

Ask individual children to write up their results on the flip chart, looking for a pattern.

LESSON 2

Repeat Lesson 1, but in the **Main teaching activity**, choose different two-digit numbers. For individual work, ask the children to complete 'Comparing numbers' (photocopiable page 195). Review the work using an A3 version during the Plenary session.

RESOURCES

Collections for estimating, then checking by counting, such as counters, pennies, small toys in a basket, shells in a dish or marbles in a jar; flip chart and pen; a pile of notebooks and some pencils (somewhere between 20 and 30, but not the same number of each); recording tables (see **Preparation**, below); pencils and paper.

PREPARATION

Put the collections into transparent containers, so that there are between 15 and about 30 objects for estimating, then counting, in each set. Prepare some simple recording tables with headings of: 'The set of'; 'My estimate'; 'I counted'. This can be done using the 'tables' option in a word-processing package. Three will fit to a page and, once printed, these can be cut into strips so each child can have his or her own copy.

LEARNING OUTCOMES
ORAL AND MENTAL STARTER
● Begin to bridge through 10 when adding a single-digit number.

MAIN TEACHING ACTIVITY
● Understand and use the vocabulary of estimation.
● Give a sensible estimate of a number of objects that can be checked by counting (eg up to about 30 objects).

VOCABULARY

Guess; how many; estimate; nearly; roughly; close to; about the same as; just over; just under; too many; too few; enough; not enough.

ORAL AND MENTAL STARTER

BRIDGING THROUGH 10: Remind children of the strategy: 6 + 8 = 6 + 4 + 4 = 10 + 4 = 14. Ask addition questions, and encourage them to break the sum down into the two stages: 5 + 7; 8 + 6; 4 + 9… For each response ask: *How did you work it out?*

MAIN TEACHING ACTIVITY

ESTIMATING: Hold up a jar with some small items in it. Ask: *How many do you think are in here? Can you make a good guess?* Ask for some estimates, write them on the flip chart, then ask a child to count the objects. Ask: *Is this about right?* and encourage the children to use the vocabulary of estimation in their responses, such as: 'There were nearly the same as my guess.' or 'My estimate was not enough.'. Show the pile of notebooks and the pencils. Ask: *Are there enough pencils for these notebooks?* then invite one child to check by counting.

The set of	My estimate	I counted
counters	25	30

Now ask the children, working in their groups, to take each collection in turn, estimate how many, then check by counting. They can record the results in their recording tables.

DIFFERENTIATION

Less able: decide whether to prepare some sets with fewer objects for this group.
More able: prepare a set with between 30 and 40 objects as a challenge.

PLENARY

Ask children to look at their results. Encourage individuals to explain whether they were: 'roughly right; close; nearly; estimated too many, too few; enough; not enough'.

RESOURCES

Counting stick; flip chart and pen; large numeral cards 0 to 30 and a set of numeral cards 0 to 30 for each pair of children (photocopiable pages 14, 15 and 16); pencils and paper; the class number line; a copy of page 196 (Random numbers) for each child.

PREPARATION

Make the required photocopies. On a flip chart sheet write:

| 7 | | 9 | 10 | | 12 |

| 3 | 4 | 8 | 6 | 7 | 5 |

Cover the second track up until it is needed.

LEARNING OUTCOMES
ORAL AND MENTAL STARTER
● Describe and extend number sequences: **count on and back in ones from any small number, and in tens from and back to zero.**

VOCABULARY

One more; 10 more; one less; 10 less; compare; order; size.

MAIN TEACHING ACTIVITY

● **Within the range 0 to 30, say the number that is 1 or 10 more or less than any given number.**

● **Order numbers to at least 20,** and position them on a number track.

ORAL AND MENTAL STARTER

COUNTING IN ONES AND TENS: Repeat this activity from Lesson 1 on page 186.

MAIN TEACHING ACTIVITY

ORDERING NUMBERS: Ask: *What is one before 6, 13, 23,....? What is one after 5, 16, 28....? What is one less than 3, 12, 24,...?* Ask a child to check on the class number line for each question. Then ask: *What is 10 more than 5, 10, 17,...? 10 fewer than 30, 26, 17...? An orange costs 17p and an apple costs 10p less. How much is the apple?* For each one, ask a child to point to the class number line and count along or back 10. Show the number track on the flip chart and ask: *What number goes here... and here...?* Ask a child to write in the missing numbers, and to explain his or her thinking. Uncover the second track and ask: *What numbers have been swapped?* Encourage the children to explain their thinking. Choose six numeral cards at random and give them out to some children. Ask them to stand at the front so that the numbers are not in any particular order, for example: 17, 10, 23, 15, 8, 30. Explain that these numbers need to be put in order, but only two can be moved at a time. The children decide which to move first. For each move, ask them to explain their thinking. Repeat with other randomly chosen numerals.

Now ask the children to work in pairs. Each pair takes a set of numeral cards 0 to 30, shuffles them, deals out six cards, at random, and places them face up. They write down the order of these cards. They then take turns to move two cards at a time, aiming to order the cards from left to right, lowest to highest. When they have finished they write down the final order of the cards, then play again.

DIFFERENTIATION

Less able: limit the cards to 0 to 10, or 0 to 20, and choosing just four cards at random. Check that the children are confident with this game.
More able: extend the line of cards to seven.

PLENARY

OUT OF ORDER: Write some numerals, out of order, on the flip chart, and ask the children to help you to write them again, in order.

LESSON 5

Repeat the **Main teaching activity** of Lesson 4, changing the numbers. For individual work, provide copies of photocopiable page 196 (Random numbers) and ask the children to rewrite the numbers in order. You may decide not to use this sheet with the less able group and instead ask them to work together, ordering randomly-dealt cards, as in the **Main teaching activity**. Encourage the more able children to make up some random number puzzles for each other to try. In the Plenary session, ask the more able children for their Random number puzzles and challenge all the children to solve them.

RESOURCES

A set of cards made from photocopiable page 167 (Addition 6 to 10); a set of numeral cards 0 to 20 for each child (pages 14 and 15); copies of photocopiable page 197 (Number trains), plus an A3 enlargement of 'Number trains'; paper and pencils; flip chart and marker pen; number lines (page 18).

PREPARATION

Make the required photocopies.

LEARNING OUTCOMES

ORAL AND MENTAL STARTER

● Begin to know addition facts for all pairs of numbers with a total up to at least 10, and the corresponding subtraction facts.

MAIN TEACHING ACTIVITY

● **Understand the operation of addition, and of subtraction (as 'take away', 'difference', and 'how many more to make') and use the related vocabulary.**

● Use known number facts and place value to add or subtract a pair of numbers mentally within the range 0 to at least 10, then 0 to at least 20.

VOCABULARY

Add; more; plus; make; sum; total; altogether; subtract; take away; minus; leave; equals; sign.

ORAL AND MENTAL STARTER

ADDITION TO 10: Explain to the children that you will hold up a card with a number sentence on it, and that you would like them to work out the answer mentally and then hold up the appropriate numeral card as their answer. If they all hold up the correct answer, move on; if some do not, ask others: *How did you work it out?*

MAIN TEACHING ACTIVITY

ADDING AND SUBTRACTING: Ask the children to use their numeral cards to show the answers to questions like: *What is 5 add 4? And 15 add 4?*; writing the number sentences on the flip chart each time. Encourage children to explain the pattern that they see. Repeat for other examples, then ask some subtraction questions: *What is 7 minus 3? And 17 minus 3? Can you see a pattern?* Pin the A3 copy of 'Number trains' to the flip chart, and ask the children to work out the sum in the first coach, then write the answer into the box in the second coach to make the next sum.

Provide a copy of 'Number trains' for the children and ask them to complete the trains quickly, using number facts that they already know to work out the answers mentally.

DIFFERENTIATION

Less able: if the children find this difficult, provide number lines to help them.
More able: challenge them, when they have finished the sheet, to find all the number facts which link together three numbers, such as: 15, 4, 11 (11 + 4 = 15; 4 + 11 = 15; 15 – 4 = 11; 15 – 11 = 4).

PLENARY

Pin up the A3 enlargement of 'Number trains' and ask individual children to write in the answers. Encourage the others to check the answers.

LESSON 7

Repeat Lesson 6, using the **Main teaching activity** suggestions to practise using known number facts to work out unknown ones. When the children are confident with this, provide some written examples for them to complete mentally. These can be taken from school resources and should take the form of: 15 + 4 = ☐; 15 + ☐ = 19; ☐ + 4 = 19. Provide less able children with number lines if they are unsure. More able children could be challenged to find all the facts for three numbers, such as 19, 14, 5 (14 + 5 = 19; 5 + 14 = 19; 19 – 5 = 14; 19 – 14 = 5). In the Plenary session encourage the children to look for the pattern in their answers.

RESOURCES

A set of Addition 6 to 10 cards from photocopiable page 167; a set of 0 to 20 numeral cards for each child (photocopiable pages 14, 15 and 16); flip chart and pen; pencils and paper; copies of photocopiable page 198 (Bridging 10 and 20) and an A3 enlargement of this sheet.

PREPARATION

Make the required photocopies and A3 enlargement of photocopiable page 198 (Bridging 10 and 20).

LEARNING OUTCOMES

ORAL AND MENTAL STARTER

● Begin to know addition facts for all pairs of numbers with a total up to at least 10 and the corresponding subtraction facts.

MAIN TEACHING ACTIVITY

● **Understand the operation of addition, and use the related vocabulary.**
● Begin to bridge through 10, and later 20, when adding a single-digit number.

VOCABULARY
Add; more; plus; make; sum; total; altogether; equals; sign.

ORAL AND MENTAL STARTER

ADDITION TO 10: Repeat this activity from Lesson 6, page 189.

MAIN TEACHING ACTIVITY

BRIDGING 10 AND 20: Asking the children to use their numeral cards to show their answers, ask questions such as: 9 add 4; 8 add 5. Ask the children to say how they worked it out, encouraging them to use two steps and cross 10 as the middle stage: 9 + 4 = 9 + 1 + 3 = 10 + 3 = 13. When the children are confident with this, introduce the idea of crossing 20 in the same way. Ask: *What is 18 add 5?* Show the children that 18 + 5 = 18 + 2 + 3 = 20 + 3 = 23. Ask them to use this strategy to answer some more questions that cross 20: 17 + 4; 15 + 9; 16 + 8, and so on. For each answer encourage the children to explain the mental steps that they took.

Now, working in pairs, ask the children to sort out a set of numeral cards; putting the teen numbers into one pile, and the unit cards into another, so that they have a set of 0 to 9 cards and another of 10 to 20. They shuffle each pile of cards, then take turns to draw two cards, write an addition sum, work mentally, and write the answer. Remind them that not all the questions will cross 20.

DIFFERENTIATION

Less able: decide whether to limit the number range by asking them to draw a unit card and add it to, for example, 8 or 9.
More able: for each two cards ask them to write three sums. So for 18 + 6 they would have: 18 + 6 = □; 18 + □ = 24; □ + 6 = 24.

PLENARY

Ask the children for some of their examples which cross 20. Challenge everyone to work quickly to answer them, and to say how they worked it out.

LESSON 9

Repeat Lesson 8 providing some different oral examples in the **Main teaching activity**. Provide each child with a copy of 'Bridging 10 and twenty' and ask them to work mentally to solve these. Work with the less able group, encouraging the children to explain how they worked each one out. Challenge the more able children to try, for example: 25 + 9; 27 + 8. In the Plenary session ask children to provide answers to the questions and to write them into the A3 enlargement. For each one, ask how it was worked out.

RESOURCES

Flip chart and pen; pencils and paper; written questions of the type: 18 + 4 = ? presented on flip chart sheets; number lines (photocopiable page 18).

PREPARATION

Find examples of the written questions from the school's resources.

LEARNING OUTCOMES

ORAL AND MENTAL STARTER

● Describe and extend number sequences: count in steps of 5 from zero to 20 or more, then back again; begin to count in steps of 3 from zero.

MAIN TEACHING ACTIVITY

● **Understand the operation of addition, and use the related vocabulary.**
● Use known number facts and place value to add a pair of numbers mentally within the range 0 to at least 10, then 0 to at least 20.

VOCABULARY
Add; more; plus; make; sum; total; altogether; equals; sign.

ORAL AND MENTAL STARTER

COUNTING IN FIVES AND THREES: Ask the children to count with you in fives, from zero to about 20 or more, and back again. Say: *5, 10, 15... What comes next? And next? 30, 25, 20... What comes next?* Repeat for counting in threes from zero. Say: *3, 6, 9... What comes next?* Count around the class, in fives, then in threes. Ask: *What number will John say?*

MAIN TEACHING ACTIVITY

ADDING TO TEENS: Ask: *What is 18 add 5? How can we work it out?* Encourage the children to suggest methods, such as: 'Well, 18 add 2 is 20 and add 3 more is 23'. Repeat for other examples, adding a single-digit number to a 'teens' number: 15 + 7; 19 + 4; 14 + 7 and so on. For each one, ask the children to describe the method they used for working it out. When they are confident with this strategy, ask them to copy and complete the written questions, setting a time limit of about 10 minutes.

DIFFERENTIATION

Less able: if children find the work difficult, provide number lines so that they can count 10, then count the units.
More able: challenge them to work quickly, using rapid recall of known facts.

PLENARY

Discuss some of the written questions that the children have completed, encouraging them to explain how they worked these out.

RESOURCES

Items for sale with price labels attached, from 1p to 20p; coins; pencils and paper.

PREPARATION

Write the price labels and attach them to the items for sale. Make up sets of price labels for each group, just using prices from 1p to 10p.

LEARNING OUTCOMES

ORAL AND MENTAL STARTER

● Describe and extend number sequences: count in steps of 5 from zero to 20 or more, then back again; begin to count in steps of 3 from zero.

MAIN TEACHING ACTIVITY

● Recognise coins of different values. Find totals and change from up to 20p. Work out how to pay an exact sum using smaller coins.

VOCABULARY

Money; coin; penny; pence; pound; price; cost; buy; sell; spend; spent; pay; change; dear; costs more; cheap; costs less; cheaper; costs the same as; how much…?; how many…?; total.

ORAL AND MENTAL STARTER

COUNTING IN FIVES AND THREES: Repeat this activity from Lesson 10, page 192.

MAIN TEACHING ACTIVITY

BUYING AND SELLING: Choose three items, each priced less than 10p, such as 3p, 4p and 6p and ask a child to be the shopkeeper. Ask: *How much will these cost?* and encourage all the children to work the total out mentally. Ask how they worked it out. Offer the shopkeeper a 20p coin and say: *How much change will you give me?* Encourage the shopkeeper to count the change into your hand: *These cost 13p; and 2p makes 15p and 5p makes 20p. That's 7p change.* Repeat for other items, keeping their prices below 10p.

Ask the children to work in small groups of about four. One child is the shopkeeper, another a customer; while the other two watch and check what happens. The customer chooses three labels, being careful not to go over 20p, and asks the shopkeeper: 'How much is this?' The shopkeeper works out the cost, then the customer decides how much money to offer and the shopkeeper counts out the change. Swap roles after each turn.

DIFFERENTIATION

Less able: decide whether to limit this initially to just two prices to be totalled and the customer to give the correct money.
More able: when they are confident, the customer can purchase items to a cost between 20p and 30p. Encourage them to give change from 30p, offering a 20p and a 10p coin.

PLENARY

Ask individuals to show examples of totalling and giving change. Discuss how they totalled the prices in their heads.

LESSON 12

Repeat 'Buying and selling' from Lesson 11, this time using all the price labels up to 20p, and just buying two items each time which total no more than 20p. Encourage the children to use mental strategies to total, including bridging through 10. Ask them to work in small groups as before, choosing two labels which total more than 10p. They take turns to buy, give change from 20p and check the calculating. Work with a less able group, encouraging them to explain their mental strategies. You could encourage a more able group to total beyond 20p and give change from 30p. The Plenary session is the same as in Lesson 11.

LESSON 13 +14

RESOURCES

A number fan for each child (photocopiable page 17); flip chart and pen; pencils and paper; coins; numeral cards.

LEARNING OUTCOMES

ORAL AND MENTAL STARTER

● **Know by heart** addition doubles of all numbers to at least 5 (eg 4 + 4).
● Identify near doubles, using doubles already known (eg 6 + 5).

MAIN TEACHING ACTIVITY

● **Use mental strategies to solve simple problems** set in 'real life' or money contexts, **using counting, addition, subtraction, doubling and halving, explaining methods and reasoning orally.**
● Choose and use appropriate number operations and mental strategies to solve problems.

VOCABULARY

Pattern; puzzle; answer; right; wrong; What could we try next?; How did you work it out?; count out; share out; left; left over; number sentence; sign; operation.

ORAL AND MENTAL STARTER

DOUBLING AND HALVING: Ask the children to use their number fans to show the answers to these: *Double 4...; half of 12...; What number do I need to double to make 8? 5 + 6...* Ask children to explain how they worked each one out.

MAIN TEACHING ACTIVITY

REAL LIFE AND MONEY PROBLEMS: Explain that the purpose of the next two lessons is to solve problems. Begin with: *I am thinking of a number, then I subtract 10. The answer is 8. What is my number?* Ask children to explain the strategies they used. Ask: *Did everyone use the same one? Which was best? Why?* Repeat this for other problems, choosing from and adapting those listed below to make new problems as needed. Encourage the children to record in their own way and to explain their methods and reasoning orally. You may want to put a time limit on some problems to encourage the children to work quickly.

1. I am thinking of two numbers. When I add them the answer is 8. What could my two numbers be? (Find three different ways.)
2. I am thinking of two numbers. When I add them the answer is 14. What could my two numbers be? (Find three different ways.)
3. Jane rolled three dice. Her total was twelve. What could the scores on the dice be?
4. Shani picked three cards from a set of 1 to 10 cards. Her total was 13. Which cards might she have picked? (Encourage the children to use numeral cards to help them.)
5. I ate four sweets on Monday, three on Tuesday, and five on Wednesday. How many have I eaten altogether? I had fifteen sweets. How many have I left now?
6. Make up some number stories for these sums: 4 + 5 = 9; 12 – 4 = 8; □ + 2 = 5; 6 – □ = 3; 13 + □ = 18; 19 – □ = 10; 14 + 13 = □.
7. I spent 6p and was given 4p change. How much money did I have to start with?
8. How much more is 15p than 12p? 18p than 7p?
9. Chews cost 5p. What do three chews cost?
10. Which amounts from 11p to 20p can you make with exactly three coins?
11. How could I pay 17p exactly? Describe different ways.

DIFFERENTIATION

Less able: begin with questions 1 and 7, as these are easier.
More able: questions 6, 10 and 11 are more challenging.

PLENARY

Ask the children how they solved the problems and which mental strategies they used. Ask individual children to write their recording on the flip chart for others to see and discuss.

LESSON 15

RESOURCES	Number fans (page 17), copies of photocopiable page 199 (Real life and money problems) and an A3 enlargement of this; flip chart and pen.
LEARNING OUTCOMES	**ORAL AND MENTAL STARTER** ● Know by heart addition doubles of all numbers to at least 5 (eg 4 + 4). ● Identify near doubles, using doubles already known (eg 6 + 5). **MAIN TEACHING ACTIVITY** ● **Use mental strategies to solve simple problems** set in 'real life' or money contexts, **using counting, addition, subtraction, doubling and halving, explaining methods and reasoning orally.** ● Choose and use appropriate number operations and mental strategies to solve problems.
ORAL AND MENTAL STARTER	DOUBLING AND HALVING: Repeat this activity from Lesson 13 (page 193).
MAIN TEACHING ACTIVITY	REAL LIFE AND MONEY PROBLEMS: Pin the A3 copy of page 199 onto the flip chart and ask the children to help you solve the first problem. Discuss possible mental strategies, then ask the children to complete the sheet.
DIFFERENTIATION	Less able: provide help with reading the problems. Decide whether to limit the problems the children try to the first two. More able: challenge them to make up word problems for others to try.
PLENARY	Discuss solutions. Ask which mental strategies were used, and why.

Name

Comparing numbers

Write these numbers.

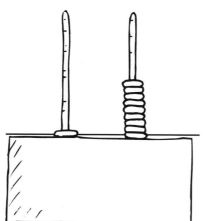
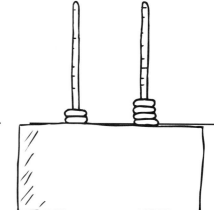

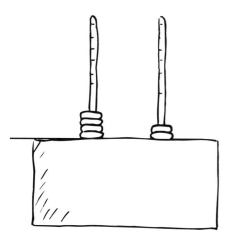
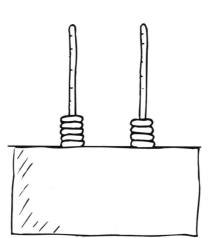
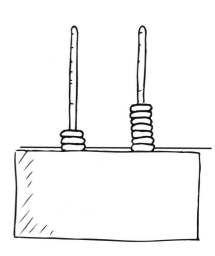

Write a number between these.

11 ☐ 18   32 ☐ 42

15 ☐ 25   13 ☐ 30

19 ☐ 24   10 ☐ 26

31 ☐ 37   23 ☐ 40

25 ☐ 30   18 ☐ 31

Random numbers

Write these numbers in order.

9   15   13   3   11 ___   ___   ___   ___   ___

18   12   16   14   4 ___   ___   ___   ___   ___

14   11   17   20   3 ___   ___   ___   ___   ___

5   1   19   13   8 ___   ___   ___   ___   ___

16   6   14   4   12 ___   ___   ___   ___   ___

19   3   16   7   5 ___   ___   ___   ___   ___

Put a ✔ if the numbers are in order.
Put a ✖ over a number which is not in order.

3	5	7	9
2	5	4	6
11	19	16	17
10	11	12	16
14	17	18	10
9	12	6	15

Number trains

Finish these sums. Put each answer in the next box.

15 + 4 | ☐ – 3 | ☐ – 5 =

18 – 8 | ☐ – 9 | ☐ + 16 =

14 + 3 | ☐ – 6 | ☐ + 4 =

5 + 9 | ☐ + 5 | ☐ – 2 =

20 – 8 | ☐ – 6 | ☐ + 7 =

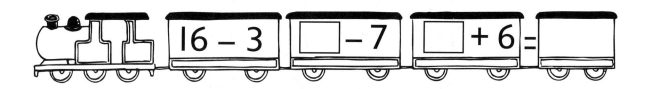

16 – 3 | ☐ – 7 | ☐ + 6 =

Name

UNIT 9-11

Bridging 10 and 20

Join matching pairs.

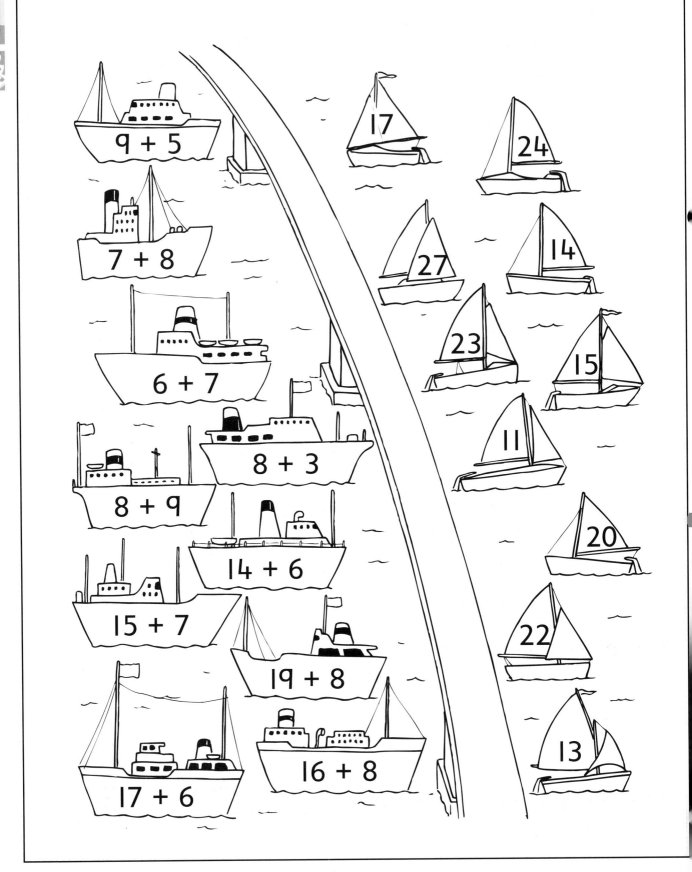

Real life and money problems

Write the answers.

Tom has 14p.
How much more does he need to make 20p? p

Draw coins to total 13p.
Find two different ways.

I buy two 9p stamps. How much does that cost? p

6 cakes   8 cakes

How many cakes altogether?

Jenny has 19 sweets.
She eats 7.

How many does she have left?

UNITS 12-13

ORGANISATION (10 LESSONS)

	LEARNING OUTCOMES	ORAL & MENTAL STARTER	MAIN TEACHING ACTIVITY	PLENARY
LESSON 1 +2	• Understand and use the vocabulary related to capacity. • **Compare two capacities by direct comparison;** extend to more than two. • Measure using uniform non-standard units (eg yoghurt pots) or standard units (eg litre jugs). • **Suggest suitable standard or uniform non-standard units and measuring equipment to estimate, then measure, a capacity,** recording estimates and measurements as 'about 3 beakers full'.	DOUBLES, HALVES AND NEAR DOUBLES: Rapid recall of known facts; using these to find unknown facts.	HOW MUCH DOES IT HOLD?: Comparing, estimating and measuring activities, including using the litre.	Discussion of the strategies used to solve the problems.
LESSON 3	• Understand and use the vocabulary related to time. Order familiar events in time. Read the time to the hour or half hour on analogue clocks.	ADDITION TO 10: Rapid recall of number facts.	TIMING: Telling the time; timing events and solving time problems.	Discussion of the solutions to the problems.
LESSON 4	• Understand and use the vocabulary related to time. Order familiar events in time. Read the time to the hour or half hour on analogue clocks.	TELLING THE TIME: Reading the time for o'clock and half hour times.	TIMING DEVICES.	Discussion of the solutions to the problems.
LESSON 5	• Understand and use the vocabulary related to time. Order familiar events in time. Know the days of the week and the seasons of the year.	TELLING THE TIME.	WHEN WAS THIS?: Ordering time events; recognising days and seasons.	TELLING THE TIME.
LESSON 6 +7	• **Use mental strategies to solve simple problems** set in measurement contexts, **using counting, addition, subtraction, doubling and halving, explaining methods and reasoning orally.**	TELLING THE TIME.	SOLVING PROBLEMS: Using mental strategies to solve measurement problems.	Discuss the solutions to the problems.
LESSON 8 +9 +10	• Solve a given problem by sorting, classifying and organising information in simple ways, such as: using objects or pictures; in a list or simple table. • Discuss and explain results.	BRIDGING 10 AND 20: Using the bridging strategy to add.	SURVEYS: Collecting, sorting, organising data, and answering questions about it.	Discussion of the decisions taken to collect and sort data.

ORAL AND MENTAL SKILLS
Know by heart: addition doubles for all pairs of numbers with a total up to at least 5 (eg 4 + 4). Identify near doubles, using doubles already known (eg 6 + 5). Begin to bridge through 10, and later 20, when adding a single-digit number. Begin to know addition facts for all pairs of numbers with a total up to at least 10, and the corresponding subtraction facts. Read the time to the hour or half hour on analogue clocks.

In Unit 12 Lessons 1 and 3 are shown in full. In Unit 13 Lessons 6 and 8 are given in detail. All other lessons are extensions of what has already been taught and follow in numerical order.

RESOURCES

A set of numeral cards 0 to 20 for each child (pages 14 and 15); a selection of containers including litre jugs, bowls, buckets, shampoo bottles, yoghurt pots, margarine tubs, spoons, scoops, egg cups, plastic beakers; commercial 1 litre containers in different materials and shapes; teapot; pouring materials such as water, sand, rice, lentils; paper and pencils; flip chart and pen.

PREPARATION

Collect together a wide range of 'junk' containers for these activities.

LEARNING OUTCOMES

ORAL AND MENTAL STARTER

● **Know by heart:** addition doubles for all numbers to at least 5 (eg 4 + 4).
● Identify near doubles, using doubles already known (eg 6 + 5).

MAIN TEACHING ACTIVITY

● Understand and use the vocabulary related to capacity.
● **Compare two capacities by direct comparison;** extend to more than two.
● Measure using uniform non-standard units (eg yoghurt pots) or standard units (eg litre jugs).
● **Suggest suitable standard or uniform non-standard units and measuring equipment to estimate, then measure, a capacity,** recording estimates and measurements as 'about 3 beakers full'.

VOCABULARY
Full; half full; empty; holds; container.

ORAL AND MENTAL STARTER

DOUBLES, HALVES AND NEAR DOUBLES: Ask the children to hold up numeral cards to show the answers to questions such as: *What is double 3? Half of 10? 8 + 7?* Encourage them to work as quickly as possible.

MAIN TEACHING ACTIVITY

HOW MUCH DOES IT HOLD? Show the children two containers. Ask: *Which do you think holds more? How could you find out?* Invite a child to fill one container with sand and pour into the other, then ask whether the estimate was reasonable. *How could we measure how much this container holds? What could we use?* Encourage the children to explain why they chose a particular unit. Show them the litre jug and a litre bottle (or other litre container, such as a tetrapak of milk or orange juice); explain that milk or other drinks bought from a supermarket often come in litre containers. Tell them that the litre jug can be used to find out how much larger containers (such as buckets and bowls) hold. Remind them that when they are measuring, they should record their estimate and measure as 'about 6 scoops; about 3 cups; about 4 litres'. Write these on the flip chart.

> **We guess the teapot holds about 5 cups.**
>
> **It holds about 4 cups.**

Ask the children to work in groups to estimate, then check by measuring, the capacity of various containers. They should make a group record, writing a sentence for their results (see figure).

Adapt the following questions to create suitable challenges for your class.

1. Put the cup, beaker and egg cup in order of how much they hold. Estimate, then check by filling and pouring.
2. Which units would you choose to measure a litre jug? Explain why. Now estimate and check by measuring to find out how much it holds. Repeat for a teapot or an egg cup.
3. How much does the bucket hold? Decide what you will use to measure, estimate, then check by filling and pouring.
4. How much do these two containers hold? (Both litre containers, different shapes: one tall and thin, the other squat.)
5. Which holds more: the jug or the litre container? Estimate, then check by measuring using your chosen unit.
6. How many cups of tea could I pour from this teapot?
7. How many children could have a beaker of juice from this bottle?
8. Which holds more: the bucket or the bowl? How much more?

DIFFERENTIATION

Less able: ask the children to begin with questions 1 and 2.
More able: question 8 is more challenging.

PLENARY

Discuss the results. Encourage the children to explain how they solved the problems and why they chose the particular units.

LESSON 2

Repeat Lesson 1, choosing different measuring challenges from the selection listed.

RESOURCES

A set of cards made from photocopiable page 167 (Addition 6 to 10); a set of 0 to 10 numeral cards (photocopiable page 14) for each child; 1, 3 and 5 minute sand timers; bricks or interlocking cubes; dice; paper and pencils; squared paper; teaching clock; coffee jar lids; Plasticine; card; coloured crayons.

LEARNING OUTCOMES

ORAL AND MENTAL STARTER

● Begin to know addition facts for all pairs of numbers with a total up to at least 10, and the corresponding subtraction facts.

MAIN TEACHING ACTIVITY

● Understand and use the vocabulary related to time. Order familiar events in time. Read the time to the hour or half hour on analogue clocks.

ORAL AND MENTAL STARTER

ADDITION TO 10: Explain that you will hold up cards with sums on and that you would like the children to hold up a numeral card for the answer. Work as quickly as possible, encouraging rapid recall of these number facts.

MAIN TEACHING ACTIVITY

TIMING: Begin by asking children to tell the times on the clock face. Set it to: 9 o'clock; half past 9; 10 o'clock. Then, with the clock set to 11 o'clock, ask: *How long will it be to 12 o'clock? What do we do at 12 o'clock? What time do we start lessons again in the afternoon? How long is the lunch break? If it is 11 o'clock now, how long ago was 9 o'clock?* Explain that today the children will be carrying out some time estimates and checks to find out how long some things take. Say: *How many times do you think you can undo and do up the buttons on your coat before the sand runs through this timer?*

Encourage the children to make their estimates then, on a signal from you (turning over the sand timer) the children carry out the task. Ask: *Did you make a good guess?* On the flip chart write one child's estimate and measure: My estimate is 10. I did about 8. Explain that you would like the children to record their estimates and measures.

Choose from the following activities. Encourage the children to try each one at least twice to see if they have the same result each time.
1. While the sand runs through the timer how many times can you write the word 'time'?
2. Before the sand runs out make the tallest tower of bricks you can. How many bricks did you use?
3. How many squares can you colour in neatly before the sand runs out?
4. Throw two dice and add the scores. How many can you do before the sand runs out?
5. Ask your friend to count, slowly, to 30. How many times do you think you can write her name before she gets to 30?
6. Make a rocker timer using card, a jar lid and some Plasticine (see figure). What do you think you can do before it stops rocking?

VOCABULARY

Quick; quicker; quickest; quickly; fast; faster; fastest; slow; slower; slowest; slowly; old; older; oldest; new; newer; newest; takes longer; takes less time hour; o'clock; half past; clock; watch; hands; How long ago?; How long will it be to …?; How long will it take to…?; How often?; always; never; often; sometimes; usually; once; twice.

7. How long will it take you to draw a house? Decide how to time this. Work with a friend.
8. Which takes longer: writing your full name or doing up your shoes? How will you find out? Work with a friend.

DIFFERENTIATION

Less able: begin with question 1.
More able: questions 7 and 8 are more difficult.
Challenge the children to solve all the problems and explain how they did them.

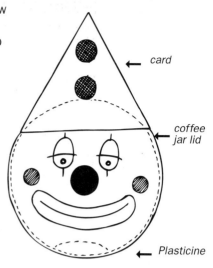

← card

← coffee jar lid

PLENARY

Discuss some of the solutions to the problems and how the children worked them out.

← Plasticine

LESSON 4

RESOURCES	1, 3 and 5 minute sand timers; bricks or interlocking cubes; dice; paper and pencils; squared paper; teaching clock; coffee jar lids; Plasticine; card; coloured crayons.
LEARNING OUTCOMES	**ORAL AND MENTAL STARTER** ● Read the time to the hour or half hour on analogue clocks. **MAIN TEACHING ACTIVITY** ● Understand and use the vocabulary related to time. Order familiar events in time.
ORAL AND MENTAL STARTER	TELLING THE TIME: Ask time questions as in the start of the **Main teaching activity** of Lesson 3, page 202.
MAIN TEACHING ACTIVITY	TIMING DEVICES: Discuss how you can tell how long something takes, such as counting, using a sand timer, looking at the clock. Use some of the activity ideas in Lesson 3 to investigate these suggestions.
DIFFERENTIATION	Less able: start with activity 2 from Lesson 3. More able: challenge them to invent their own timing activities.
PLENARY	Discuss some of the solutions to the problems and how the children worked them out.

LESSON 5

RESOURCES	Teaching clock; flash cards for days of the week and seasons (these could be printed from the NNS *Mathematical Vocabulary* CD-ROM).
LEARNING OUTCOMES	**ORAL AND MENTAL STARTER** ● Read the time to the hour or half hour on analogue clocks. **MAIN TEACHING ACTIVITY** ● Understand and use the vocabulary related to time. Order familiar events in time. Know the days of the week and the seasons of the year.
ORAL AND MENTAL STARTER	TELLING THE TIME: Repeat this activity from Lesson 4, above.
MAIN TEACHING ACTIVITY	WHEN WAS THIS? Recite the days of the week in order, using the days of the week flash cards. Ask: *What day is it today... yesterday... tomorrow?* Discuss what time of year it is and how you can tell, holding up the seasons flash cards for the children to read. Ask questions about the seasons, encouraging children to say their names and features. 　Display the days of the week flash cards in order as a circle. Ask questions and let the children write down answers individually. *Which day comes between Monday and Wednesday? Which day comes after Sunday? Which days make the weekend? Today is Thursday – what day was two days ago? If today is Thursday, what will tomorrow be?* Discuss answers, then ask: *Which is your favourite day of the week? Why?* Discuss.
DIFFERENTIATION	Less able: Encourage them to copy down the circle of days of the week before answering the questions. More able: Challenge them to think of things they might do during the summer, but not during other seasons; can they explain why?
PLENARY	TELLING THE TIME: Repeat this activity from the **Oral and mental starter**.

RESOURCES

Teaching clock; one copy per child of photocopiable page 81 (Clock); paper fasteners; pencils and paper.

PREPARATION

Provide copies of photocopiable page 81 for children to make their own clock faces, fastening the hands with paper fasteners or bolts.

LEARNING OUTCOMES

ORAL AND MENTAL STARTER
● Read the time to the hour or half hour on analogue clocks.
MAIN TEACHING ACTIVITY
● **Use mental strategies to solve problems** set in measurement contexts, **using counting, addition, subtraction, doubling and halving, explaining methods and reasoning orally.**

VOCABULARY

Pattern; puzzle; answer; right; wrong; What could we try next?; How did you work it out?; count out; share out; left; left over; number sentence; sign; operation.

ORAL AND MENTAL STARTER

TELLING THE TIME: Repeat the telling the time activity from the **Main teaching activity** of Lesson 3, page 202.

MAIN TEACHING ACTIVITY

SOLVING PROBLEMS: Explain that the next two lessons are about using mental strategies to solve problems. Ask the children to set their clocks to the times that you say: 6 o'clock; 4 o'clock; half past 9. Ask: *What time does your clock say now? What time will it be in two hours? What time was it three hours ago? What will it be in half an hour?*

Choose from, or adapt, the problems below. Read them out, asking the children to solve them mentally, recording in their own way how they solved the problem. Encourage them to write a number sentence using +, – and = , where appropriate.

1. I have a garden stick eight straws long. If I cut it in half, how long will each piece be?
2. The pencils are five cubes long. How long would three pencils be?
3. A classroom is 18 metres long and 14 metres wide. How much longer is it than wide?
4. A full jug holds six cups of water. How much will two jugs hold?
5. The small teapot will fill four cups, and the large teapot will fill eight cups. How many cups will they fill together?
6. The bucket holds 17 beakers of water. If I pour out five beakers, how many are left?
7. The apple weighs six cubes and the orange weighs seven cubes. How much do they weigh altogether?
8. I have a banana and a pear which together weigh the same as 12 cubes. If the banana weighs five cubes how much does the pear weigh?
9. I have a bag of eight sweets which weighs the same as 16 cubes. I eat half of them. How many have I eaten? What do the rest of the sweets weigh?
10. How long is it from 1 o'clock to 7 o'clock?
11. It is now half past eight. What time was it half an hour ago?
12. It is 4 o'clock. If you go to bed at 8 o'clock, how many hours until bedtime?

DIFFERENTIATION

Less able: encourage them to try problems 1, 4, 7 and 10 first. Remind them of mental strategies that they have learned and, if necessary, suggest appropriate ones to use.
More able: problems 3, 6, 9 and 12 are more challenging. Suggest that the children invent some problems for their friends to try.

PLENARY

Discuss the solutions to some of the problems and the mental strategies used.

LESSON 7

Repeat Lesson 6, using different challenges to those used in the previous lesson.

RESOURCES

Large sheets of paper; squares of sticky paper; paper and pencils; cubes; a set of 0 to 30 numeral cards for each child (photocopiable pages 14, 15 and 16); flip chart and pen.

PREPARATION

Decide what questions the children will investigate. Draw a table on the flip chart to record how many teeth the children have lost (with columns headed 'Teeth lost' and 'Number of children'). Label a large sheet of paper with appropriate columns for a graph (see below).

LEARNING OUTCOMES

ORAL AND MENTAL STARTER
● Bridge through 10, and later 20, when adding a single-digit number.

MAIN TEACHING ACTIVITY
● Solve a given problem by sorting, classifying and organising information in simple ways, such as: using objects or pictures; in a list or simple table. Discuss and explain results.

VOCABULARY

Count; sort; vote; list; group; set; list; table.

ORAL AND MENTAL STARTER

BRIDGING 10 AND 20: Revise bridging (see page 192). Ask questions such as 8 + 6; 14 + 7. The children hold up numeral cards to show answers. Discuss the strategies used.

MAIN TEACHING ACTIVITY

SURVEYS: Ask the children to help you make some lists. *List all the counting numbers from 15 to 27; list all the days of the week; list all the first names in the class which have five letters.* Write each list on the flip chart, and ask them to help you put the items in order. Now say that you want them to find the answers to some questions. They will need to make and organise their own lists, then help you to make a simple graph. Ask: *How many teeth have you lost?* Show the chart you have drawn and begin to fill it in by asking some children how many teeth they have lost. Once the data is collected, ask for ideas about how to make a graph. Suggest that they stick squares of paper onto a large sheet of paper with columns labelled '0 teeth', '1 tooth' and so on. Ask: *How many children have lost two teeth? Which is the least usual? How many children did we ask? How can you tell?*

Ask one or more questions for the children to investigate in groups of about eight. All the children can work on one question, make lists and then combine them to make a class chart. Suitable questions include: *Which would you like to go to most – a beach, a safari park, a theme park or a castle? What is your favourite colour/drink/TV programme? How many pets do you have, and what sort of animals are they? What time do you go to bed? How many marbles can you hold in one hand? Who is your favourite pop star?*

Encourage the children to decide quickly what information to collect and how to organise their list. Ask groups questions about their list, eg: *How many... How many more/fewer liked... than ...?* Make a chart, asking children from each group to stick squares onto paper or build towers of cubes. Ask questions about the chart, eg: *How many children did we ask? How do you know? How many liked... best? Which one did most people vote for?*

DIFFERENTIATION

Less able: encourage them to decide what information to collect. Help them make their lists. Encourage them to answer questions during whole-class discussion.
More able: ask them to think of their own question, then survey their group and one other. Challenge them to make their own chart of their results.

PLENARY

Discuss the strategies that children chose to collect and sort the data.

LESSONS 9 AND 10

Repeat Lesson 8, choosing one or more different questions for the children to investigate.

UNIT 14: Assess & Review

Choose from these activities. During the group activities, some children can complete assessment worksheets 6A and 6B which assess their skills in comparing and ordering numbers, addition and subtraction, and solving simple problems using mental strategies, while others work with you on practical tasks. The specific assessment criteria for the assessment sheets can be found at the bottom of each sheet.

RESOURCES

A set of numeral cards 0 to 30 for each child (pages 14, 15 and 16); a variety of containers including litre containers and jugs, buckets, scoops, spoons; filling material such as water, rice, dried peas.

ORAL AND MENTAL STARTER

ASSESSMENT

Do the children:

- **Within the range 0 to 30, say the number that is 1 or 10 more or less than any given number?**

10 MORE 10 LESS: Count together in tens from zero to one hundred and back again. Ask: *What is 10 more than 20, 15, 13,...? What is 10 less than 30, 20, 10, 25,..?* If children are not sure help them to count forward or back 10, using their fingers to keep count.

GROUP ACTIVITIES

ASSESSMENT

Can the children:

- **Use mental strategies to solve simple problems, using counting, addition, subtraction, doubling and halving, explaining methods and reasoning orally?**

PROBLEMS: Explain that you will say a word problem, which you would like the children to think about, then answer by either writing a sum or by saying the answer, explaining how they worked it out. Check that they can explain their mental strategies and write, where appropriate, a suitable number sentence. Choose from this selection of problems.

- If my clock says 6 o'clock, what will the time be in three hours from now?
- My clock says half past two. What will it be in one hour?
- If I pay 10p for two stamps, how much would they be each?
- If Sandip has twelve marbles, and Meena has nine, who has fewer? How many fewer?
- An orange weighs five cubes. I put it on the scales with a grapefruit and balance them with 11 cubes. How much does the grapefruit weigh?
- Jane is playing a game. She takes five strides and stops. Then she takes another seven strides. How many strides in total is that?
- One jug is filled with 10 cups of squash, and another holds eight cups. How many cupfuls altogether?
- The bucket holds 18 litres. If I take out five litres of water, how much is left?

Assessment 6A

Write these numbers in order.

9　4　11　18　13 _____　_____　_____　_____　_____

14　18　12　6　10 _____　_____　_____　_____　_____

15　13　14　17　16 _____　_____　_____　_____　_____

Write in the missing numbers.

| 7 | 8 | 9 | | | | 13 |

| 19 | 18 | 17 | | | | 13 |

| 8 | 9 | | | 12 | | 14 |

Finish these addition walls.　　　　Finish these difference walls.

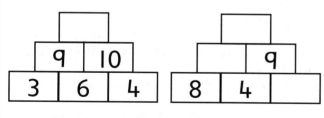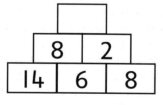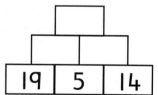

Finish these subtraction walls.

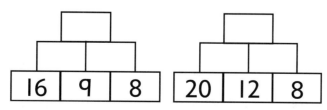

- Read, write and order numbers from 0 to at least 20; understand and use the vocabulary of comparing and ordering these numbers.
- Understand the operation of addition, and of subtraction (as 'take away' or 'difference'), and use the related vocabulary.

Assessment 6B

Put a ✔ on the heavier pan.

How much heavier?

How many litres do the buckets

hold in total?

18 litres   8 litres

How much more does the big bucket hold?

Marika gets up at

How many hours until the clock says this?

Tom measured the ribbon with this ruler.

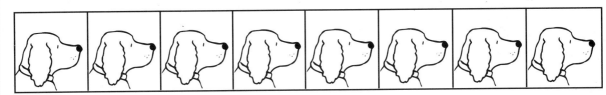

About how long is the ribbon?   dogs long

● Use mental strategies to solve simple problems, using counting, addition, subtraction, doubling and halving, explaining methods and reasoning orally.